# A MESSAGE FROM

♥

*Independence Blue Cross
and Pennsylvania Blue Shield*

*T*he tremendous interest in health care, which has virtually exploded during the past few years, has brought with it an equally tremendous increase in public demand for knowledge and information about the health care system.

At Independence Blue Cross, the region's largest health insurer, we are acutely sensitive to this need and deeply aware of our own responsibility to educate and inform our two million subscribers and other residents of the Delaware Valley.

Constantly, we are asked, and respond to, questions about why health care costs are so high and why they increase so dramatically from year to year.

With equal frequency, we are asked why so many people are uninsured and left economically vulnerable in the event of illness.

And recently, the questions have taken on an added dimension: How can I take better care of myself? How can I prevent illness? What should I do to lead a healthier life? What about my children? How can I get insurance that's affordable? How can the system be reformed?

What we have discovered is a greater need than ever to communicate. As a major institution, in partnership with Pennsylvania Blue Shield, serving two million people on the one hand, while dealing on a daily basis with hospitals, doctors and other providers on the other, we are committed to providing answers to as many questions as possible.

If, for example, you are employed by an organization that offers health insurance as an employee benefit, you will want to inquire about the availability of traditional Blue Cross and Blue Shield indemnity insurance which offers maximum freedom in choosing hospitals and doctors with a broad array of coverage.

We also offer what is known as a Preferred Provider Organization (PPO), called Personal Choice℠, which provides a broad range of benefits and provider selection but which has built-in cost controls that can save you, and your employer, valuable dollars. Or, if you think you'd be better off in a health maintenance organization (HMO) with your health managed by a primary care physician who is part of an HMO network, you should know that you can choose our new Keystone Health Plan East, the fastest growing HMO in the nation.

If you don't have health insurance, and can't afford a traditional policy, you should know that we have an insurance plan called *Special Care*℠ which may meet your needs.

If you have, or know of, children who lack health insurance because their parents are not able to afford it, and are at an income level not low enough to qualify for Medical Assistance, you should know that we have established *The Caring Foundation for Children* which provides a basic health insurance policy paid by private contributions to our Caring Foundation at no cost to children or their families.

If you have medical problems and think you can't get insurance because of them, you should know that we don't turn anyone down. We don't medically underwrite and have open enrollments for individuals on a year round basis.

If you are just plain angry at rising health care costs, you ought to know that we have kept our administrative costs to 6 cents on the dollar, one of the lowest administrative expense ratios in the insurance industry, while the other 94 cents has gone directly into the payment of your health care bills. And we're on your side when it comes to professional charges. We have devoted much time and effort to the negotiation of hospital agreements which will hold down costs for our subscribers.

If recent revelations about the questionable solvency of some insurers worry you, you can be assured in knowing we are a financially sound and solid institution.

To get these messages out, we have employed a variety of tools.

Each year, we make a report to the community on health care trends. It's called *The Community Health Care Report* and a copy of it is available to you upon request. Its approach and its language are primarily geared toward a professional and technical audience.

Recently, we have begun to promote wellness and good health through a variety of video productions, some of which you may see on cable television or at your place of work, if your employer is an Independence Blue Cross group subscriber.

Many of our senior executives spend hours speaking, lecturing or participating in panels which are designed to address health care issues.

And written publications to our subscribers and group benefits managers deliver a more targeted story to special audiences.

And so, when PHILADELPHIA Magazine approached us to distribute their new publication, *A Guide to Health Care in the Delaware Valley*, we readily accepted the opportunity to communicate the health care message to our subscribers and the community-at-large in a new and different way.

You will find this Guide full of valuable information about healthy living, top doctors, hospital specialties, support groups and other issues. But the difference between this Guide and so many other publications is its readability. Employing the crisp and colorful style which has made PHILADELPHIA Magazine a journalistic leader, the Guide delivers its advice and information in a highly readable, enjoyable and sometimes controversial manner. Some of the opinions given and approaches taken may not be the way we would have expressed them. But the content of this Guide is bound to get your attention in a way that traditional writing about health care never could. And if that style helps you to live better, take better care of yourself, consult an appropriate physician, choose the best hospital, change your diet, become more cost conscious or confront an emergency with more knowledge and confidence, then it will have done its job.

We think it will. And we believe you will consult it many times when those nagging questions about health care come to mind.

Fortunately, when you do so, you will act with the knowledge that you are living in one of the world's great centers of health care, with internationally renowned hospitals and highly respected practitioners who have access to the most advanced research, medical technology and quality care.

One last point. In the pages of this Guide you will find valuable lists of institutions, associations and individuals to call or write. In keeping with the spirit of this publication, we would like to list our own important numbers to call. We are here to serve you. All you need to do is pick up the phone and hopefully we, too, can help to guide you through the maze known as the American system of health care. ♥

# Carry Us For Life.℠

*Independence Blue Cross*

General Offices
241-2400

Group Sales
241-3400

*Customer Service*

Non-Group
568-8204

Small Group
568-3800

Large Group
567-5959

National Group
567-5667

Caring Program for Children
1-800-464-5437

Personal Choice
1-800-626-8144

Keystone Health Plan East
241-2001

Corporate Communications
241-3131

Hearing Impaired
241-2944 (TDD)

*Philadelphia Magazine's*

# GUIDE TO HEALTH CARE

## in the Delaware Valley

**BY CAROL SALINE**

**RESEARCHED BY PHIL YANELLA, JR.**

**1 9 9 3**

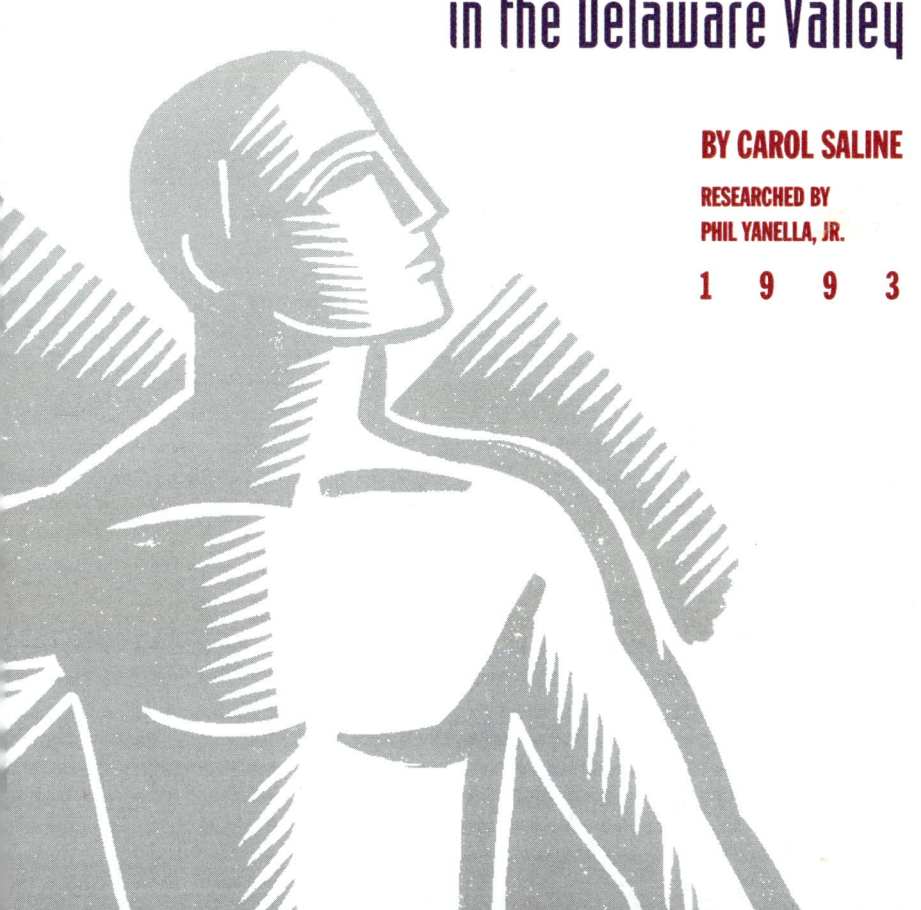

BOOK DESIGN: ANDREA HEMMANN / HEMMANN DESIGN
ILLUSTRATIONS: ANTHONY RUSSO

The articles and advertisements in this Guide are published by *Philadelphia Magazine* and do not necessarily represent the opinions or viewpoints of Independence Blue Cross and Pennsylvania Blue Shield. The advice and recommendations in this Guide are provided by *Philadelphia Magazine* for your general information only. For any medical problem you should consult your physician.

*Philadelphia Magazine's Guide to Health Care in the Delaware Valley* is published annually at 1818 Market St., Philadelphia, PA 19103-3683, (215) 564-7700. All contents of this guide are copyrighted 1992 by *Philadelphia Magazine* and Metro Health, division of METROCORP™.

# Health Care Coverage Based On The Theory That No Two Million People Are Exactly Alike.

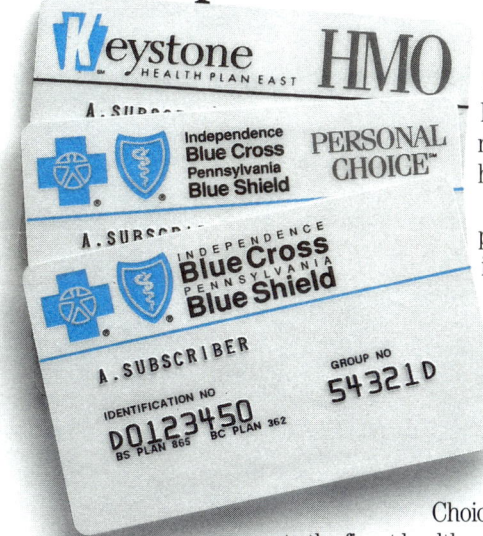

If there's one thing we've learned about our two million Delaware Valley subscribers, it's that no two of them have exactly the same health care requirements.

No doubt the same is true for the people in your organization. Which is why you should offer them the *only* health insurance programs that carry the true-blue trust and security we've maintained for over five decades.

Our Traditional Indemnity plan, our new Keystone Health Plan East HMO and our Personal Choice product provide affordable access to the finest health care in the world, each in its own unique way. That's why we call our new package the Blue Solution. It's designed to meet all your health insurance needs from one source.

All this from the companies that insure far more people than any other in this part of the country. Because no two people in your organization are exactly alike, make sure you offer each one a health insurance program that meets their individual requirements. One they can carry for life.

## Two Million People Carry Us For Life.

® Registered mark of the Blue Cross and Blue Shield Association. ℠ Service marks of Independence Blue Cross and Pennsylvania Blue Shield.

# What's the best way to find the right doctor? Ask the right nurse.

Call a specially trained Einstein RN. She can help you find a doctor who's right for you. Whether you're looking for a doctor who specializes in family medicine or older adults. Orthopaedics or cardiology. With an office near your home or job. And hours that fit your schedule.

Last year, 28,755 people called us and tapped into the genius of Einstein. Now's a good time for you to be the next one.

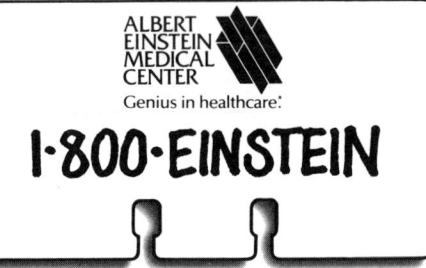

ALBERT EINSTEIN MEDICAL CENTER
Genius in healthcare.

1·800·EINSTEIN

©1992 AEHF

♥ I began writing about health nearly 15 years ago, with an article on insomnia. At the time, like any good reporter covering a new subject, I was motivated by curiosity. I certainly never expected to become infected with a fever of fascination for the world of medicine—a fever that still burns. While I've learned a great many things, what has surprised me the most is the hunger people have for medical advice they can trust. I get more questions on health–related topics from readers—and from friends—than on anything else I write about. People want reliable, well–researched information about everything from who are the area's top doctors to whether it's safe to take estrogen replacements. That need is why I asked David Lipson to publish this book. ♥ We compiled a great deal of information from *Philadelphia Magazine* articles and added many new resources that I thought would be valuable. My thanks go to Phil Yannella Jr. for his research assistance and Sandy Hingston for her unerring copyediting. ♥ When I was a child, we had memo–pads from an insurance company lying around our house, imprinted with a message I've never forgotten: "It is better to have it and not need it, than to need it and not have it." That's what I hope this health guide will be for you—something useful you won't need too often, and something helpful when you do have a problem. ♥

–*Carol Saline*

# This sticker could
# SAVE
## the one you love

The Mr. Yuk poison prevention sticker may be used as a learning tool to teach children that Yuk means **NO! Stay Away!** FREE Mr. Yuk stickers and literature are available at Thrift Drug Stores.
If you suspect a poisoning has occured, call your Poison Control Center at **215-386-2100.**

# Table of Contents

**SECTION ONE: CHOOSING A DOCTOR**

13  Chapter 1:  *The Superdoctors.*
    A review of the medical and surgical specialists considered tops by their peers.

33  Chapter 2:  *For Children Only..*
    Who are the area's most respected pediatric specialists?

**SECTION TWO: CHOOSING A HOSPITAL**

51  Chapter 3:  *Why Are the Bills So High?*

57  Chapter 4:  *The Wise Patient:*
    How to take care of yourself in the hospital.

63  Chapter 5:  *Under and Out:*
    News from the netherworld of medicine–anesthesia.

69  Chapter 6:  *Inside Story:*
    A glossary of the many techniques used to see inside the body.

79  Chapter 7:  *A Shopper's Guide to Area Hospitals.*

**SECTION THREE: MENTAL HEALTH**

117  Chapter 8:  *Matter Over Mind:*
    Using drugs to treat depression, anxiety, and other problems once reserved for the shrink's couch.

125  Chapter 9:  *High Anxiety:*
    While you are reading this, some 20 million Americans are having an anxiety attack. Makes you nervous, doesn't it?

131  Chapter 10:  *Where To Go For Help:*
    A list of psychiatric hospitals and mental health centers.

7

## SECTION FOUR: A PRESCRIPTION FOR WELLNESS

**142** Chapter 11: *Testing, Testing...*
and more testing. Billions of dollars' worth of medical tests may be unnecessary. And that includes the all-purpose annual physical.

**151** Chapter 12: *The Dark Side of the Sun:*
Summer can leave you with more than a tan.

**157** Chapter 13: *Why Fat Makes You Fat:*
And why there is only one real way to get thin.

**163** Chapter 14: *A Change of Thought on Change of Life:*
For years menopausal women worried about the risks of hormone therapy. Now they're talking about the benefits.

**169** Chapter 15: *How Can You Sleep At Night?*
If you chronically take sleeping pills, the probability is, you can't.

**175** Chapter 16: *Pain Is Their Speciality:*
Physiatrists seem to be able to do what other doctors can't.

**179** Chapter 17: *That Certain Smile:*
What's new at the dentist's office.

**183** Chapter 18: *Season of the Itch:*
Beating the bugs of summer.

**187** Chapter 19: *A Few Good Words About Chiropractors:*
If your physician can't fix the pain, let a chiropractor take a crack at it.

**193** Chapter 20: *A Separate Piece:*
What biopsies are, and why they aren't always right.

**197** Chapter 21: *Under Your Skin:*
Doctors know what causes acne. And it has nothing to do with pepperoni pizza.

**201** Chapter 22: *Everybody Must Get Stones:*
For the millions who get gallstones or kidney stones, two new forms of surgery provide faster relief.

**205** Chapter 23: *A Little Traveling Medicine, Please:*
How to wage germ warfare overseas.

**209** Chapter 24: *Cold Comfort:*
How to fight the winter blahs.

**215** Chapter 25: *Light Fantastic:*
Lasers are the next bright idea in surgery.

**223** Chapter 26: *Nothing to Sneeze At:*
A look at some new ways of treating allergies.

**231** Chapter 27: *Heart of Gold:*
Organ transplants turn death into life.

## SECTION FIVE: WISDOM FOR THE AGING

**249** Chapter 28: *Those Tarnished Golden Years*

**257** Chapter 29: *Remembrance of Things,*
uh, huh, well, hmmm...

**263** Chapter 30: *Sweatin' With the Oldies:*
There's plenty of fresh evidence that says, if you don't like old age, walk away from it.

**269** Chapter 31: *Services for the Aging*

## SECTION SIX: FOR YOUR INFORMATION

**287** Chapter 32: *Help!*
An A-to-Z listing of area support groups, from Alzheimer's disease to the Zipper Club.

**301** Chapter 33: *Getting Better:*
A survey of treatment centers, from substance abuse to physical therapy.

**309** Chapter 34: *Hot Numbers:*
A potpourri of hot lines and resources for health-related problems.

## PROFESSIONAL DIRECTORY

**315** *Special Advertising Section*

**SECTION ONE**

# CHOOSING A DOCTOR

Dr. John Macdonald
Medical Director
Temple University
Comprehensive Cancer Center

## Temple University Comprehensive Cancer Center

"We are dedicated to providing our patients the best standard and research treatments available. Along with treatments aimed at prolonging life, we also offer many services to increase quality of life. We are very pleased that the Temple University Comprehensive Cancer Center continues to grow as a unique facility providing on-site programs and services for prompt detection, diagnosis, treatment, support and follow-up care for people with cancer and their families."

 **THE TEMPLE UNIVERSITY COMPREHENSIVE CANCER CENTER**
CALL (215) 221-4000

*The Temple University Comprehensive Cancer Center is a subsidiary of Salick Health Care, Inc., the nation's leading disease-specific health care provider.*

# 1

# Doctor! Doctor!

*These 300–plus physicians practice the best medicine in the region. And who doesn't want the best?*

♥ On the short list of life's important choices, choosing Dr. Right may well rank up there with choosing a spouse. Like the latter, a doctor can be a confidante, adviser and caretaker. But while love helps people pick a life partner, there's no such built–in honing device for finding a physician. However, there are criteria you can use to make an informed decision.

Do you need a doctor if you're not sick? Yes. Everybody should have a family practitioner or internist, if only from a prevention perspective. When something does go wrong, this is the physician you'll turn to first, and it helps if you've got an existing relationship. Whenever possible, go doctor–shopping when you're healthy, so you can think logically and aren't forced into making a hurried or desperate choice.

Consider the doctor's qualifications. Where did he go to school? Is he board–certified? Does he admit at a hospital that's easily accessible, and is it a place where you'd want to be treated? Robert Cathcart, who for many years was president of Pennsylvania Hospital, says, "Ultimately, I'd select the doctor ahead of the hospital. The hospital can be very supportive to the doctor, but it doesn't practice medicine."

Don't be embarrassed about scheduling a get–acquainted visit with a doctor you're interested in. These are the kinds of things you'll want to examine: What are the doctor's fees, and will he discuss them openly? Will he accept your insurance plan? Will he file the claims or leave that to you? Is the location of the office convenient? Are the hours compatible with your schedule? Is there parking or public transportation? How long does it take to get an appointment? How long will the doctor keep you waiting once you arrive? (Drop in at the waiting room and check this out.) Would the doctor make house calls in an emergency, or at least meet you at the office? Who covers for him nights and weekends?

How are you treated by the office personnel? Are they courteous and clear? For that matter, is their boss? Will the doctor take your phone calls to ask a question, and are your suggestions about treatment valued? Do you feel you get enough time and attention during your appointment? Can you have access to your medical records? Above all, does the doctor talk to you in language you understand, or is his style to issue orders and instructions?

If you need a special procedure or an operation, find out how many your doctor has done, how often she does it, her success rate (and rate of complications), and, where applicable, why she's recommending this new method over the old–fashioned way. In cases where you've heard rumors that your doctor has been slapped with malpractice suits, you can check that with *9479 Questionable Doctors*, published by the Public Citizen Health Research Group in May 1991. The book should be in large libraries, or call the Washington–based group at 202–833–3000. The Pennsylvania Health Care Cost Containment Council has just compiled statistics on the coronary bypass survival rates for individual surgeons throughout the state. You can obtain the free report by calling 717–232–6787, or by writing the council at the Harrisburg Transportation Center, Suite 208, 4th and Chestnut sts., Harrisburg, PA 17107.

When it comes to choosing a specialist, we've done some of the work for you by compiling the following list of those practitioners considered outstanding by their peers. We found them by mailing a detailed survey to some 3,000 doctors and nurses throughout the Delaware Valley. Our sample included the department chairs of over three dozen area hospitals, the fellows of the American College of Physicians and the American College of Surgeons, and members of several nursing associations. We asked: "If a member of your family had a medical or surgical problem, to whom would you send him for the best care and treatment?" The responses gave us a working list of top–notch practitioners, which we then refined and edited through extensive personal interviews with our own respected sources.

Are the results subjective? You bet, but that doesn't mean they aren't accurate. It was easy to eliminate those doctors who ought to be fixing televisions instead of people. It was harder to cull the best from a crowded field of nearly 16,000 physicians in the Delaware Valley. We think we succeeded, even though plenty of people complain every time we do this kind of thing that it's nothing more than a popularity contest. We disagree. While some doctors may get named by their pals for the wrong reasons, in our experience likability alone does not propel anyone to universal prominence. One doctor actually telephoned us when he received the survey, to say he thought he deserved to be included but didn't expect to get any votes: "I'm too aggressive. I market myself. I'm rich and successful. That's why other doctors don't like me. But I must be good, or patients wouldn't keep sending me their friends." Our research showed that he wasn't well–liked, but *was* excellent at what he did. We put him on the list.

No doubt there are doctors we should have mentioned but didn't.

Some we omitted on purpose; others we missed by accident. It's not hard to imagine that some first–rate physicians—especially those who aren't connected with major hospitals—escaped our attention. If your doctor is among them and you're satisfied with your care, don't switch.

We only included physicians who spend a majority of their time seeing patients. That automatically eliminated big–name researchers, as well as department chairmen whose administrative responsibilities limit their clinical hours.

Use this list as a guide, not as a bible. The ultimate selection of a personal physician is yours, not ours. When you're looking for a doctor, pay attention to your instincts. Steer clear of any physician who treats you like an object. Fortunately, Philadelphia happens to be a major medical center with an abundance of qualified docs—that's why there is such fierce advertising and marketing going on here. If something tells you that you're not getting the kind of medical attention you're entitled to, or that your doc is one of those who believes M.D. stands for Medical Deity, complain or move on. You are the buyer, and your health deserves at least as much consumer research as you'd give your next car.

## STATE OF THE ART

*The practice of medicine has undergone epochal changes in the last generation. Doctors earn more money than ever, but their dissatisfaction with the profession is also at record levels. Technology has made the once–miraculous seem routine, but these miracles fetch a price that society is increasingly unwilling to pay. What's it like to practice medicine in these times? We asked 18 of our top doctors some of the questions you'd want to ask if you knew it wouldn't get added to your bill.*

**Dr. Bradley Fenton, internist, Presbyterian Hospital:**
**Q:** Are better–informed patients a bonus or a burden for doctors?
**A:** It's a mixed blessing. Today's public knows all about the advances in medicine from the media, but they don't know how to interpret a lot of the information. That raises unrealistic expectations, and often forces doctors to rely too heavily on fancy technology, which isn't necessarily better than clinical judgment.

**Dr. Myron Yanoff, ophthalmologist, Hahnemann University Hospital:**
**Q:** What has been the most significant advance in your specialty?
**A:** Clearly, it's the increased technology. We can do things today with safer and better instruments that weren't possible when I started practice. We're using lasers in every part of the eye. We have sutures thinner than eyelashes. We can control glaucoma without cutting, and prevent most diabetics from going blind. The changes have really been dramatic.

**Dr. David Paskin, surgeon, Pennsylvania Hospital:**
**Q:** Why are medical school applications dropping?
**A:** Doctors have been hit hard by litigation. They've lost respect in the community. The profession is seen as less glamorous and more demanding. And that's really too bad, because there is no job in the world that has greater rewards. Nothing can match the gratitude of a patient you've cured.

**Dr. Michael Perstchuk, psychiatrist, Graduate Hospital:**
**Q:** What's been your greatest disappointment?
**A:** That medicine has increasingly become a business. An incredible amount of my time is taken up dealing with insurance companies over payments–time that could be much better spent doing research and seeing patients. I'd like to just deal with giving patients what they need, instead of trying to find a way to work the system to get those needs filled.

**Dr. Max Ronis, otolaryngologist, Temple University Hospital:**
**Q:** Do patients expect too much from doctors?
**A:** Media hype and publicity have led people to have unrealistic expectations about medicine in general. In the old days, I could tell somebody their hearing was bad and they'd have to learn to live with it. They'd say, "Okay, Doc." Now they say, "Well, fix it." The technology is so dazzling that people believe there must be a pill or operation to cure everything.

**Dr. Stephen Gluckman, infectious disease specialist, Cooper University Medical Center:**
**Q:** How has AIDS changed the way you practice medicine?
**A:** I had to learn how to cope with dying, how to deal with all the social and emotional issues of a long–term, lingering disease. This process of developing a rich relationship with patients has actually been quite gratifying and uplifting. I'm able to be like the old–fashioned doctor I wanted to become when I started medical school.

**Dr. Paul Gross, dermatologist, Pennsylvania Hospital:**
**Q:** How can advertising assist patients in choosing a doctor?
**A:** Unless someone is shopping for a specific service at a specific price, advertising doesn't help patients, because you can't tell anything about quality from an ad. Its one advantage is making people aware of a new procedure, like treating leg veins. Don't be presold by reading an ad. Go meet the doctor, and try to get a personal recommendation.

**Dr. Virginia LiVolsi, pathologist, Hospital of the University of Pennsylvania:**
**Q:** How did you choose your specialty?
**A:** I loved solving the puzzle of what's wrong with a patient. So often we're the ones doctors turn to for explanations. That's very gratifying intellectually. I also get tremendous satisfaction knowing I can serve patients without having to deal with the emotional aspects of their care.

**Dr. Ronald Bolognese, obstetrician, Pennsylvania Hospital:**
**Q:** How does concern about malpractice influence what you do?
**A:** It's become a constant factor. It drives up the cesarean rate, because doctors are afraid to take any risk. It forces us to do more tests to protect ourselves, which drives up costs. And it's become a barrier in the doctor–patient relationship, made it more adversarial. You're always worried: If a patient is unhappy or dissatisfied, will she sue me? Doctors are much warier.

**Dr. Leonard Bruno, neurosurgeon, Germantown Hospital:**
**Q:** What's the patient's responsibility in a treatment program?
**A:** The best outcomes occur when patients see doctors as a resource and themselves as active members of the health–care team. Often patients wind up being too passive. They don't question the doctor enough, don't discuss their problems. I've had people stop taking medicine instead of telling me it upsets their stomachs.

**Dr. Stanton Smullens, vascular surgeon, Jefferson Hospital:**
**Q:** What's been the most rewarding aspect of your work?
**A:** Without a doubt, dealing with patients. It's a privilege to be involved with people at very dramatic times in their lives. The closeness that comes out of that is immensely satisfying. There's also the reward of fine craftsmanship, when I've performed a difficult surgical problem well.

**Dr. R. Barrett Noone, plastic surgeon, Bryn Mawr Hospital:**
**Q:** What do your colleagues complain about the most?
**A:** In general, the paperwork related to insurance; in my specialty, the loss of ethics due to advertising and competition. I also hear complaints about the loss of prestige. When I entered medicine, doctors were highly regarded members of the community. Today they're viewed merely as service providers. Some of that's our fault, for being too eager to make a buck. But it's changing.

**Dr. Michael J. O'Connor, neurosurgeon, Graduate Hospital:**
**Q:** What's the value of a second opinion?
**A:** It's not wise to question a doctor every step of the way, but it's certainly reasonable in any long course of medical care with one doctor, who's treating you for something like high blood pressure, to get a second opinion about major surgery. If that doesn't agree with the first, get a third, and make your doctor explain his position.

**Dr. Warren Katz, rheumatologist, Presbyterian Hospital:**
**Q:** Do you spend enough time with your patients?
**A:** Not as much as I'd like, but I do try to make the time count. That means listening to patients very closely, answering their questions, and addressing their fears, especially the unexpressed ones. And I believe greatly in therapeutic touch. Medications are more effective when the doctor is tuned into his patients psychologically and recognizes the

value of touching.

### Dr. Dominic Corrigan, endocrinologist, Abington Hospital:
**Q:** Is there a downside in the evolution of medicine from an art to a high-tech science?
**A:** Yes. The complexity and sophistication of technology has the effect of sometimes separating us from our patients. We can measure every little thing, but it's harder and harder to explain to people what we're doing. We have a real problem translating this highly complicated information into something our patients can understand.

### Dr. Barbara Fowble, radiation oncologist, Hospital of the University of Pennsylvania:
**Q:** When should a patient choose a university hospital over a community hospital?
**A:** Many things can be done equally well in both. But more complicated treatments can be handled better in places where doctors have a combination of experience and expertise. Ask how many of the procedures the doctor has done. What are his or her results? If it comes down to a choice between care and convenience, always choose care. The convenience is temporary.

### Dr. Francis L. Hutchins Jr., gynecological surgeon, Graduate Hospital:
**Q:** When should a patient change doctors?
**A:** When they are not getting a clear picture of what the problem is and what their options are, or if the doctor says this is the *only* way to do things and is unwilling to discuss the pros and cons of other possibilities. Patients should feel like partners with their doctors, not like they're being told what to do as if they were children.

### Dr. David Langer, neurosurgical intern, Hospital of the University of Pennsylvania:
**Q:** What do the words "best doctor" mean to someone like you, just entering the profession?
**A:** I've been impressed with how much of medicine is unscientific, and how important clinical judgement is. The doctors I admire are those who have technical skill, the ability to educate their patients, an interest in advancing their field through research, a concern for the doctor-patient relationship, and a sense of ethics. I'm kind of glad doctors are no longer seen as gods. In the long run, it's better for us to be humanized.

# MEDICAL SPECIALISTS

## ♥ ALLERGY & IMMUNOLOGY

Any allergy, be it hay fever or a penicillin reaction, is an abnormal response by the body's immune system to something ingested or inhaled. The allergist will do skin or sometimes blood tests to identify the cause of the symptoms (hives, rashes or sneezing). If the irritant can't be avoided—by eliminating an offending food, for instance—a series of injections is used to develop immunity.

Paul C. Atkins, *HUP*
Eliot H. Dunsky, *Hahnemann*
George R. Green, *Abington*
Herbert Mansmann Jr., *Jeff*
Sheryl F. Talbot, *Pennsylvania*
Burton Zweiman, *HUP*

## ♥ ANESTHESIOLOGY

A critical part of any surgical procedure is the choice of how to numb the patient. Should he be awake or asleep? Should she have local, general or regional anesthesia? Patients frequently leave these decisions up to the surgeon, but there is no reason why you cannot discuss the options yourself with an anesthesiologist.

James Duckett, *Presbyterian*
James R. Harp, *Pennsylvania*
Thomas D. Mull, *Bryn Mawr*
Stanley Muravchic, *HUP*
Henry Rosenberg, *Hahnemann*
Joseph Seltzer, *Jeff*
Linda Sundt, *Wills*

## ♥ CARDIOLOGY

Heart problems are classified as congenital (murmurs, valve abnormalities) or acquired (angina, heart failures). The cardiologist treats both kinds. Following diagnosis, this doctor will either recommend surgery to correct the defect, or manage the condition with noninvasive measures, such as drugs, diet and exercise.

David J. Eskin, *Abington*
William S. Frankl, *Hahnemann*
Irving M. Herling, *HUP*
Mark E. Josephson, *HUP*
*(sp: electrophysiology)*
Morris N. Kotler, *Einstein*
Terry Langer, *Presbyterian*
Bernard L. Segal, *Presbyterian*
Harvey L. Waxman, *CMC*
*(sp: electrophysiology)*

**Cardiac Catheterization:**
A number of heart problems related to blocked arteries are handled by this specialist, who is an expert at threading an ultrathin tube through the blood vessels for diagnostic reasons and for therapeutic applications, such as opening passageways and dissolving clots.

Sheldon Goldberg, *Jeff*
John W. Hirshfeld, *HUP*
Hratch Kasparian, *Graduate*
William J. Untereker, *Presbyterian*

## ♥ DERMATOLOGY

Any kind of skin irritation would be cause to visit a dermatologist—severe dandruff, acne, psoriasis, nail fungus, rashes, moles, eczema, even wrinkles. Because of the rise in skin cancer, anyone with a family history of melanoma or suspicious dark spots on the skin should see a dermatologist for an assessment.

Edward E. Bondi, *HUP*
Paul R. Gross, *Pennsylvania*

Gerald S. Lazarus, *HUP*
James Leyden, *HUP*
Marie Uberti–Benz, *Presbyterian*

**Cosmetic Dermatology:**
Many dermatologists develop specialties that focus on appearance. Their face–saving techniques include dermabrasion, collagen and silicone injections, and surgery to remove skin cancers.
Leonard Dzubow, *HUP*
Steven S. Greenbaum, *Jeff*
Paul Gross, *Pennsylvania*
Waine Johnson, *Graduate*
Albert M. Kligman, *HUP (sp: aging skin)*
James Leyden, *HUP*

### ♥ DIABETOLOGY

Great strides have been made in the management of diabetes, which occurs in two forms. The milder type, adult–onset diabetes, can usually be controlled through diet and medication; the more severe juvenile diabetes occurs in adults as well as children, and requires daily insulin intake. The following specialists treat adult diabetics with either problem.
Seth Braunstein, *HUP*
Harry Gottlieb, *MCP*
Charles Shuman, *Temple*

### ♥ ENDOCRINOLOGY

Endocrinologists treat a variety of problems stemming from the body's hormone–related systems. These include metabolic malfunctions, thyroid disorders, and adrenal diseases like Addison's disease and Cushing's syndrome.
Dominic Corrigan, *Abington*
Sol Epstein, *Einstein (sp: osteoporosis)*
Elihu W. Goren, *Germantown*
John G. Haddad, *HUP (sp: metabolic bone disease)*
Alan D. Marks, *Temple*
Leslie I. Rose, *Hahnemann*
Peter J. Snyder, *HUP*
John L. Turner, *Graduate (sp: AIDS)*

### ♥ FAMILY/GENERAL PRACTICE

In the good old days before every medical school graduate opted to became a specialist, GPs were the backbone of medicine. Now family medicine is itself a specialty, although it's still almost impossible to find a family doctor who makes house calls.
Irwin Becker, *Einstein/Germantown*
Barry R. Cooper, *Abington*
Harry Frankel, *Graduate*
Paul McCausland, *Bryn Mawr*
Robert Perkel, *Jeff*

### ♥ GASTROENTEROLOGY

Digestive disorders—ulcers, cancer, inflammatory bowel diseases, hiatal hernias—afflict some 20 million Americans, who visit this specialist so they can quit bellyaching.
Harris S. Clearfield, *Hahnemann*
Sidney Cohen, *Temple*
Julius J. Deren, *Graduate*
Anthony J. Dimarino Jr., *Presbyterian*
Susan J. Gordon, *Jeff*
William H. Lipshutz, *Pennsylvania*

### ♥ GERIATRICS

This relatively new specialty grew from the explosion of longer–liv-

ing Americans, who require care targeted to the medical problems of aging. While most physicians can and do treat older patients, it often can be useful to see someone with increased knowledge of the aging body.
 Raymond Cogen, *Einstein*
 Sarle Cohen, *Logan Square East*
 Martin Leicht, *Philadephia Geriatric Center*
 Joel Posner, *MCP*

## ♥ GYNECOLOGY/OBSTETRICS

Once a kindly doctor who delivered babies and talked a woman through menopause, this physician has developed into a sophisticated specialist treating the range of female medical conditions that begin with menstruation and continue through a woman's life. We divided this group into areas of primary concentration.

### General Gynecology:
Whether it's for a Pap smear, a mammography, or a discussion of hormone replacement therapy, every woman should see a gynecologist on a yearly basis.
 William Beck, *Pennsylvania*
 Eileen Engle, *Pennsylvania*
 David M. Goodner, *Jeff*
 Marvin R. Hyett, *Jeff*
 Kaighn Smith, *Lankenau*
 Michael Spence, *Hahnemann (sp: gynecologic infectious diseases)*
 Robert Weinstein, *HUP*

### Gynecologic Oncology:
These specialists restrict their gynecologic practices to treating various cancers of the female reproductive system.
 John A. Carlson Jr., *HUP*
 Enrique Hernandez, *MCP*
 W. Michael Hogan, *Lankenau*
 Charles E. Mangan, *Pennsylvania*
 John J. Mikuta, *HUP*

### Obstetrics:
William Beck, *Pennsylvania*
David Goodner, *Jeff*
Joel I. Polin, *Abington*
Robert Weinstein, *HUP*

### Gynecologic Surgery:
This covers those procedures related to noncancerous problems of the female reproductive organs, including hysterectomies, sterilization, endometriosis and fibroids.
 Francis L. Hutchins Jr., *Graduate/Lankenau (sp: operative laparoscopy)*
 Joseph Montello, *Jeff (sp: urogynecology)*
 Martin Weisberg, *Jeff (sp: operative laparoscopy)*
 Craig Winkel, *Jeff (sp: laparoscopy/pelviscopy)*

### High-Risk Pregnancy:
As more and more women delay childbearing until their 30s, complications in pregnancy have increased to the point where they are now handled by a select group of obstetricians. Consider this specialist when age or an existing medical problem like diabetes threatens either the life of the fetus or the mother's ability to carry to term.
 Ronald J. Bolognese, *Pennsylvania*
 Arnold Cohen, *HUP*
 Linda K. Dunn, *Abington (sp: genetics)*
 Michael T. Mennuti, *HUP (sp: genetics)*
 Nancy S. Roberts, *Lankenau*
 Ronald J. Wapner, *Jeff*

**Infertility:**
Remarkable scientific advances like in–vitro fertilization have made the old temperature chart practically obsolete. Couples should consider a fertility specialist when a year of trying to conceive has not produced a pregnancy.
  Jerome Check, *CMC*
  Stephen Corson, *Pennsylvania*
  Martin Freedman, *Holy Redeemer*
  Celso–Ramon Garcia, *HUP*
  Luigi Mastroianni Jr., *HUP*

♥ **HEMATOLOGY/ONCOLOGY**

In general, these physicians deal with blood diseases like anemia, hemophilia, leukemia, leukopenia, etc. But a number of them (as noted) concentrate their practices on treating cancer patients.
  Isadore Brodsky, *Hahnemann*
  *(sp: bone marrow)*
  Peter A. Cassileth, *HUP*
  *(sp: leukemia)*
  John Durocher, *Pennsylvania*
  John H. Glick, *HUP*
  *(sp: non–Hodgkin's lymphoma and breast cancer)*
  Donna J. Glover, *Presbyterian*
  Jack Goldberg, *CMC*
  Rosaline Joseph, *MCP*
  S. Benham Kahn, *Hahnemann*
  John S. MacDonald, *Temple*
  Michael J. Mastrangelo, *Jeff*
  *(sp: melanoma)*

♥ **INFECTIOUS DISEASE**

An infinite number of bacteria and viruses cause infections as they're transmitted person–to–person, or from other species to humans, as in the case of Lyme disease. This specialist identifies the source of the infection and selects drugs to help the immune system fight it. In recent years, AIDS has become a major thrust of this practitioner.
  R. Michael Buckley, *Pennsylvania*
  Stephen J. Gluckman, *CMC*
  Donald Kaye, *MCP*
  Bennett Lorber, *Temple*
  Rob Roy MacGregor, *HUP*
  Jerome Santoro, *Lankenau*

♥ **INTERNAL MEDICINE**

Often referred to as the doctor's doctor, the internist is a medical detective trained to identify elusive disorders. Besides being expert diagnosticians, internists also manage patients with complicated medical histories.
  Richard Baron, *Chestnut Hill*
  *(sp: geriatrics)*
  Roger Daniels, *Pennsylvania*
  Bradley W. Fenton, *Presbyterian*
  David R. Goldmann, *HUP*
  Edward H. McGehee, *Jeff*
  Wilbur W. Oaks, *Hahnemann*
  Paul M. Roediger, *Abington*
  Marie Savard, *Presbyterian*
  *(sp: family practice)*

♥ **NEPHROLOGY**

Far more kidney diseases are treated with dialysis than by transplants, so choose this physician carefully. You're likely to have a long–term relationship.
  James F. Burke, *Jeff*
  Martin Goldberg, *Temple*
  Robert A. Grossman, *HUP*
  Diane K. Jorkasky, *Presbyterian*
  Brendan P. Teehan, *Lankenau*
  Charles J. Wolf, *Pennsylvania*

♥ **NEUROLOGY**

The neurologist uses medication to treat a wide range of disorders involving the nervous system, from headaches to epilepsy to the aftereffects of a stroke. You'd also consult one for muscular dystrophy, movement or memory loss, pain, myasthenia gravis or Parkinson's disease.

   Robert D. Aiken, *Jeff*
   Rodney D. Bell, *Jeff (sp: cerebral vascular)*
   Christopher Clark, *Graduate (sp: Alzheimer's)*
   David G. Cook, *Pennsylvania*
   June Fry, *MCP (sp: sleep disorders)*
   Jeffrey I. Greenstein, *Temple (sp: neuro–immunology, multiple sclerosis)*
   Gunter Haase, *Pennsylvania*
   Richard N. Harner, *MCP (sp: epilepsy)*
   Howard I. Hurtig, *Graduate*
   Fred D. Lublin, *Jeff (sp: multiple sclerosis)*
   Elliot L. Mancall, *Hahnemann*
   Donald Silberberg, *HUP*

## ♥ OPHTHALMOLOGY

You can have your vision checked by an optometrist or get your glasses from an optician, but an ophthalmologist is the only medical doctor qualified to diagnose and treat problems of the eye. This speciality divides into several sub-specialities, as noted.

### General Ophthalmology:
   Dion R. Ehrlich, *Jeanes*
   Louis A. Karp, *Pennsylvania/Scheie*
   Micheal L. Kay, *Wills*
   Micheal A. Naidoff, *Wills*
   Charles W. Nichols, *HUP*
   Myron Yanoff, *Hahnemann*

### Cataracts:
As part of the natural aging process, the lens of eye gradually clouds like a frosty window. The resulting blurred or fuzzy vision is corrected by surgically removing the damaged lens and replacing it with an intraocular implant.

   Raymond Adams, *Graduate*
   Daniel Merrick Kane, *Wills*
   Stephen B. Lichtenstein, *Wills/Lankenau*
   Steve B. Siepser, *Wills/Montgomery*

### Cornea:
Anything from a scratch to herpes simplex can damage the transparent membrane covering the eye. Most problems are medically treated; some necessitate cornea transplants.

   Elisabeth J. Cohen, *Wills/Lankenau*
   Peter R. Laibson, *Wills/Lankenau*
   Irving M. Raber, *Lankenau*

### Glaucoma:
One of the leading causes of blindness is a buildup of pressure within the eye, which can usually be controlled with drugs. Early detection is important, and one reason to get a regular eye check-up after age 35.

   Marlene Moster, *Wills*
   George Spaeth, *Wills*
   Elliot B. Werner, *Hahnemann*
   Richard P. Wilson, *Lankenau*

### Neuro–Ophthalmology:
Deals with visual disturbances that stem from medical (and neurological) conditions such as brain tumors, multiple sclerosis, stroke and myasthenia gravis.

   Thomas Bosley, *Wills*
   Steven L. Galetta, *HUP*
   Mark L. Moster, *Temple*

Peter J. Savino, *Wills*
Robert C. Sergott, *Wills/Lankenau*

**Ocular Oncology:**
Treats cancers of the eye.
James J. Augsberger, *Lankenau*
Jerry A. Shields, *Wills*

**Ophthalmic Plastic Surgery:**
This specialist corrects drooping eyelids, removes tumors on the lids, fixes defects of the orbit and tear ducts, and also performs a popular cosmetic procedure called blepharoplasty.
Joseph Flanagan, *Wills/Lankenau*
James A. Katowitz, *Scheie*
David B. Soll, *CMC*
Mary Stefanyszyn, *Wills/Lankenau*
Allan E. Wulc, *Scheie*

**Retina and Vitreous:**
The retina is the lining on the back of the eye, comparable to the film that takes the picture in a camera. Any severe blow to the head may cause the retina to detach. The vitreous is the clear gel that fills the center of the eye. It may shrink for a variety of reasons and cause, among other things, retinal tear. Diabetes often damages these parts of the eye.
William Annesley *Wills/Lankenau*
William E. Benson, *Wills/Lankenau*
Alexander J. Brucker, *Scheie*
Jay L. Federman, *Wills*
Stephen H. Sinclair, *Hahnemann*
William Tasman, *Wills*

## ♥ OTOLARYNGOLOGY

Back when this speciality was known as ENT (ear, nose and throat), tonsillectomies and earaches were its bread and butter. Today these physicians, many of whom also do surgery, treat a range of problems of the head and neck: hearing loss, cancer of the larynx, taste and smell disorders, tinnitus and vertigo.
Joseph P. Atkins Jr., *Pennsylvania*
William Keane, *Pennsylvania*
David Kennedy, *HUP*
Louis D. Lowry, *Jeff*
Max Lee Ronis, *Temple*
Robert Sataloff, *Jeff/Graduate (sp: voice problems)*
Harvey D. Silberman, *Einstein/Rolling Hill*

## ♥ PATHOLOGY

Most patients have little contact with this specialist, who microscopically examines small pieces of tissue (known as biopsies) to determine the cause of an illness, be it cancer or an elusive microbe. When a biopsy is questionable, patients can and should request another expert opinion.
Barbara Atkinson, *MCP (sp: cytopathology)*
Hugh Bonner, *HUP/Chester County (sp: lymphoma)*
John S.J. Brooks, *HUP (sp: soft tissue)*
Harry S. Cooper, *Hahnemann*
David E. Elder, *HUP (sp: pigmented lesions)*
Virginia LiVolsi, *HUP*
Francis X. McBrearty Jr., *Lankenau*
Arthur S. Patchefsky, *Hahnemann*
Giuseppe Pietra, *HUP (sp: lung and heart disease)*
Emanuel Rubin, *Jeff (sp: liver)*

## ♥ PHYSICAL MEDICINE

Also known as physiatrists, these doctors not only provide rehabilitation to victims of accidents, strokes and sports–related injuries; they also treat persistent neck and back pain with exercise and therapy rather than surgery or drugs.

Ernest M. Baran, *Lafayette Hill Medical Center*
(sp: electrophysiology)
Francis J. Bonner Jr., *Graduate*
John F. Ditunno Jr., *Jeff*
Gerald J. Herbison, *Jeff*
Nathaniel Mayer, *Moss*
Frank Naso, *Jeff*
William E. Staas Jr., *Jeff/Magee*

## ♥ PSYCHIATRY

Unlike psychologists, who use only a wide variety of talk therapies for coping with emotional problems, psychiatrists are permitted to augment such treatment with drugs. Those below spend the majority of their time as clinical practitioners.

Joseph DiGiacomo, *HUP*
William R. Dubin, *Belmont Center*
Gary L. Gottlieb, *HUP*
(sp: geriatrics)
Alan Gruenberg, *Institute of Pennsylvania Hospital*
(sp: diagnostic testing)
Bradley H. Sevin, *Pennsylvania*
Barry Jay Schwartz, *HUP/Institute of Pennsylvania Hospital*
Levon D. Tashjian, *Institute of Pennsylvania Hospital*
James L. Stinnett, *HUP*
Robert M. Toborowsky, *Pennsylvania*

**Adolescent Psychiatry:**
Mary Anne Delaney, *Hahnemann*
Harold Kolansky, *Einstein*
Herbert E. Mandell, *Belmont Center*
G. Pirooz Sholevar, *Jeff*

**Eating Disorders:**
Susan Ice, *Belmont Center*
Michael Pertschuk, *Graduate*
Neal Satten, *Institute of Pennsylvania Hospital*

**Substance Abuse/Addiction:**
Charles Giannasio, *Belmont Center*
Donald Gill, *Institute of Pennsylvania Hospital*
Edward Gottheil, *Jeff*
Joseph Volpicelli, *HUP*

## ♥ PULMONARY

Lung specialists handle diseases like emphysema, bronchitis, pleurisy, pneumonia and lung cancer. The symptoms that might send you to one of these doctors include prolonged coughing, shortness of breath, chest pains, or blood in the sputum.

Michael P. Casey, *Pennsylvania*
Paul E. Epstein, *Graduate*
Stanley Fiel, *MCP*
(sp: cystic fibrosis)
William Figueroa, *Lankenau*
John Hansen–Flaschen, *HUP*
Eugene Lugano, *Pennsylvania*
Richard Snyder, *Abington*
Micheal Unger, *Pennsylvania*
(sp: laser bronchoscopy)

## ♥ RADIOLOGY

High–tech equipment like CAT scans and MRIs have taken this speciality light–years away from simply reading X–rays. The modern radiologist falls into one of two major subgroups: diagnosing problems from pictures, or treating diseases with radiation.

**Diagnostic Radiology:**
Abass Alavi, *HUP*
*(sp: nuclear medicine)*
Constantin Cope, *HUP*
*(sp: interventional)*
Murray Dalinka, *HUP*
*(sp: bone radiation)*
Stephen Feig, *Jeff*
*(sp: mammography)*
Mary Fisher, *Temple*
Barry B. Goldberg, *Jeff*
*(sp: ultrasound)*
Robert I. Grossman, *HUP*
*(sp: neuroradiology)*
Herbert Y. Kressel, *HUP*
*(sp: MRI)*
Marc S. Lapayowker, *Abington*
Igor Laufer, *HUP (sp: G.I.)*
David Levin, *Jeff*
*(sp: interventional)*
Wallace Miller, *HUP*
Bernard J. Ostrum, *Einstein*
Howard M. Pollack, *HUP*
*(sp: uroradiology)*
Vijay Rao, *Jeff (sp: neuroradiology)*

**Radiation Oncology:**
Luther W. Brady, *Hahnemann*
Barbara Fowble, *HUP*
*(sp: breast cancer)*
John R. Glassburn, *Pennsylvania*
Gerald E. Hanks, *Fox Chase*
Carl M. Mansfield, *Jeff*
Melvyn Richter, *Abington*

### ♥ RHEUMATOLOGY

Most of the rheumatologist's practice revolves around patients with arthritis. This inflammatory disease of the joints manifests itself in a variety of forms, from gout to crippling rheumatoid arthritis. This specialist also treats lupus, a connective–tissue disease.
Robert A. Gatter, *Abington*
Warren A. Katz, *Presbyterian*
Barry M. Schimmer, *Pennsylvania*
H. Ralph Shumacher Jr., *HUP*
Charles Tourtellotte, *Temple*

## SURGICAL SPECIALISTS

### ♥ CARDIAC/THORACIC

Some studies suggest that heart bypass surgery is performed more frequently than necessary. If you are a candidate for this procedure, it's wise to get a second opinion from a cardiologist. Most heart surgeons also operate on the chest, where they may remove tumors from the lung, the esophagus or the trachea.
Stanley K. Brockman, *Hahnemann*
Richard N. Edie, *Jeff*
Scott M. Goldman, *Lankenau*
W. Clark Hargrove, *Presbyterian*
Gerald M. Lemole, *Christiana (Delaware)*
James Sink, *Presbyterian*
John Bell–Thomson, *Einstein*

### ♥ COLON AND RECTAL

The most common reason for visiting this type of surgeon is hemorrhoids. Others include ulcerative colitis, Crohn's disease, and colon cancer, which now now ranks third among adult cancers in the United States. However, the prognosis is good if it's detected early.
Thomas L. Dent, *Abington*
Gerald J. Marks, *Jeff*
Alan M. Resnik, *Graduate*

## ♥ GENERAL SURGERY

In addition to all kinds of routine operations like hernia repair, appendectomy, and gallbladder removal, most skilled general surgeons also devote a large part of their practices to excising cancerous tumors.
>Herbert E. Cohn, *Jeff*
>*(sp: thoracic)*
>Julius A. Mackie, *HUP*
>Moreye Nusbaum, *Presbyterian*
>David L. Paskin, *Pennsylvania*
>Ernest F. Rosato, *HUP*
>Francis E. Rosato, *Jeff*
>Charles C. Wolferth Jr., *Graduate/Hahnemann*

**Oncologic Surgery:**
Practice restricted to cancer.
>John M. Daly, *HUP*
>James L. Weese, *Presbyterian*

**Breast cancer:**
>Harvey J. Lerner, *Germantown*
>Anne Rosenberg, *Jeff/HUP*
>Gordon F. Schwartz, *Jeff*
>Robert G. Somers, *Einstein*

## ♥ NEUROSURGERY

The advent of the operating microscope has greatly increased the scope of procedures these surgeons can successfully perform on the brain and spinal cord. These include operating on aneurysms, brain and pituitary tumors, seizure sites, and discs.
>Leonard Bruno, *Germantown*
>William A. Buchheit, *Temple*
>Eugene S. Flamm, *HUP*
>H. Warren Goldman, *MCP*
>Michael J. O'Connor, *Graduate*
>Frederick Simeone, *Pennsylvania*

## ♥ ORGAN TRANSPLANTS

The introduction of drugs to fight rejection made it possible to successfully transplant not only kidneys, but hearts and, increasingly, the liver and pancreas, too. The need for organs continues to outdistance supply, however. Anyone desiring information about organ donation should call KIDNEY–1.

**Heart:**
>Jeffrey B. Alpern, *Hahnemann*
>Verdi J. DiSesa, *HUP*

**Kidney:**
>Leonard Perloff, *HUP*

**Liver:**
>Clyde F. Barker, *HUP*
>Ali Naji, *HUP*
>Michael Moritz, *Jeff*

**Pancreas:**
>Michael J. Morris, *Einstein*
>Ali Naji, *HUP (sp: islets)*
>Leonard J. Perloff, *HUP*

## ♥ ORTHOPEDICS

Broken bones, severed tendons, defective or deteriorated joints, and sports injuries are the reasons people seek orthopedists, who, as noted below, tend to concentrate on particular body parts.

**General:**
>Arthur Bartolozzi, *Pennsylvania*
>Michael Clancy, *Temple/Shriners*
>Malcolm L. Ecker, *Chestnut Hill*
>John Esterhai, *HUP*
>*(sp: bone infections)*
>Robert P. Good, *Bryn Mawr*
>Eric L. Hume, *Jeff*
>Mary Ann Keenan, *Einstein*
>*(sp: neuro–orthopedics)*

Frederick S. Kaplan, *HUP*
(sp: medical osteoporosis)
Richard D. Lackman, *Jeff*
(sp: orthopedic oncology)

**Joints:**
Robert E. Booth, *Pennsylvania*
John M. Cuckler, *HUP (knees)*
John M. Fenlin Jr., *Jeff*
(sp: shoulders)
Paul A. Lotke, *HUP (sp: knees)*
James E. Nixon, *Graduate*
(sp: knees)
Richard Rothman, *Pennsylvania/Jeff*

**Hands:**
F. William Bora Jr., *HUP*
James Hunter, *Jeff*
Mark Nissenbaum, *Abington/Holy Redeemer*
A. Lee Osterman, *HUP*
Lawrence Schneider, *Jeff*

**Spine:**
Richard A. Balderston, *Pennsylvania*
Jerome M. Cotler, *Jeff*
Parvis Kambin, *Graduate*
Henry H. Sherk, *MCP*
Ronald Wisneski, *HUP*

**Sports Medicine:**
Nicholas A. DiNubile, *Delaware County Memorial*
(sp: rehab and performing arts)
Vincent J. DiStefano, *Graduate*
John R. Gregg, *Graduate/CHOP*
Phillip J. Marone, *Methodist/Jeff*
Lawrence S. Miller, *Lankenau*
(sp: shoulders)
Ray A. Moyer, *Temple*
Joseph S. Torg, *HUP*

♥ **PLASTIC SURGERY**

The leaders in this category excel in both reconstructive and cosmetic surgery, dividing their time between the two. They repair the disfigurements caused by burns, injuries or birth defects, and they are also in the beauty business, correcting everything from small breasts to large noses as well as counteracting the effects of aging.
James W. Fox IV, *Jeff*
Ralph W. Hamilton, *HUP*
(sp: rhytidectomy)
Donato D. LaRossa, *HUP*
(sp: cleft palate)
R. Barrett Noone, *Bryn Mawr/Lankenau*
Harvey M. Rosen, *Pennsylvania*
Murray W. Seitchik, *Einstein*
Linton A. Whitaker, *HUP/Pennsylvania*

**Facial/Cosmetic Surgery:**
These doctors, some of whom are not board–certified plastic surgeons, concentrate on procedures to improve appearance, such as face–lifts, eye–lifts, nose jobs and chemical peels.
Paul S. Kim, *Paoli Memorial*
Herbert Kean, *Jeff*
Emil P. Leibman, *Temple*
Julius Newman, *Graduate*
Charles E. Pappas, *Chestnut Hill*

**Liposuction**
The trendiest of the cosmetic procedures is usually quite safe in the right hands.
Leonard Dzubow, *HUP*
Richard L. Dolsky, *Graduate*
Zaki Ftaiha, *Graduate*
R. Barrett Noone, *Bryn Mawr/Lankenau*

♥ **TRAUMA SURGERY**

If you've been injured in an accident, try to get to a hospital where one of these people do emergency

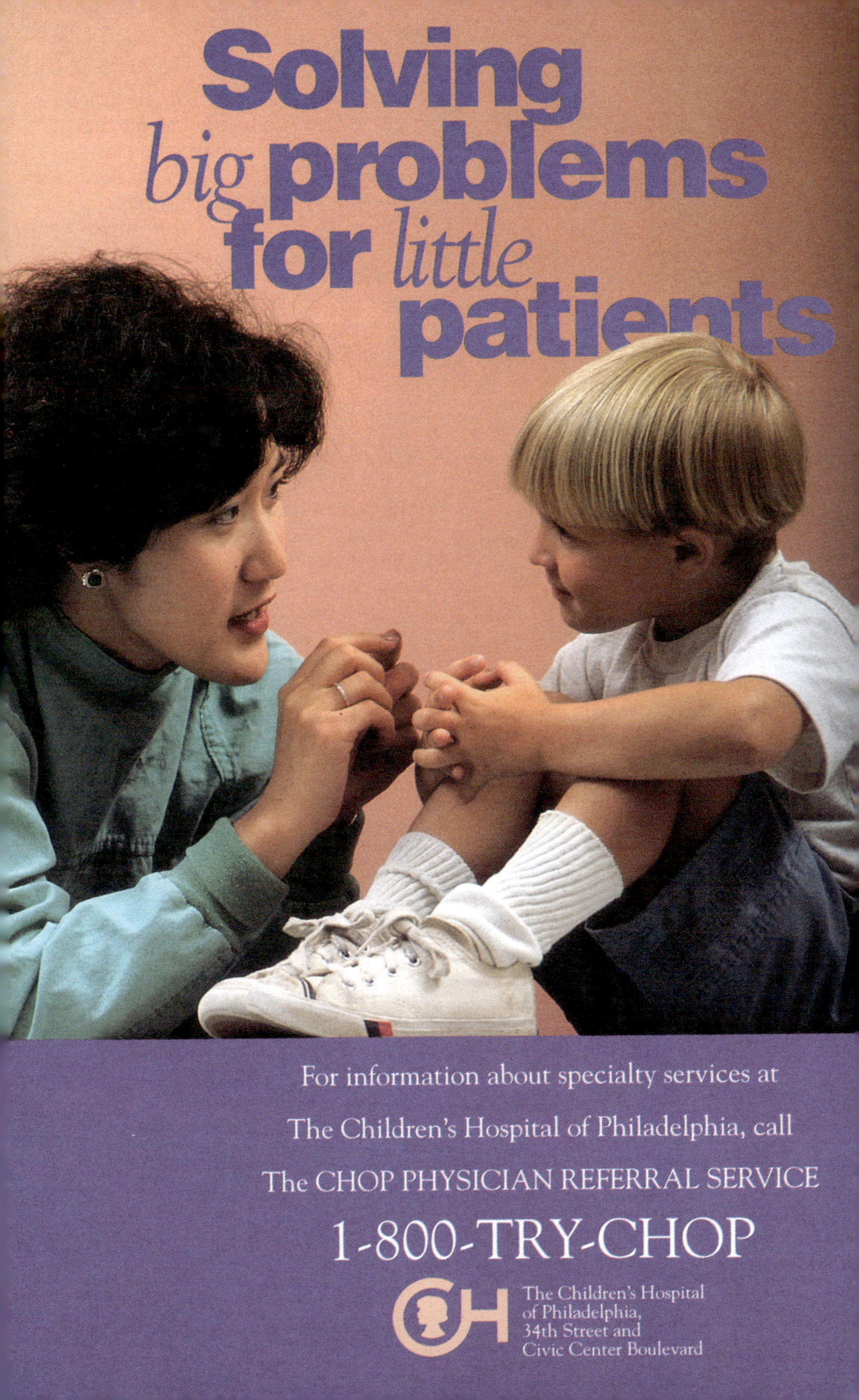

# Solving *big* problems *for little* patients

For information about specialty services at The Children's Hospital of Philadelphia, call

The CHOP PHYSICIAN REFERRAL SERVICE

## 1-800-TRY-CHOP

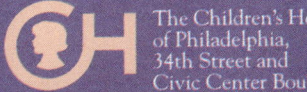

The Children's Hospital of Philadelphia, 34th Street and Civic Center Boulevard

operations.
    Robert F. Buckman, *Temple*
    William G. DeLong Jr., *CMC*
    C. William Schwab, *HUP*
    Jerome Vernick, *Jeff*

## ♥ UROLOGY

This speciality deals with organs of the urinary tract—kidneys, bladder, ureters—and the problems they manifest, such as cystitis, kidney stones and incontinence. It's also the male counterpart to the gynecologist, for matters of the prostate and genitals.
    Demetrius H. Bagley, *Jeff*
    *(sp: kidney stones and sexual dysfunction)*
    Richard E. Greenberg, *Abington/Fox Chase*
    *(sp: urologic oncology)*
    Irving H. Hirsch, *Jeff*
    *(sp: male fertility)*
    A. Richard Kendall, *Temple/Abington*
    Terrence R. Malloy, *Pennsylvania*
    Joel L. Marmar, *CMC*
    *(sp: male fertility)*
    S. Grant Mulholland, *Jeff*
    Alan Wein, *HUP*

## ♥ VASCULAR SURGERY

When a narrowing or blockage of the arteries impedes blood flow, bypass surgery provides an alternate route for the blood to reach tissues. This specialist operates mainly on the arteries of the abdomen and limbs, rather than the heart or brain.
    Henry D. Berkowitz, *Presbyterian*
    Anthony J. Comerota, *Temple*
    Dominic A. DeLaurentis, *Pennsylvania*
    Peter R. McCombs, *Abington*
    Leonard J. Perloff, *HUP*
    Louis Pierucci, *CMC*
    Stanton Smullens, *Jeff*

---

*Abbreviations have been used for the following area hospitals:*
Abington—Abington Memorial Hospital; Belmont Center— Belmont Center for Comprehensive Treatment; CHOP— Children's Hospital of Philadelphia; CMC–Cooper Hospital, University Medical Center; Einstein—Albert Einstein Medical Center, Northern Division; Fox Chase—Fox Chase Cancer Center; Germantown—The Germantown Hospital & Medical Center; Hahnemann—Hahnemann University Hospital; HUP—The Hospital of the University of Pennsylvania; Jeff—Thomas Jefferson University Hospital; Logan Square East—Logan Square East Care Center; Magee—Magee Rehabilitation Hospital; MCP—Hospital of the Medical College of Pennsylvania; Moss—Moss Rehabilitation Hospital;Presbyterian—Presbyterian Medical Center of Philadelphia; Scheie—Scheie Eye Institute; Shriners—Shriners Hospital for Crippled Chiuldren; Temple—Temple University Hospital; Wills—Wills Eye Hospital.

# Only one hospital can offer this combination of cardiac experience, technology and facilities...
## The Graduate Hospital.

♥ The cardiologist who performed the Delaware Valley's first coronary arteriogram in 1962.

♥ The specialist who has done more than 3,800 artery-clearing balloon angioplasty and 150 atherectomy procedures, making him one of the most active and experienced interventional cardiologists on the East Coast.

♥ Over 11,000 diagnostic and therapeutic cardiac catheterization procedures performed during the past five years by six hospital-based cardiologists with 138 years of combined experience.

♥ Two brand new and totally digitalized cardiac catheterization laboratories.

♥ An advanced non-invasive diagnostic laboratory headed by the immediate past president of the American Heart Association's Delaware Valley chapter.

♥ A state-of-the-art electrophysiology laboratory to diagnose and treat abnormal heart rhythms.

♥ An active and responsive second opinion program.

♥ A clinical research program offering the latest investigational drugs.

♥ An on-site cardiac surgery program providing a full range of open heart surgical procedures, including coronary artery bypass and valve repair and replacement.

*If you or a loved one has a heart problem, choosing the right hospital and the right doctors may be the most important decision you will ever make. Before you make that decision, ask your most pressing questions and demand straightforward answers. When you do,* **we're confident you'll choose Graduate.**

Physician Referral Service
1-800-654-GRAD

**THE GRADUATE HOSPITAL**
Divisions of Cardiology and Cardiothoracic Surgery
One Graduate Plaza  1800 Lombard Street  Philadelphia, PA 19146

Graduate Health System

# PLEASANT DREAMS

Not long ago, Becky's life had become a nightmare.

Becky's family didn't know *what* to do, or where to turn. Emotional problems made her act in ways her parents couldn't understand. Even her brother could tell that *something* was wrong. Now, Becky and her family are resting comfortably again.

They called **Child Assist Network**, a service of Philadelphia Child Guidance Center. Our referral specialists match the needs of children and adolescents with mental health and human service resources.

## Call 1-800-359-0800
TDD & Voice

**Serving Southeastern PA, Southern NJ, Northern DE**

 Philadelphia Child Guidance Center

34th Street & Civic Center Boulevard, Philadelphia, PA 19104

Dedicated to the mental health care of children, adolescents and their families since 1925. Affiliated with the University of Pennsylvania School of Medicine, The Children's Hospital of Philadelphia, Children's Seashore House.

**Child Assist Network** is supported by grants from The Pew Charitable Trusts and the City of Philadelphia, Department of Public Health, Office of Mental Health/Mental Retardation.

# 2

# For Children Only

*Who are the area's most respected pediatric specialists?*

♥ The doctors on this list are those most highly recommended by their peers. We compiled it the same way that we put together our list of adult specialists—by surveying over 1,000 pediatricians throughout the Delaware Valley and asking, "If your child had a medical or surgical problem, to whom would you send her?" The responses provided a working roster, which was then refined through extensive interviews with our sources. Doctors who spend most of their time in research and administration rather than in dealing with patients were eliminated.

We did our best to get a geographical spread, but despite that effort a preponderance of the doctors who made the cut work at Children's Hospital and, to a lesser extent, at St. Christopher's. We are extremely fortunate to have in Philadelphia two renowned institutions for treating children one world–class, the other of national stature. Obviously, these places are top–heavy with leading physicians.

Some readers may be disappointed that their wonderful and caring neighborhood pediatrician isn't included. The difficulty in compiling these kinds of lists is that qualified doctors quietly doing very good work outside of hospital settings are very hard to judge. And, generally speaking, they're perfectly fine for handling routine care. Almost all the pediatricians named here are people you'd turn to for a special problem. We hope you don't need them very often.

## THE DOCTOR IS IN

There are certain questions about children and their health that worry every parent: Does my child eat enough? When is a fever dangerous? Are vitamins necessary? Things like that. So we put together a short list of common concerns, and asked some of the best pediatricians in the city to address them. Here's what they said.

### Dr. Bruce Taubman, general practice, Cherry Hill

**Q:** My child won't eat anything except peanut–butter sandwiches. Should I be worried?

**A:** The rate at which a child grows and gains weight can be one of the most sensitive indicators of general health. When children are poor eaters, it may be difficult to tell simply by observation whether or not they're eating enough. That's why it's a good idea to have your pediatrician plot a height and weight chart as a guideline. Say, for example, a child at age two is very tiny, and ranks in the fifth percentile of the national average. If he remains in that percentile year after year, he's growing normally. But if at age four a child's in the 50th percentile and at age seven he's fallen much lower, that's a sign there's a problem.

Normal children usually manage to get the calories they need to grow without being forced to eat. In fact, I never saw a child who was losing weight because the mother wasn't trying hard enough to get food in him. If your child goes through a phase of eating nothing but hot dogs and macaroni and cheese, let him have as much as he wants, and don't worry about it. Your role is to limit his options: no dessert without dinner first, no chips between meals if lunch is left on the plate.

### Dr. Patrick Pasquariello Jr., general practice, Children's Hospital of Philadelphia

**Q:** What qualities should I look for in choosing a pediatrician?

**A:** A good guideline is the three As: Is the doctor affable, available and able? Since everybody goes through the same basic training, what's more significantly important is how doctors translate their knowledge into care. Here's where chemistry enters the picture. The doctor must relate well to the patient, and not everybody clicks. If your child doesn't like the doctor, pay attention to the complaint, and find out why. At the same time, the doctor needs to have a rapport with the parent, too, so he can interpret her needs. Is Mrs. S. the kind of mother who calls every time her child sneezes, or only when there is a real problem? This can be one of the difficulties with a group practice, where you see a different doctor on every visit. If you are unhappy with this arrangement, you can insist on seeing the one doctor you prefer; if that doesn't work, find another group. Finally, you want a pediatrician who is willing to spend time with you when you need the time.

### Dr. Stephen Ludwig, general practice, Children's Hospital of Philadelphia

**Q:** When should I be alarmed about a high fever?

**A:** Parents tend to be overly concerned about fevers. They are usually a sign of a common, minor viral infection, but sometimes they do indicate a more serious problem. What causes the worry is wondering which it is, and that depends more on the sick child's behavior than on the thermometer reading. There is little reason to be upset with a 104° fever if the child is playing with his toys and acting normally. On the other hand, a child can be much sicker with a 102° fever if he is extremely lethargic, weak, and not eating.

Another thing to look for is how the fever responds to medication. Within a half–hour of a dose of Tylenol, the fever should drop one or two degrees. A study at CHOP showed that two–thirds of the children brought to the emergency room with high fevers had not been given enough medication. The dosage changes with the weight of the child, so read the package insert to be sure you're using the right amount.

You can put a child in a tepid water bath to lower the fever, though usually that's not necessary. Alcohol rubs are definitely not recommended. And there is no need to fear febrile seizures. They occur in only 2 to 5 percent of children between the ages of six months and six years, and are more frightening than dangerous.

### Dr. Leonard Graziani, neurologist, Thomas Jefferson University Hospital

**Q:** My little boy seems so much more wild than his friends. How can I tell if he's hyperactive?

**A:** About 10 to 15 percent of boys under five are diagnosed with attention deficit disorder, compared to just 3 to 5 percent of girls. While it's accepted that little boys are supposed to be more active, it exceeds normal bounds when the child is viewed as disruptive and a troublemaker. There are a number of things you can observe to determine if your child falls in that category: Does he have trouble sitting still at school or at the dinner table? Can he sit long enough to watch the full segment of a favorite TV show, like *Sesame Street*? Do you find yourself saying, "I can't invite children over, because he gets too wild and starts fights when he's excited"? Does he get invited to other children's homes more than once? Does he get out of control at birthday parties? Does he trip and fall frequently? Does he go to bed willingly, or collapse from exhaustion after a nightly argument?

There are also certain age–appropriate signposts. A three–year–old should be speaking clearly enough so that family members understand him. At four, he should be understood by strangers and able to answer "why" questions. For example, "Why does Mommy wear a watch?" should not elicit an answer like "On her arm." Also at four, he should be able to take turns and play in an organized way, and at five he should be playing outdoors without supervision.

If your child has any one of the problems listed or fails to meet a signpost, that's a warning. If he has two or more, he should be evaluated by a neurologist.

### Dr. William Zavod, general practice, Philadelphia

**Q:** When should I call the doctor in the middle of the night?

**A:** If you are really concerned about something, you should always feel free to call your pediatrician. However, some things are more important to check out than others. They include the following: Any temperature above 100° in a child under three months, or a fever above 100° in an older child who is extremely lethargic, hard to rouse or crying uncontrollably; severe, persistent abdominal pain that isn't helped by Tylenol and lasts more than 30 minutes; the sudden onset of a croupy cough that sounds like a barking seal and doesn't respond to steam within 30 minutes; the acute onset of ear pain that doesn't respond to ear drops or an analgesic after 45 minutes; when a child with a bad cold wakes up and can't catch his breath; when a baby cries for over three-quarters of an hour and can't be consoled.

In general, vomiting and diarrhea often look more threatening than they are, and don't require special attention unless they persist for 12 to 18 hours. Since sick children may have trouble taking medication by mouth, it's a good idea to keep acetaminophen suppositories in your medicine cabinet for wee-hour emergencies.

### Dr. Gail Slap, adolescent medicine, Children's Hospital of Philadelphia
**Q:** When do I need to take my teenager to the doctor?
**Q:** Adolescents should be seen at least once a year, whether they are sick or not, so that they have an established relationship with a health provider when they do need one. While all doctors may be medically qualified to treat adolescents, it's important to choose one who understands puberty and feels comfortable talking to teens. Prevention is the core of adolescent medicine, and that often boils down to having a conversation about things like birth control and drug abuse. Teenagers who have connections with physicians are more likely to seek help before they do something, instead of when a crisis occurs. A doctor can also be helpful in addressing those doubts that teens tend to suffer through in silence: Am I developing the way I should, are my breasts too big for my age, why is my period late, why am I so scrawny?

Certain persistent physical symptoms, such as "My stomach hurts" or "I'm always tired," should be looked into. In addition, behavior problems can be a sign of ill health. Take note of a decline in school performance, withdrawal from normal activities and friends, excessive anger and rebellion. And because eating disorders are common at this age, watch for rapid weight gain or loss. In general, the three danger areas to keep an eye on are changes in sleeping, eating and energy.

### Dr. Glenn Isaacson, otorhinolaryngologist, St. Christopher's Hospital for Children
**Q:** Why do so many children today get ear infections, and how are they best treated?
**A:** One explanation for the increase is day care. More children are repeatedly exposed to infections at an early, vulnerable age. In fact, inner-ear infections and fluid in the middle ear are the most common reasons children get referred to my office. I think pediatricians are simply more aware of these problems, because of better diagnostic techniques and an understanding of the potential hearing loss they may cause.

The initial treatment for ear infections is antibiotics. When these aren't effective in controlling recurrent problems (six bouts a year or more), we put in ear tubes. This very safe and highly effective surgery became popular in the mid '60s, and is today the most common operation performed on children. In response to complaints that it was being performed too often, a study was done, which led to guidelines that most otorhinolaryngologists strictly follow. Since the introduction of ear tubes, complications once caused by ear infections have almost disappeared, and we see far less ear disease in young adults, as a result of prompt treatment in childhood.

### Dr. Virginia Stallings, nutritionist, Children's Hopital of Philadelphia
**Q:** Should children take vitamins?
**A:** Genuine isolated vitamin deficiencies, like scurvy and rickets, are extremely rare in this country, partly because many of our foods are fortified. If children eat an age–appropriate and varied diet, they really don't need vitamins. However, most children eat funny. They get very picky, and often eat only those foods they like. While some narrow ranges are fine, others are not. Because parents worry their children aren't getting the proper nutrition, there is no harm in a one–a–day multiple vitamin. But I'm concerned about giving too much of a supplement, so parents should stick to the recommended dose.

I prefer those vitamins that have iron, and I'd also suggest that if a child has an allergy or intolerance to milk, the parent should consider a calcium supplement.

### Dr. Rosemary Casey, general practice, Children's Hospital of Philadelphia
**Q:** My child gets sick a lot and often takes antibiotics. Is there any danger in taking these medicines too often or for too long?
**A:** There are definite advantages to antibiotics in treating bacterial infections and preventing the development of possible complications. But as with all good things, there are problems, such as allergic reactions ranging from mild hives to serious rashes, and side effects that show up as diarrhea, nausea and vomiting.

The important consideration is whether the illness is bacterial or viral. There is rarely any reason to put a child on an antibiotic for a viral infection, like a cold, the flu, bronchiolitis, mononucleosis, or a sore throat that cultures negative for strep. Parents sometimes ask whether taking antibiotics will create resistance to them. It's possible, but it's not common, and when it does occur, there are always alternate choices that can be used. The risk of not treating the bacterial infection is greater than the risk of taking an antibiotic.

### Dr. Lillian Kravis, allergist, Children's Hospital of Philadelphia
**Q:** My child has hay fever and a chronic runny nose. How do I know if she needs allergy shots?
**A:** Immunotherapy—allergy shots—need not be undertaken until other measures have failed. These include environmental adjustments, like removing a pet from the home, changing feather pillows and down comforters for foam pillows and blankets, and removing from the child's room dust collectors like heavy drapes and items stored under the bed. There are also many excellent antihistamines, decongestants

and nasal steroids which may do the job. Unfortunately, sometimes they have to be discontinued because they aren't well-tolerated.

What ultimately determines treatment is the severity of the child's symptoms. Are they causing secondary complications and interfering with the quality of life? If a child can't get a good night's sleep because she can't breathe, and medication isn't helping, then allergy shots may be necessary.

### Dr. Eric N. Faerber, radiologist, St. Christopher's Hospital for Children

**Q:** My little girl was sent for an ultrasound because she had a urinary tract infection. Are these diagnostic tests dangerous for children?
**A:** Children today are far more likely to visit a radiologist than their parents were, but this is no cause for alarm. Certain of the techniques we use, like ultrasound and MRI, do not involve ionizing radiation, and have no known side effects at this time. Renal ultrasound—a way to get information about the kidneys—is noninvasive, and has actually replaced a riskier technique called IVP, which required injecting dye into the child's blood vessels. As for MRI, the worst that could happen is a small reaction to the oral sedation sometimes needed to help the youngster remain still inside the machine.

There are times—say, when a bone is broken or pneumonia is suspected—that radiation is unavoidable. Usually the number of X-rays ordered will be less than for an adult. Certain hospitals have a special film/screen combination that decreases the dose of radiation; you may want to ask about it. Similarly, when CAT scans are necessary, we try to limit the number of images, to keep the risk as low as possible.

### Dr. Anthony L. Rostain, psychiatrist, Philadelphia Child Guidance Center

**Q:** What is the best way to handle a tantrum?
**A:** If your child has tantrums, it certainly doesn't mean you are a bad parent. For most children, a tantrum is a normal way to express frustration and/or anger, or to gain control of a situation. Some children are just born with a higher level of aggression and a lower level of tolerance, which makes them more prone to tantrums. While it's difficult not to respond when a child is kicking and screaming, or even banging his head and holding his breath, the rule of thumb is to ignore the tantrum whenever possible. Walk away. Don't try to argue or talk the child down. However, when you see a shift into uncontrolled sobbing, where the child almost seems to be in an altered state of anxiety, you will need to interfere. That's not the same as giving in. It means calming the child by holding him, stroking his hair, rocking and soothing him with words like "Mommy loves you." When he's quieter, distract him to an activity different from the one that triggered the tantrum.

In public places, tantrums are harder to ignore. They often succeed in getting the child what he wants because the parent, wrestling with feelings of anger and intimidation, gets too embarrassed to let the outburst run its course. The better approach would be to say something like, "Fine. Have a tantrum. You are not getting what you want." Then walk away (but stay within the child's vision), and continue your shopping or whatever you were doing until the child stops carrying on. If that is out of the question, you could substitute a more acceptable alternative, like a cheap toy for an expensive one, to quiet the child. What's least helpful is capitulation, because the child learns that screaming is the way to accomplish his goal.

If your child has more than one or two tantrums a day, consult your doctor. It may be a sign that something else is happening—inadequate sleep, stress, a learning disability.

### Dr. Allan M. Arbeter, infectious diseases, Albert Einstein Medical Center

**Q:** With so many stories appearing about complications due to vaccines, should parents be concerned about routine immunizations?

**A:** One of the standard components of routine care for healthy children is an immunization schedule. Every vaccine used for infants and toddlers has been developed, licensed, and put into circulation because of a bona fide need to prevent a disease that's life–threatening or could alter a child's ability to function at a peak level. Virtually every one of these vaccines has some clinical side effects, which in recent years has been severely overblown and sensationalized by the media. Real public– health data and close scrutiny of pediatric practices don't support the fear generated by this hoopla. To the contrary, they show the overwhelming safety and efficacy of routine childhood immunizations compared to the problems caused by the diseases they're targeted to prevent.

## MEDICINE

### ♥ ADOLESCENT MEDICINE

When your child seems too old to visit a doctor's office teeming with crying babies and not old enough for the doctor you use, you may want to schedule an appointment with this specialist, who treats not only the physical ailments of adolescents, but some of the sensitive emotional issues as well—i.e., sexually transmitted diseases and drug and alcohol abuse. While not trained as gynecologists, they do pelvic examinations and discuss things, like birth control, that would make some pediatricians blush.

Paula Braverman, *St. Chris*
Samuel K. Parrish, *MCP*
Donald Shwarz, *CHOP*
Gail Slap, *CHOP/HUP*

### ♥ ALLERGY

Allergies are abnormal responses by the immune system to a substance that's been ingested or inhaled. Allergists attempt to pinpoint the cause for the responses primarily through skin tests and food–elimination tests. They then create treatment programs combining diet, environmental management, medication and injections. Since asthma, a major childhood disease, is often caused by an allergic reaction, a large portion of this speciality is devoted to treating asthma cases.

Eliot Dunsky, *Hahnemann*
Jeffrey Greene, *CHOP*
Lillian Kravis, *CHOP*
Herbert Mansmann, *Jefferson*
Stephen J. McGeady, *Jeff*
Stephen A. Raphael, *St. Chris*

## ♥ ANESTHESIA/INTENSIVE CARE

While the primary thrust of this specialty is sedating children for surgery, a large part also involves providing breathing assistance to critically ill children in intensive care units. These doctors are experts in treating shock and monitoring life–support systems.
John Downes, *CHOP*
Robert G. Kettrick, *du Pont*
David Lowe, *St. Chris*
Russell Raphaely, *CHOP*

## ♥ CARDIOLOGY

More and more congenital heart defects are being discovered in childhood by these specialists, who, in addition to evaluating patients for heart surgery, also treat acquired heart problems, like rheumatic fever and arrhythmias.
Iain F.S. Black, *St. Chris*
Richard Donner, *St. Chris*
Sidney Friedman, *CHOP*
Jim Huhta, *Pennsylvania*
Victoria L. Vetter, *CHOP*
Henry Wagner, *CHOP*
Paul M. Weinberg, *CHOP*
*(sp: neonatology)*

## ♥ DERMATOLOGY

It would be natural to assume that the bulk of the pediatric dermatologist's practice consists of acne patients, but in fact this specialist is more likely to see eczema cases and problems like chronic hives and port–wine stains.
Paul J. Honig, *CHOP*
Peter Koblenzer, *St.Chris*
Walter Tunnesen Jr., *CHOP*

## ♥ DIABETIES

One in 600 children is diabetic. The warning signs are frequent urination, unusual thirst, and weight loss. When this disease occurs in childhood, it affects normal development, so besides manipulating insulin doses, this specialist also gets involved in the dietary and psychological management of the patient.
Lester Baker, *CHOP*
Robert Kaye, *MCP*
Iraj Rezvani, *St. Chris*

## ♥ EMERGENCY MEDICINE

Few children make it to adulthood without at least one visit to the emergency room, for a fracture, a cut requiring stitches, ingestion of a poisonous substance, a severe head injury, or any of the other accidents that put gray hair on a parent's head. Today these specialists are trained to pick up signs of child abuse in what look like routine injuries.
Fred Henretig, *MCP/CHOP*
*(sp: pediatric toxicology)*
Mark Joffe, *St. Chris*
Steven Selbst, *CHOP*
David Wagner, *MCP*
*(sp: pediatric surgery)*

## ♥ ENDOCRINOLOGY

In youngsters, endocrine disorders other than diabetes tend to show up as problems with growth (the child is unusually short or tall) or sexual development (the changes related to puberty appear too soon or too late). The treatment plan usually involves drugs or hormones.

 Angelo M. DiGeorge, *St. Chris*
 Thomas Moshang, *CHOP*
 Judith L. Ross, *MCP/Mercy Catholic*
 Charles A. Stanley, *CHOP*

## ♥ GASTROENTEROLOGY

The symptoms that would send a child here include chronic vomiting, internal bleeding, diarrhea, constipation, and stomach aches. The problems seen by this specialist include inflammatory bowel disease, ulcers, chronic liver and pancreatic disease, and lactose intolerance.

 Steven Altschuler, *CHOP*
 Emanuel Lebenthal, *Hahnemann*
 Ian Gibbons, *Jeff*
 David Piccoli, *CHOP*
 Steven Widzer, *St. Chris/Einstein/Bryn Mawr*

## ♥ GENERAL PEDIATRICS

It would go beyond the scope of this list to name every competent neighborhood pediatrician in the Philadelphia area. If you are satisfied with your doctor, stay where you are. We have noted three highly regarded diagnosticians. These are the experts a pediatrician calls when there's a problem figuring out what's wrong with a child or the need for a second opinion. You can use them, too. The others are considered by their peers to be outstanding generalists.

*Diagnosticians*
 David Cornfeld, *CHOP*
 Patrick Pasquariello Jr., *CHOP*
 David Smith, *St. Chris*

*Generalists*
 Stewart Barbera, *Holy Redeemer/St. Chris*
 Rosemary Casey, *CHOP*
 J. Ronald Halenda, *private practice, Media*
 Stephen Ludwig, *CHOP*
 Edward Rosof, *private practice, Marlton*
 Bruce Taubman, *private practice, Cherry Hill*
 John M. Tedeschi, *private practice, Cherry Hill*
 William Zavod, *private practice, Philadelphia*

## ♥ GENETICS

As advanced techniques in gene analysis have made it possible to identify so many inherited disorders, from Tay–Sachs to Down's syndrome to muscular dystrophy, this specialty has mushroomed. It includes a wide variety of pre– and post–natal diagnostic procedures and family counseling.

 Laird G. Jackson, *Jeff* (sp: internal medicine)
 Adele Schneider, *Einstein*
 Kathleen E. Toomey, *St. Chris*
 Elaine Zackai, *CHOP/Lankenau*

## ♥ HEMATOLOGY

In the old days, a mother would pull down the lower lid of her child's eye, and if the rim was pink instead of red, she'd start spooning in cod–liver oil. Today anemia is more appropriately treated by a hematologist, who also handles other blood diseases, such as sickle–cell anemia and thalassemia.

 Alan Cohen, *CHOP*

Carlton D. Dampier, *St. Chris*
*(sp: sickle–cell anemia)*
Gregory Halligan, *St. Chris*
Kwaku Ohene–Fremong, *CHOP*
*(sp: sickle–cell anemia)*
Marie J. Stuart, *St. Chris*

## ♥ IMMUNOLOGY

Some immunologists concentrate on allergic problems; those listed here focus on identifying and treating chronic, severe and frequent infections which do not respond to normal antibiotics.
Steven Douglas, *CHOP*
Harold W. Lischner, *St. Chris*

## ♥ INFECTOUS DISEASES

Any parent with a school–age child will attest to the fact that infections seems to leapfrog from one kid to another. But you wouldn't visit this specialist unless your child had a virus or bacteria that failed to respond to traditional antibiotics and required more aggressive therapy.
Alan Arbeter, *Einstein*
Margaret C. Fisher, *St. Chris*
Sarah Long, *St. Chris/Temple*
Stuart Starr, *CHOP*
Terrence L. Stull, *MCP*
Sidney J. Sussman, *Cooper*

## ♥ METABOLIC DISORDERS

When the body has difficulty converting food to energy in a way that interferes with normal physical or mental function, the problem may be metabolic. Diseases in this category include fructose intolerance, amino acid disorders, Gaucher's syndrome, Lesch–Nyhan syndrome, and carbohydrate abnormalities. To counteract the defect, the doctor will create a combination drug–and–diet program.
Gerard T. Berry, *CHOP*
Paige Kaplan, *CHOP/Einstein*
*(sp: genetic disorders)*
Stanton Segal, *CHOP*
Marc Yudkoff, *CHOP*

## ♥ NEONATOLOGY

When newspapers report the miraculous survival of a one–pound infant, the doctors responsible for saving the baby are neonatologists. Biomedical advances have contributed enormously to the burgeoning of this speciality and its enhanced ability to diagnose and treat sick newborns who years ago would have died shortly after birth.
Soraya Abbasi, *Pennsylvania*
Roberta Ballard, *CHOP*
Vinod K. Bhutani, *Pennsylvania*
Frank W. Bowen, *Pennsylvania*
Maria Delivoria–Papadopoulos, *HUP*
John G. DeMaio, *Lankenau/Paoli*
Jeffrey S. Gerdes, *Pennsylvania*
Hallam Hurt, *Einstein*
Richard Polin, *CHOP*
S. David Rubenstein, *St. Chris/Temple*
Pamela B. Russell, *Lankenau/Paoli*
Alan Spitzer, *Jeff/Methodist (sp: apnea)*
Alan B. Zubrow, *MCP/Roxborough*

## ♥ NEPHROLOGY

Don't be alarmed if your pediatrician sends you to a nephrologist to have your little girl's urinary–tract infection treated. That's one of the common child-

hood problems seen by this specialist, who also deals with kidney disorders and hypertension, which in youngsters is often a result of kidney malfunction.
   Jorge Baluarte, *St. Chris*
   Bonita Falkner, *MCP*
   Bruce Kaiser, *St. Chris*
   Bernard Kaplan, *CHOP*
   Mike Norman, *Christiana/du Pont*
   Martin Polinsky, *St. Chris*

## ♥ NEUROLOGY/CHILD DEVELOPMENT

This covers a wide range of disorders of the nervous system, from birth injuries to seizures to chronic headaches to sleep disorders. In addition, when little Johnny is far too slow in walking, talking, or even rolling over, the developmental delay may be the first sign of a neurological problem. School-age children are also referred to neurologists for suspected attention-deficit disorders and some learning disabilities.
   Peter Berman, *CHOP*
   Lawrence Brown, *MCP*
   Thomas J. Casey, *Bryn Mawr*
   Robert Clancy, *CHOP*
   *(sp: neonatal epilepsy)*
   Leonard J. Graziani, *Jeff*
   Sam Tucker, *CHOP*

## ♥ NUTRITION

This specialist works in consultation with others to treat children whose problems require special diets and/or feeding supplements.
   Virginia Stallings, *CHOP*

## ♥ ONCOLOGY

While oncologists treat all kinds of malignancies, the most commonly occuring cancer in children is leukemia. As the treatment-team captain, the oncologist manages chemotherapy, works with the radiotherapist, and supports the emotional needs of the family. Because you will have an intense and long-term relationship with this physician, it's especially important that you feel comfortable and develop a good rapport.
   Milton H. Donaldson, *Cooper*
   Audrey Evans, *CHOP*
   Beverly Lange, *CHOP*
   Anna T. Meadows, *CHOP/HUP*
   Robert S. Wimmer,
   *Einstein/Temple (sp: hematology)*

## ♥ PATHOLOGY

It's unlikely you would have any personal contact with the person who microscopically examines small pieces of tissue (known as biopsies) to determine the cause of an illness. If you have doubts about a biopsy report, don't hesitate to request a second opinion.
   Jane Chatten, *CHOP*
   J.D. deChadarevian, *St. Chris*
   Lucy B. Rorke, *CHOP*
   *(sp: neuropathology)*

## ♥ PSYCHIATRY

Some of the emotional problems of children and teenagers—depression, anxiety, sexual identity, anorexia—are no different from those plaguing adults. But with the increase of divorce, drugs, and sexual abuse has come a whole new range of issues that require the special training of these physicians, who are permitted, when necessary, to prescribe medication as an adjunct to therapy.

Mary Anne Delaney, *Hahnemann*
Harold Kolansky, *Einstein–Belmont*
Herbert S. Lustig, *Temple/Belmont*
Herbert E. Mandell, *Einstein–Belmont*
Anthony L. Rostain, *Child Guidance/CHOP*
John Sargent, *Child Guidance/CHOP/HUP (sp: adolescents)*
Alberto C. Serrano, *Child Guidance/CHOP*
G. Pirooz Sholevar, *Jeff*

### ♥ PULMONARY MEDICINE

The function of this specialist is to help children breathe easier. Many patients come from the one in every 3,000 to 5,000 youngsters suffering from cystic fibrosis. These doctors also treat severe asthma, recurrent lung infections, and breathing abnormalities.

Michael M. Grunstein, *CHOP/HUP*
Douglas S. Holschlaw Jr., *Hahnemann*
Howard B. Panitch, *St. Chris*
Thomas F. Scanlin, *HUP*
Craig M. Schramm, *CHOP/HUP*
Daniel V. Shidlaw, *St. Chris*

### ♥ RADIOLOGY

Once upon a time, this was the doctor who just read X–rays. But the modern radiologist works in an imaging center whose tools include ultrasound, nuclear medicine, MRIs, CAT scans, angiography, and various intervention techniques to help repair vessel problems without surgery.

Eric N. Faerber, *St. Chris (sp: CAT, MRI)*
Kenneth E. Fellows, *CHOP/HUP*
Sydney Heyman, *CHOP*
Soroosh Mahboubi, *CHOP (sp: CAT, MRI)*
Henrietta Rosenberg, *CHOP/HUP (sp: ultrasound)*
Eleanor M. Smergle, *St. Chris (sp: angiography)*
Barbara J. Wolfson, *St. Chris*
Robert A. Zimmerman, *CHOP/HUP (sp: neuro–radiology)*

### ♥ REHABILITATION MEDICINE

This rapidly expanding speciality includes a wide range of diagnostic, evaluation and treatment services. For those with physical or neurologic handicaps, such as cerebral palsy and muscular dystrophy, they provide occupational and physical therapy. They also work with children who have speech and hearing impairments, learning or retardation problems, developmental delays, and hyperactivity.

Mark L. Batshaw, *Seashore House/CHOP*
Edward B. Charney, *Seashore House/CHOP*
Maureen A. Fee, *St. Chris/Paoli Memorial*

### ♥ RHEUMATOLOGY

The painful inflammation of the joints known as rheumatoid arthritis strikes children as well as adults. However, a large number of patients referred to this specialist in recent years turn out to be suffering from Lyme disease, which affects the joints in its more severe stage.

Balu H. Athreya, *Seashore House/CHOP*

Donald P. Goldsmith, *Cooper/Allentown*

## SURGERY

### ♥ CARDIO-THORACIC

This surgeon repairs rare and congenital heart defects in infants and children.
William I. Norwood, *CHOP*
Pierantonio Russo, *Temple/St.Chris*

### ♥ GENERAL SURGERY

The bulk of this surgeon's practice involves fairly common procedures such as hernias, obstructions of the bowel and bile ducts, malformations of the GI tract, and, of course, appendectomies.
James A. O'Neill Jr., *CHOP*
Louise Schnaufer, *CHOP*
John M. Templeton, *CHOP*
Charles P. Vinocur, *St. Chris*
William H. Weintraub, *St. Chris*

### ♥ NEUROSURGERY

The delicate work of correcting defects of the central nervous system is the domain of this surgeon. These would include hydrocephalus (swelling of the brain caused by fluid retention), spina bifida, epilepsy that doesn't respond to drug treatment, and brain tumors.
Paul Kanev, *St. Chris/Temple*
Louis Schut, *CHOP*
Leslie N. Sutton, *CHOP/HUP/Pennsylvania*

### ♥ OPHTHALMOLOGY

About 80 percent of the operations performed by this specialist involve correcting defects of the eye muscles, the most common being turned eyes, caused by a deviation that prevents the eyes from working in sync, and amblyopia, the term for decreased vision. Other conditions include congenital cataracts, glaucoma, droopy eyelids and blocked tear ducts. It's important to treat vision problems early, so the child doesn't miss out on the visual stimulation so critical to learning.
Joseph H. Calhoun, *Wills*
Leonard B. Nelson, *Wills/Lankenau/CHOP*
Graham E. Quinn, *CHOP*
David B. Schaffer, CHOP

### ♥ ORTHOPEDICS

In addition to dealing with the inevitable fractures and sports injuries that accompany the growth of active children, these surgeons correct congenital deformities of the spine, such as scoliosis, and of the limbs, such as clubfoot.
Philip D. Alburger, *St. Chris*
Randall Betz, *Temple/Shriners*
Richard Bowen, *du Pont*
Richard S. Davidson, *CHOP/Shriners (sp: clubfoot)*
Denis S. Drummond, *CHOP*
John R. Gregg, *CHOP*
A. Lee Osterman, *HUP/CHOP (sp: hands)*
Peter D. Pizzutillo, *Jeff*

### ♥ ORGAN TRANSPLANTS

With the advent of drugs to fight rejection, no one is considered too young for a transplant these days. The dramatic pleas of parents who turn to the media to solicit organs

for their children attest to how greatly the need exceeds the supply.
**Bone Marrow:**
  Nancy Bunin, *CHOP*
**Heart:**
  Marshall L. Jacobs, *CHOP*
**Kidney:**
  Stephen P. Dunn, *St. Chris*
  Pierantonio Russo, *Temple/St. Chris*
**Liver:**
  Stephen P. Dunn, *St. Chris*
  Henry T. Lau, *CHOP*

### ♥ OTORHINOLARYNGOLOGY

A few decades ago, the ear, nose and throat specialist was best known for removing tonsils. Today his bread and butter is putting tubes in kids' ears, to combat chronic infections. They also operate on tumors of the head and neck.
  Steven Handler, *CHOP*
  Glenn Isaacson, *St. Chris/Holy Redeemer*
  William P. Potsic, *CHOP*
  Ralph F. Wetmore, *CHOP*

### ♥ PLASTIC/CRANIOFACIAL

These highly skilled surgeons are able to perform wonders on children who were once doomed to live with disfigurements. Their face–saving techniques repair birth defects such as cleft palate, deformities due to injuries (including burns), tumors, and other aesthetic problems.
  Don LaRossa, *CHOP/Presbyterian*
  Peter D. Quinn, *CHOP* (sp: maxillofacial)
  Linton Whitaker, *CHOP/HUP*

---

# Doylestown Hospital

### *The best of tradition and technology.*

Specialists in Primary Care  - Gastroenterology
Cardiology - Rehabilitation - Maternity Services
Expanded Emergency Medicine and Surgery Departments

*Located at Routes 202 and 611 in the heart of Bucks County.  Serving Greater Bucks and Eastern Montgomery Counties and Western New Jersey.*

**For more information on our programs and facilities, please call 345-2121 and ask for a complimentary copy of our**

## Consumer Guide to Services.

## ♥ UROLOGY

Pediatric urology involves repairing complications of the bladder, the kidney, and the urinary and genital tracts. In addition, these surgeons do reconstruction of inadequately developed sex organs which can make it impossible to tell if a baby is a boy or girl or both.

John W. Duckett, *CHOP*
Hyman H. Rabinovitch, *St. Chris/Bryn Mawr*
Howard McCrum Snyder III, *CHOP/HUP*

---

*Abbreviations have been used for the following area hospitals:* **Belmont**—Belmont Center for Comprehensive Treatment; **Child Guidance**—Philadelphia Child Guidance Center; **CHOP**—Children's Hospital of Philadelphia; **Christiana**—Christiana Medical Center of Delaware, Christiana Hospital; **Cooper**—Cooper Hospital–University Medical Center, Camden, NJ; **du Pont**—Alfred I. du Pont Institute for Children, Wilmington, DE; **Einstein**—Albert Einstein Medical Center; **Hahnemann**—Hahnemann University Hospital; **Holy Redeemer**—Holy Redeemer Hospital and Medical Center; **HUP**—Hospital of the University of Pennsylvania; **Jeff**—Thomas Jefferson University Hospital; **MCP**—Hospital of the Medical College of Pennsylvania; **Paoli**—Paoli Memorial Hospital; **Presbyterian**—Presbyterian Medical Center of Philadelphia; **Roxborough**—Roxborough Memorial Hospital; **Seashore House**—Children's Seashore House; **Shriners**—Shriners Hospital for Crippled Children; **St. Chris**—St. Christopher's Hospital for Children; **Temple**—Temple University Hospital; **Wills**—Wills Eye Hospital.

---

We'd do anything for that kid. And our love goes beyond mere sentiment. We're Children's Seashore House, a 70-bed regional hospital providing diverse specialized and rehabilitation care for children with special needs.

Our five treatment areas range from a respiratory rehabilitation unit for tracheostomy patients and children who are ventilator dependent, a biobehavioral unit for children unit for children with severe behavioral problems secondary to developmental disabilities, a neurorehabilitation unit for children who have had neurosurgery or suffered head trauma to a feeding disorder unit for children with feeding problems that compromise nutrition and health and a musculoskeletal unit for children who have had orthopedic or other surgical procedures or medical conditions that require intense rehabilitation.

We also provide outpatient programs in the areas of cerebral palsy, rheumatic diseases, Down Syndrome, learning and behavior disorder, mental behavior disorders, mental retardation and other disabling conditions of childhood, physical, occupational and speech/language therapies, as well as behavioral and cognitive psychological services.

All the services, resources and latest technology needed to completely address special medical and rehabilitation needs can be found within one hospital.

For more information, contact Children's Seashore House, Philadelphia Center for Health Care Sciences, 3405 Civic Center Boulevard, Philadelphia, PA 19104-4302. (215) 895-3600

## ALL THE LOVE MEDICAL SCIENCE CAN OFFER

### Children's Seashore House
A Regional Hospital for Specialized Care and Rehabilitation

*THE MOST IMPORTANT WORK ON EARTH.*

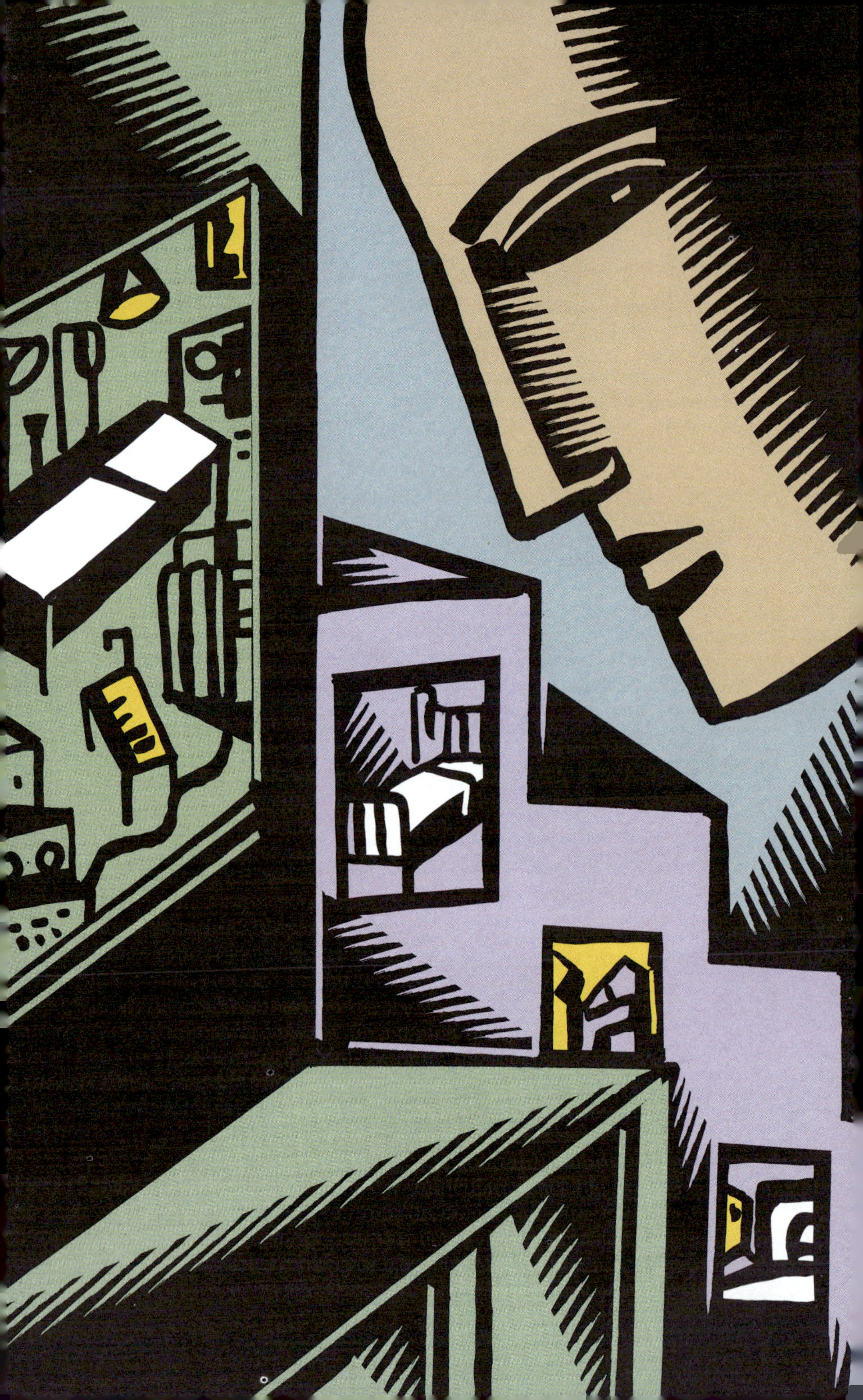

## SECTION TWO

# CHOOSING A HOSPITAL

# FREE PRESCRIPTION PROGRAM

**For people with Diabetes, Lupus, Hypertension, Arthritis, High Cholesterol, Transplants, Ulcers, and for You!!!**

All Rx maintenance medications *(such as: Mevacor, Zantac, Insulin, Diabeta, Naprosyn, Sandimmune, Plaquenil, Blood Glucose Meters, Lopressor, Cardizem, etc.)* are available at NO COST TO YOU *(in most cases)*.

Once you've met your Major Medical Insurance Policy yearly deductible requirement, Advantage Health Services' *Rx Freedom Program* can step in and provide you with your prescription drugs and medical supplies... at absolutely no cost to you (in most cases).

## INTRODUCING
# THE Rx FREEDOM PROGRAM™

- We do all of the claim filing to your insurance company. No more paperwork!
- We accept insurance reimbursement as payment in full! (In most cases)
- Next day free nationwide delivery!
- No membership fee.
- Relief from financial burdens.
- No out-of-pocket expenses.

## ADVANTAGE HEALTH SERVICES, INC ™

THE Rx FREEDOM PROGRAM™ offers you an opportunity to improve your quality of life...

**Call us NOW at 215-443-7667 or 1-800-682-8283**

ANYONE ON MAINTENANCE MEDICATION AND WHO HAS A MAJOR MEDICAL INSURANCE POLICY WHICH REIMBURSES FOR PRESCRIPTION DRUGS QUALIFIES. WE'RE SORRY WE CANNOT ACCEPT MEDICAID OR MEDICARE.

# 3

# Why Are the Bills So High?

*America can get control of rising medical costs.*

♥ Just a generation ago, it would have seemed downright foolish to ask the question, "Can I afford to be sick?" Excellent medical care was considered one of the benefits of being born under the Stars and Stripes. In the future, this may not be such an automatic assumption. The quality of medical care in America will not diminish, but the system—in particular, who gets what care—is out of control. Medicare costs are projected to soon outstrip Social Security payments. We spend $2,500 per person for health care in the United States, which is 50 percent more than Canada, twice Japan's cost and triple that of England. Yet people in those countries live as long as we do, and have lower infant mortality rates.

Are we getting the best bang for our buck when approximately 37 million Americans, mostly the working poor, carry no health insurance whatsoever? Meanwhile, those who do are increasingly being ordered by employers to kick in a portion of their salaries to pay for it, because companies can't afford the escalating premiums.

"American hospitals are supposed to symbolize the ideals of charity, altruism and community spirit," writes Rosemary Stevens, Ph.D., in her book *In Sickness and in Wealth*. The newly appointed dean of the college of arts and sciences at the University of Pennsylvania is an expert on hospital management and health-care policy. So she seemed the logical person to ask about the future of American hospitals. Why is it cheaper to buy a car than to have an operation? Can hospitals maintain their social commitment under the pressure to perform as businesses? What follows is a summation of her ideas.

Before 1850, people of means avoided hospitals because they were largely asylums for the poor—rowdy, undisciplined places that took in anybody in need of care, from vagrants to pregnant girls to the mentally ill. The modern hospital emerged after the Civil War. There was a growth in professional nursing guided by the work of Florence Nightingale, and new understanding of germs made it possible to do surgery under aseptic conditions. Suddenly doctors could slit open someone's belly without having that patient die from infection. By the 1920s, fear of hospitals was replaced by hope. An enormous optimism arose about the curative powers of hospitals and the promise of medicine as a source for social change.

After World War II, with the introduction of health insurance and third–party payments, hospitals drifted away from their roots in charity and began to view themselves more like their counterparts in business and industry. This emerging business model created increasing conflicts with the more traditional model of community service. The result today is tremendous tension in a system that tries to be an expression of both American business enterprise and American humanitarian ideals.

Much of the impetus pushing hospitals to operate like businesses has come from government money, which to a large degree drives the system. Of every dollar spent on health care, 40 cents come from the government. The pay nexus—that is, fees for service—influences everything from the selection and distribution of patients to decisions about care.

When Medicare was created in 1966, it initially gave hospitals a license to spend. Whatever a hospital claimed, within reason, was reimbursed by the federal government. As a result, there was very little control over expenditures. It's the same old story: Whenever a third party picks up the tab, sensitivity to price becomes blunted. Neither patients nor doctors pay the kind of attention to what a procedure costs that they would if the money came out of their own pockets. That's a key reason why medical costs soared, and it finally led to the government's attempt to contain rising costs via a system of standardized payments. By the 1980s, hospitals were being given a flat fee based on a patient's diagnosis, regardless of how long or how much effort it took to get him well.

This system of DRGs (diagnosis–related groups) was supposed to level out the playing field by introducing healthy, even cutthroat competition between hospitals. Theoretically, if insurance paid the same amount to every hospital, patients would shop for the best care. The idea was to reduce overall costs, but it didn't work. Instead it beefed up marketing, and forced hospitals to develop more creative programs to lure patients to their facilities. Like savvy taxpayers finding loopholes in new tax laws, hospitals learned to get around the system by shifting costs into areas, like rehab or outpatient facilities, that weren't covered by DRGs.

The increasing business emphasis has been particularly hard on doctors, who were always pretty much the lords of the manor. Whereas once they exerted a powerful influence on hospital policy, today somebody is always looking over their shoulders and questioning why they ordered this test or that test. (Usually the answer is, they're driven by the fear of malpractice litigation.) More and more doctors see themselves at odds with the professional hospital managers who find it necessary to put the dollar at the forefront of medical decisions. Management now identifies which procedures are money producers for the hospital and which ones are money losers. To promote an institution as the best in the marketplace, administrators court specialists and lure superstars with promises of better facilities and more cash—just like any Fortune 500 company.

These are the kinds of things that contribute to high hospital bills. In addition, we *like* expensive science in this country. We're proud that American medicine is the best in the world, and we've never really looked at whether we're getting value for our money. Can we go on assuming that more technology is always good for individuals? Perhaps not. Also, Americans put a high premium on convenience and choice. If one hospital has an expensive piece of equipment, then everybody else wants the same one, to maintain their competitive edge. And once a hospital has bought a special high–tech machine, it has to justify the expenditure by using it often, which leads to more tests and procedures than may be necessary. High–priced equipment and the interest paid on the money borrowed to buy it gets fed back into the cost of care. Thus, for example, a report in the *Journal of American Medicine* that we have too many centers for mammograms will probably not be heeded, because fewer centers would mean longer waits, and we don't like to put up with that.

Studies lately are questioning why a procedure done in hospital A is more expensive than the same procedure done in hospital B across town. (A study a few years ago by the Pennsylvania Business Roundtable found that Philadelphia led the state in average charges per patient per day. The reason given was the expensive nature of teaching hospitals.) But what's the link between cost and quality? Does one exist, and if so, how do you define quality care and apportion who gets it? That's the hot issue of the moment, and it pits the historical mission of hospitals to provide care to the public against the need to balance the books.

There's a growing belief that the inevitable response to uniform, affordable health care in America is some form of de facto national system. We need universal coverage instead of what we have now, which is selective coverage—Medicare covers only the elderly, Medicaid covers those on welfare. But that still leaves huge numbers of poor people in this country without any insurance. We can't expect hospitals to keep providing services to the poor just because they've always done it. And it's crazy and irresponsible of Washington to go on denying the federal role in health care. (There are many national health–care proposals currently floating around Congress, ranging from a national health system based on the Canadian model to a variety of public–private partnerships. For example, the National Blue Cross and Blue Shield Association believes all Americans under 65 should be guaranteed private insurance coverage for basic benefits, but in its view the federal government ought to regulate, not operate, health–care coverage. Consequently it supports a national health insurance reform proposal which would assure universal and affordable coverage through the present system of private health insurance.)

Something's wrong when much–needed hospitals that deliver care to poor populations are the ones closing because they're financially weak. One option for change would be overall national hospital regulation; another would be planning at the local or regional level. Yet another would be having the great majority of people belong to health maintenance organizations, which would internally regulate decisions about what services are needed where.

The increased costs of having everyone in some kind of HMO would be offset by unified control of the capacity of the health system. Because we have no coordination of hospital services or joint planning at any local level, there is tremendous duplication and waste. If you were starting from scratch to assess health needs in Philadelphia, you'd no doubt have fewer hospitals and fewer physicians. Some hospitals would have more services than others; there would be coordinated decisions about where new services would go, and maybe fewer centers where highly technological procedures are done. Of course, hospitals and their boards don't like the idea of giving up autonomy. But it could be better for some patients to go to a regional center that had highly experienced full–time doctors and nurses doing specialized operations like transplants.

While a redesigned system might give patients fewer choices, it could improve their satisfaction. Right now, consumers feel helpless. They complain about hospitals and doctors and insurance companies, but there is no single group to whom they can address their grievances.

In essence, the very term "hospital" is ripe for redefinition. What should the hospital of the future be, and what kinds of trade–offs are we willing to make? Are hospitals doing too many things? Maybe they should be centers for surgery and treating the curable, rather than intensive care units for the old and the very ill as they've increasingly become. Maybe patients need to be allowed more options about where they want to end their lives, and how. We're just starting to talk about what a good life is, and what a good death is. Wonderful things are being done with artificial joints and other innovations intended to make life better at an older age, but at the same time, tremendous effort goes into people who are dying. Maybe we have to reevaluate what people want to have done to them in the last years of life. And there's no maybe that we should reform the malpractice system, and put a cap on financial awards.

There's no reason for anyone to fear that these changes would mean some people will get less than they do now. The debate must focus more on what's valuable in medical care and less on matters of cost. If we really look at *value*, we can bring costs down. But if we keep tinkering at the edges of the system, talking about cost controls and putting in new procedures, costs will only go higher. If we want to keep the system we have, we should stop bitching about it. If we don't, we need to make fundamental changes.

*For more information:* Dr. Rosemary Stevens' book, *In Sickness and In Wealth: American Hospitals in the Twentieth Century* ($24.95), is published by Basic Books.

## Special Care Facility Exclusively for Children

At Voorhees Pediatric Facility, we provide comprehensive and progressive subacute health care for medically complex children ages 6 weeks to 21 years.

- An alternative to acute care hospitalization (**with dramatic cost savings**)
- State of the art ventilator unit (including pressure vents)

- Strong medical and rehabilitative interdisciplinary team approach
- Attending Pediatricians and Pediatric Residents on Premises
- Board certified pediatric pulmonologists
- Affiliated with St. Christopher's Hospital for Children and Cooper Hospital's Child Dvlpmt. Center
- Respite care available

1304 Laurel Oak Rd. Voorhees, NJ
609-346-3300 fax: 609-435-4223
"Accreditation with Commendation"
Joint Commission on Accreditation of Hospital Organizations

**Voorhees Pediatric Facility**

Caring for children from the Mid-Atlantic states since 1983

# The Most Important Thing in the World...

## Your Health and the Health of Your Loved Ones.

Holy Redeemer Hospital and Medical Center is committed to providing you and your family with the area's finest health care services. Call our Physician Referral Service for a FREE copy of our Medical Staff Directory.

## (215) 938-DRDR

### HOLY REDEEMER HOSPITAL & MEDICAL CENTER

Ministry of the
Sisters of the
Holy Redeemer.
Part of the
Holy Redeemer
Health System.

1648 Huntingdon Pike
Meadowbrook, PA 19046
(215) 947-3000

# 4

# The Wise Patient

*How to Take Care of Yourself in the Hospital*

♥ Everybody has heard or read one of those "you won't believe what happened to me in the hospital" stories. Hospitals are big, hectic place, operating under intense pressure. So it's not surprising that sometimes somebody gets the wrong medication, develops an infection other than the condition he was being treated for, or wets the sheets because it took too long for a nurse to bring a bedpan. While you aren't always able to prevent these kinds of things, there are ways you can control them.

Healthcare is the nation's major business. It eats up the largest chunk of our GNP—12.5 percent, compared to 6 percent for defense and education. Yet where hospitals are concerned, there's often not enough correlation between cost and customer satisfaction. Charles Inlander, president of People's Medical Society, a nonprofit consumer watchdog group, points out that as consumers we're more likely to consult the Better Business Bureau about a roofer we're thinking of hiring than to check on the record of the hospitals we're entrusting with our lives. While nobody expects a stay at the hospital to be a day at the beach, we do expect that as long as a hospital has accreditation, it's a safe place to be. Yet sometimes hospitals fail state inspections even after having been granted the seal of approval of the Joint Commission of Healthcare Organizations which has been known to allow slipshod conditions to persist for long periods without revoking accreditation.

Even when the institution is performing up to standard, an article in the Los Angeles Times reported that on a national level "as many as six percent of all people admitted to hospitals end up with infections they would not otherwise get." In the trade these hospital–acquired diseases are called nosocomial infections and before you check into a hospital in the Delaware Valley, you can call and ask for its rate of nosocomial problems, which range from urinary tract infections to pneumonia. At least half of these could be prevented, says Inlander, if staffs used better hygiene. Before anyone in the hospital touches you, don't be embarrassed to ask: Did you remember to wash your hands?

Actually, you shouldn't be embarrassed to ask anything at all in the hospital. "Patients need to express their needs, because nurses can't guess what they are, and physicians don't try," says Susan Miller, one of four patient representatives at Thomas Jefferson University Hospital. "Yet most people are reticent about asking for service. They're afraid if they rock the boat, the nurse will take it out on them." In reality, she admits it's just the opposite: "The more noise you make, the more help you get."

The average patient would just as soon keep silent and assume that Doctor knows best. In several surveys examining what role patients wanted to play in making decisions about their medical treatment, almost half preferred to leave the choices to their physicians. Claire Fagin, Margaret Bond Simon dean of nursing at the University of Pennsylvania and a strong advocate of consumerism in health care, says, "The hospital system is innocently designed to make patients powerless. You must intervene and be assertive. Become a participant in your care. What's the worst thing that can happen to you if you speak up and ask questions? You'll be called a crank."

What should you question? Just about everything. If your doctor orders tests, don't submit automatically. Studies indicate that far more tests than necessary are performed. You want to know what the doctor is looking for in results, what will happen to you if you don't have the procedure done, what risks are involved in the test, and whether the potential advantages outweigh the dangers. Don't allow anybody in a lab coat to come into your room to draw blood or haul you off to X–ray without asking who ordered the test and reminding yourself that you can refuse it. "They go nuts in a hospital when a patient says no," Inlander points out. "Suddenly everyone rushes to explain what's happening."

Pay particular attention to the drugs you're given and when you're given them. Nationally the average hospital makes 60 medication errors a day, administering the wrong drug or the wrong dosage or the right drug at the wrong time. Question all medication: What is this? Why am I taking it? If you've been getting green, red and purple pills and the nurse brings blue and yellow, don't swallow them until you talk to the doctor. If you are on a 2–6–10 o'clock schedule and the nurse comes with medicine at 4, make sure you ask to see the written order.

Although hospitals seem inflexible, rooms can be changed, and so can nurses. Should you get stuck with one who is sullen or unacceptably inattentive, request someone else. In most hospitals, every patient is assigned a particular nurse, and he or she is accountable for your case. That nurse is where the buck stops. Find out who your nurse is, and then have a little chat up front about your specific needs. Let the nurse know as soon as you have a problem.

Regardless of how solicitous the nurses are, you'll probably feel that nursing care isn't what it used to be. You're right. Nobody gives back rubs or sponge baths like they did in the old days. As hospitals have increasingly come to cater to acutely ill people, the priorities of nursing have changed, and the Florence Nightingale philosophy is obsolete. Today's nurse, no matter how well–intentioned, is overworked, overpressured, understaffed, and perhaps more focused on efficiency than on compassionate care. Often the nurse's goal isn't taking care of you; its getting you to take care of yourself. A floor nurse at Pennsylvania Hospital explains, "Nursing now is geared toward making the patient as independent as possible."

The more dependent the patient, the greater the need for the family to take over. When you're worried about a desperately ill relative, ask permission to say after hospital visiting hours end, and, if necessary, tell the nurse you want to spend the night. Would you leave a frightened, bewildered child alone in the hospital? Then why should you be forced to abandon an adult too sick or confused to fend for himself? While the hospital may not be particularly pleased to have you as an overnight guest, if there is a medical reason for your presence and you aren't interfering with the delivery of care, they can't send you home. In some cases, they'll even order a cot for you.

Don't assume that anything reasonable is impossible until you talk to the patient advocate. The law in Pennsylvania requires hospitals to have some kind of grievance procedure. In the little handbook you're given at admission (which too few people take the time to read), you'll find the the name of a patient representative or advocate whose job it is to help you in the hospital. Patient reps can get all kinds of things done for you. When a man at Jefferson Hospital demanded "a goddamn bedboard" and the nurse couldn't find one, patient rep Susan Miller got the carpentry shop to build one. When a woman who was very anxious about a scheduled test voiced her worries to Miller, she arranged for some TLC as well as special cushions to alleviate back pain during the long test. A teenager in the pediatric intensive care unit who couldn't sleep because of the incessant ringing of the phone near his bed was given earplugs until he could be moved. The rule of thumb in the hospital is, if you need something, ask for it.

While patient reps can sometimes move mountains, they can't do much about hospital food. Inlander's solution to the dreaded hospital tray—"Send out for pizza." Unless you're limited to a special diet, that's not a bad idea, and there are no rules against it. Nor are there any laws requiring you to eat the tasteless oatmeal and dry pork chops lovingly prepared by the food service. You can make arrangements for your family to supply your meals, and alert the hospital upon admission that you do not want the meal plan and will not pay for it. Some hospitals have actually introduced gourmet menus, complete with wine. Check on their availability.

You don't have to be a VIP to get VIP treatment. Although special services may not be automatically offered to you, they won't be denied if you're willing to pay the extra charges. Most hospitals have plush suites, reserved for board members or doctors' families, that are available to the general public when not in use. Jefferson, for instance, has two suites with fancy meals that will add $200 a day to your hospital bill. Requests for these or for private rooms should be made in advance through the patient services office, with the understanding that emergencies may make it impossible for the hospital to deliver what was promised. We heard of a woman who threatened to check herself out of one Philadelphia hospital because she didn't like her room and quickly found herself in the private quarters she'd originally asked for. Nurses may complain about the complainer, but she's the one who gets the attention.

Finally, some general dos and don'ts that can make your hospital stay safer and more pleasant. When you're scheduled for an elective procedure, tour the facility in advance. If the rooms look dirty and dreary and the staff seems surly and uncooperative, go somewhere else. Be certain to see the doctor before your sedation starts, or pin a note on your gown reminding him what he's supposed to be doing. A surgeon told me he had a patient who drew a circle on her leg with a marker and wrote, "This is the spot where you're operating." Don't take valuables or money with you. Do take a pad and pencil, to jot down questions you may have for the doctor, as well as some family photos or a poster to decorate your room and a Walkman with your favorite tapes. It's widely believed that the more cheerful your attitude, the more quickly you'll heal.

It's also smart to demand an itemized bill for your stay, and to check it line by line. A study by a national auditing company found that 98 percent of hospital bills in excess of $10,000 had errors, approximately 75 percent of which were in the hospital's favor. Lastly, don't go home without a copy of your medical records. When your car leaves the repair shop, you're entitled to a slip detailing exactly what the mechanic did to it. You deserve at least the same information about your body.

***If you need help***: People's Medical Society, 462 Walnut Street, Allentown, PA 18012, 770–1670, is a first–rate resource for help in getting the best care and advice on what to do when you feel you've been wronged. For general information, I highly recommend the society's paperback, *Take This Book to the Hospital With You*, published by Rodale Press and available at local bookstores.

**DON'T SMOKE**

**EAT YOUR VEGGIES**

**WATCH THE DRINKING**

**CHEW YOUR FOOD**

**USE SUNSCREEN**

**WATCH YOUR STEP**

**Cool-it**

**BUCKLE-UP**

A few words from Independence Blue Cross and Pennsylvania Blue Shield, who happen to think your Mother was right.

Independence **Blue Cross**
Pennsylvania **Blue Shield**

® Registered marks of the Blue Cross and Blue Shield Association.

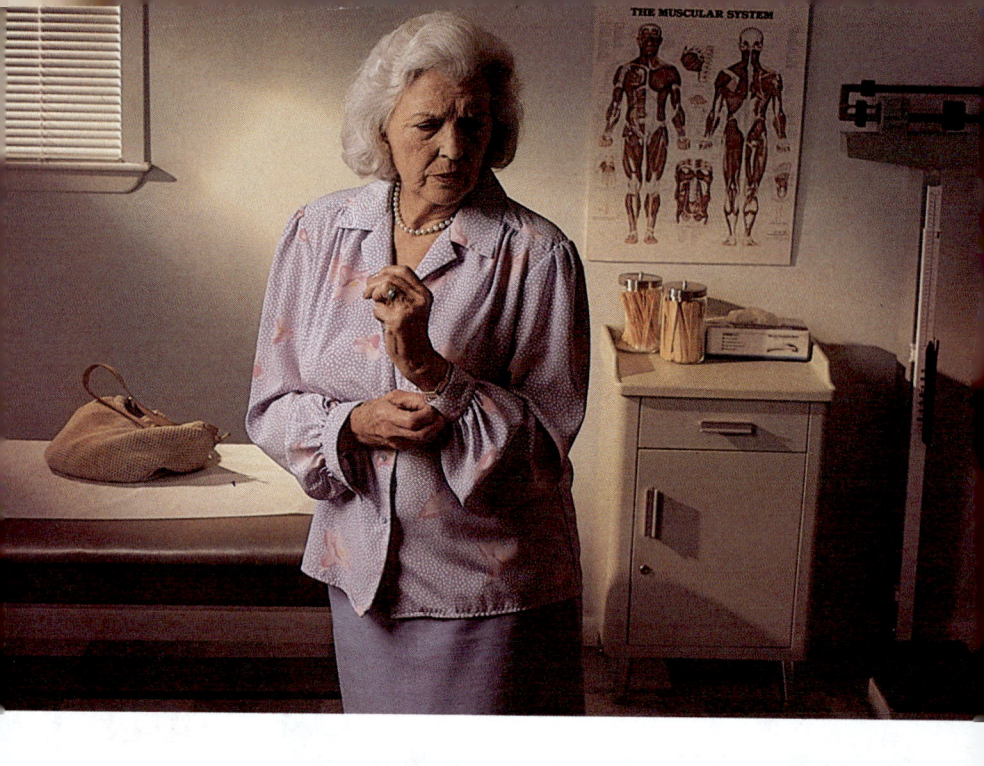

# "Doctor, if it were your mother's heart, where would you take her?"

This is a question Philadelphia Magazine asked over 3,000 doctors in "The Super Doctors" which appears in this guide. Whom did they recommend? Philadelphia Heart Institute doctors. For cardiology, cardiac catheterization and cardiothoracic surgery, we had the most doctors singled out as the best in their specialty. The most Super Doctors. By far.

If you or a loved one have a heart problem or suspect you have a heart problem, call the doctors' doctors. Call the Philadelphia Heart Institute. And put your heart in the right place.

### Philadelphia Heart Institute
at Presbyterian Medical Center

39th & Market Streets, Philadelphia, PA 19104 (215) 662-9045

## Put your heart in the right place.™

© 1992 The Philadelphia Heart Institute

# 5 Under and Out

*News from the underworld of medicne – anesthesia.*

♥ "I'd love to have a face–lift," said the physician's wife, smoothing the sag from her cheeks with the palms of her hands. "But I've heard too many anesthesia horror stories from my husband. I'm scared to death of surgery, especially if it's elective. The risks from anesthesia just aren't worth it." While she may have been exaggerating, until recently no doctor worth his salt would have denied privately that a good part of the danger in any surgical procedure came from possible complications caused by anesthesia.

The first public demonstration of anesthesia was in 1846, when a Boston dentist put a patient to sleep with a stiff whiff of ether. A year later, a Scottish obstetrician repeated the feat with chloroform, and thus began a new era of pain–free surgery. Today ether and chloroform have been replaced by much safer drugs, which, along with high–tech monitoring techniques, have eliminated most of the dangers once associated with anesthesia. "Of all the associated fields in medicine, anesthesiology has most successfully accomplished what it has set out to do," says Dr. Harry Wollman, professor of anesthesiology and pharmacology at Hahnemann University. "We can provide safe relief of pain during surgery even for very, very sick people."

The more sick the patient, the more likely there may be heart and lung problems related to anesthesia. Here in the United States, statistics pinpointing deaths specifically linked to anesthesia are not collected, but studies done abroad a decade ago pegged the mortality rate then at two to four per 10,000 operations. Current evidence suggests that number has declined considerably. As measured by insurance claims, anesthesia today causes only one in 10,000 deaths in hospitals. Even that number is skewed by the fact that advances in the field have made it possible to operate on extremely ill people who not long ago would never even have been considered as surgical candidates. In outpatient surgical centers, where the patients tend to be relatively healthy, the mortality rate drops to one in 100,000. In the view of Dr. David Brown, author of *Risk and Outcome in Anesthesia*, "Anesthesia is incredibly safe today, safer in fact than most people realize, when it's performed correctly by competent people."

That caveat is particularly significant. Most people leave decisions about anesthesiology in the hands of their surgeons, but a patient can and should choose an anesthesiologist as carefully as he would any other medical specialist. There are 20,000 board-certified anesthesiologists in this country, and you want one of them on your case. If the doctor is more than five years out of anesthesiology residency and *not* certified, you have every right to ask why. In many smaller hospitals, anesthesia may be administered not by doctors, but by nurse–anesthetists, who may be highly skilled and well–qualified but who have not attended medical school. If that is the circumstance, you might want to find out who will be supervising the anesthetist—a surgeon or a trained anesthesiologist—and how many nurses will be supervised at once. A doctor hopping between four operating rooms with a nurse–anesthetist in each is not quite the same as having a board–certified anesthesiologist standing next to a table watching your pulse.

Once you've established the anesthesiologist's credentials, you'll want to examine your anesthesia options. Depending on the type and length of surgery and your physical condition, there are three choices: local, general or regional.

As a rule of thumb, says Dr. Deborah Ritter, vice chair of the anesthesia department at Thomas Jefferson University Hospital, "The safest anesthesia is the least you can have." Where possible, that means local, because it puts less stress on the respiratory system. As the name suggests, local anesthesia confines itself to the area being treated; the site is numbed by an injection that temporarily blocks feeling in the surrounding nerves.

Local anesthesia does involve minimal risks. Injections are at best a blind procedure, and sometimes the numbing agent is accidentally inserted into a blood vessel rather than the tissue, throwing the patient into a seizure or unconsciousness. In many outpatient cosmetic procedures done under local anesthesia, the surgeon doubles as anesthesiologist, doing the injections and IV sedation himself. That means he has to operate and worry about the patient's response to anesthesia at the same time. To avoid the obvious pressure of this kind of arrangement, some hospitals, such as the University of Pennsylvania, offer AMS—anesthesia monitoring and sedation. If you request this service, you'll have a trained anesthesiologist working alongside the surgeon, freeing him or her to concentrate on the operation, since someone else is concentrating on your chart, blood pressure and breathing.

Dr. Stanley Muravchik, associate professor of anesthesia at the Hospital of the University of Pennsylvania, suggests AMS as "the safest option for limited elective surgery on patients who are comfortable being awake in the operating room." Despite the advantages of local anesthesia, there are those whose anxiety level during any kind of surgery is so high that it's better—for them *and* the surgeon—if they're asleep. Take the elderly patient who'd had cataract surgery twice, once under local and once under general anesthesia. Later she required a minor adjustment procedure, and the surgeon did it under a local. Afterward he told the family, "Now I know why the other doctor put her under. She was such a nervous wreck that every time I approached her, she flinched."

In our culture, it's become traditional to associate surgery with general anesthesia—being put to sleep. "Most Americans expect it," says Hospital of the University of Pennsylvania anesthesiologist Dr. Angelina Castro, "and most doctors prefer it, because within a minute after pentothol is injected, the patient is unconscious and the doctor can start work." The sleep of general anesthesia has no relation to natural sleep, and none of its therapeutic benefits. Rather, it's a disruption and depression of all normal functions, and therein lies the danger. Almost all anesthetics are cardiac depressants, and problems in anesthesia happen very fast. Dr. Castro describes her profession as one that features "great stretches of boredom and moments of great panic."

The panic is often precipitated by a breathing problem due to insufficient oxygen, or by a severe change in blood pressure. Today there are machines to warn doctors of impending disasters from breath to breath and heartbeat to heartbeat. The monitors even sound an alarm when there's a glitch in the equipment itself. Two of the most important high–tech advances in anesthesia monitoring are the pulse oximeter and the capnograph. The former checks the patient's breathing by measuring the oxygen concentration in the blood, while the latter charts the amount of carbon dioxide exhaled. These invaluable monitors are not standard equipment in all operating rooms. Because they're such major safeguards against human error, you should question not only whether your hospital has them, but whether you'll definitely be hooked up to these machines during the surgery.

With the risks of general anesthesia greatly reduced by technology, what still remain are the debilitating aftereffects, which can include disrupted sleep patterns, nausea, loss of appetite, depression, and the overall feeling that you've been hit by a truck. The powerful drugs of general anesthesia include not only the initial shot of sodium pentothol (the barbiturate that sends you into a temporary drug–induced sleep), but also a variety of muscle relaxants, narcotics and inhaled gases that keep you asleep and reduce the pain when you do wake. This drug package knocks the central nervous system for a loop, and hangs on in the body for hours and sometimes days. Combine the effect of these drugs with the body's own metabolic response to surgery—roughly akin to marshaling the troops for war—and you can understand why patients often grumble that anesthesia makes them sick.

Within the next decade this could change, with the introduction of more new drugs that act quickly, last as long as necessary, and leave the body fast. One example is a drug called propofol, which is rapidly replacing sodium pentothal. It puts patients under more quickly, and its effects dissipate more rapidly, making it especially good for short procedures. Another trend is toward giving more medication by continuous infusion (intravenously) and less by single injection or inhalation.

Meanwhile, there is a good but underutilized alternative to general anesthesia. In the opinion of Pennsylvania Hospital anesthesiologist Dr. James Springstead, "`Regional' anesthesia is an excellent option for certain surgical procedures if everybody's comfortable with it." It seems the discomfort may rest more with doctors than with patients. A survey of anesthesiologists in the United States disclosed that while they overwhelmingly preferred regional anesthesia when possible, the majority of them didn't use it, apparently because it demands a high level of special skill. These "nerve blocks," as they're often called, may be injected into the space outside the spinal cord. They work by numbing the nerves in the region and blocking the pain message to the brain. But this technique requires experienced practitioners, to reduce the risk that the needle may damage a nerve or deliver a toxic overdose through a blood vessel.

Which anesthesia is right for you? Essentially, that's a question of relative risk vs. relative comfort. By and large, it's safer to be awake: There's less assault on your system, and if your heart starts pounding or you're having trouble breathing, you can alert the doctor. "But," says HUP's Dr. Muravchik, "if you're asking whether general anesthesia is safe enough to be a reasonable alternative when you do have a choice, my answer is yes." In short, no promises of pleasant dreams, but less worry than ever before.

*If you need help:* Don't wait until the night before surgery to talk to the anesthesiologist. Request a telephone appointment. Find out if he or she is board–certified, and ask what anesthesia is recommended for your surgical procedure, why, and what the risks and advantages are, particularly as they relate to your personal medical history. Be sure to tell the doctor if you've ever had a problem with anesthesia, and whether you're taking any kind of medication, including something as seemingly innocuous as eye drops. For general anesthesia, ask about the monitoring equipment to be used. Will you be hooked up to a pulse oximeter and a capnograph? For local, don't forget to inquire about the possibility of AMS.

**Department of Internal Medicine
Cooper Hospital/University Medical Center**

**University of Medicine and Dentistry/Robert Wood Johnson Medical School at Camden**

**Offices:**
3 Cooper Plaza, Suite 215
Camden, NJ 08103
609-342-2439

Bunker Hill Plaza, Suite 103
Chapel Heights and Hurffville-Crosskeys Rd.
Washington Township
Sewell, NJ 08080
609-589-3300

**"Many Philadelphians and South Jerseyans** may be unaware of the dramatic metamorphosis that has taken place at Cooper Hospital/University Medical Center over the past decade. The institution is now a major University Hospital and serves as the clinical campus for Robert Wood Johnson Medical School at Camden. The Department of Internal Medicine faculty members are engaged in a group practice, which includes all subspecialties of Internal Medicine providing state-of-the-art care in each.
**The subspecialty Division Heads** and major services offered through the Cooper and Washington Township offices are highlighted in the Physician Directory."

Edward D. Viner, M.D.
Professor and Chief
Department of Internal Medicine

*Cooper Hospital/University Medical Center*

## "There has to be a better way to treat cancer."

Today, over 50% of people who have cancer can be cured. At Fox Chase Cancer Center, we don't think that's good enough. We also know that everyone who has ever undergone treatment or watched a husband, wife, child or friend go through it, understands that even successful treatment is often a long, difficult road.

There has been real progress in treating cancer. More people are surviving each year, but the research under way will help bring about a whole new era in medical care. We will prevent, treat, and cure cancers better by unlocking the secrets of when and why they occur. Fox Chase Cancer Center is at the forefront of that research today, and is expanding to meet the challenges and opportunities of tomorrow.

For cancer information, call 1-800-4-CANCER.

### FOX CHASE
CANCER CENTER

**DISCOVERY & HOPE**
7701 Burholme Avenue
Philadelphia, PA 19111

*Robert C. Young, M.D.*
*President, Fox Chase Cancer Center*

# 6

# Inside Story

*A glossary of the many techniques used to see inside the body.*

♥ Wilhelm Roentgen, a German physicist, holds the distinction of having been the first man to get under anybody's skin. In 1895, while experimenting with the cathode ray, Roentgen accidentally generated electromagnetic radiation so powerful that it could pass through virtually any substance and make an impression on a plate painted with a photographic emulsion. One of the first "pictures" he took was of the bones in his wife's hand. He called it an X–ray because of its mysterious nature. Within a year, doctors all over the world were taking X–ray pictures.

Before that time, the knife was the only tool for seeing inside the human body. Doctors would use their hands and ears to locate internal problems, and when their probing and tapping indicated trouble, they had no alternative to cutting open the patient to see what was wrong. By then, it was often too late. The X–ray provided a window onto a previously invisible world, and enabled doctors to diagnose all kinds of problems at the crucial early stages. Amid all the excitement, nobody realized how dangerous X–rays were—until people working with them began to die from overexposure. From that point on, the search was launched to find safer ways to reveal the body's intricacies.

From the crude still photos of bones that were early X–rays, radiology has progressed to the stage today where it's possible to view the heart and brain in action. It's a world Roentgen would hardly recognize. Here are explanations of some of its latest techniques.

## CAT SCANS: A SLICE OF LIFE

More than anything else, medical imaging owes its spectacular advancement to computers—and to Godfrey Hounsfield, a British scientist with an ear for music. While working on a project with the Beatles that involved the use of X–rays and electronic music, he began toying with other applications for bytes and rads. His inventiveness was later combined with the research of a mathematician. The result was computerized axial tomography, popularly known as the CAT or CT scan–the first practical application of the marriage of computers and X–rays. He and the mathematician won the Nobel Prize in medicine for creating a way to take cross–sectional pictures of the body from head to toe.

What made these pictures so amazing was their unique perspective. Before the CAT scan, X–rays could photograph only through the front or side of the body, frequently showing organs superimposed on each other, which made accurate readings difficult. But these new pictures seemed to dissect the body without a knife, depicting body parts in thin, individual cross sections, each as clearly defined as a drawing in a biology textbook.

For the patient, the procedure is quite painless. You report to the hospital or imaging center as an outpatient, and soon find yourself lying on a table in a brightly lit room, with the part of your body to be examined placed in the hole of what looks like a huge metal doughnut. A physician usually begins the scan by injecting a contrast solution into your bloodstream through a vein at the end of your elbow. This solution affects how much X–ray will be absorbed, and also enhances certain features of the final image. A computer uses the information on the amount of X–ray being transmitted through the tissue, and translates it into numbers, from which it makes a picture. In just seconds, images of your lung or brain or stomach, one slice after the other, appear on a computer screen. Not only is there an outline of the suspicious organ, but a sense of its density as well.

About one in 1,000 to 5,000 people gets a severe allergic reaction to the contrast solution. More typical symptoms are nausea, hives, a warm flush, or an unpleasant metallic taste, though many people experience nothing more annoying than the prick of the injection itself.

CAT scans aid in evaluating tumors by showing their exact size, their location, and whether they are solid or filled with fluid, an important clue to whether a growth is benign or malignant. CAT scans are useful as well for checking the extent of an injury or infection. Where X–rays would show only a bone fracture, a more exacting CAT scan could reveal internal bleeding, or cuts on an organ.

## MAGNETIC RESONANCE IMAGING:
## MAY THE FORCE BE WITH YOU

Although scientists have managed to reduce the dosage of radiation from X–rays, their dream has long been to find a way to see inside the body without using any ionizing radiation at all. Now that's possible, with a procedure that depends entirely on magnetic force.

Magnetic resonance imaging (MRI) first appeared as a laboratory technique for chemical analysis in the '30s, when it became known that parts of every cell had magnetic properties. Forty years later, researchers learned that normal and abnormal tissues respond differently in a magnetic field. In the '80s, technology advanced to the point where it became possible to translate these differences into a picture. The "camera," if you will, is a piece of high–tech machinery that looks like a giant tunnel and exerts a magnetic force as high as 30,000 times the power of the Earth's magnetic field. When a patient lies on a bed inside this tunnel, the intense magnetic force shakes up the protons present in every molecule of the body and causes them to line up in certain patterns. During this process of spinning and aligning, the protons give off energy signals that can be measured by a radio frequency and assembled into photographic images. Pictures can be made from three different planes: side to side, front to back, and head to toe. The images are actually cross sections, like slices in a loaf of bread, and some machines can take as many as 40 "slices" in eight minutes.

Other than a slight claustrophobic reaction to lying quietly inside a tunnel, MRI patients have reported no ill effects from the procedure. Any alteration to the body's molecules is slight and transient. According to Dr. Stanley Blum, chairman of radiology at the Hospital at the University of Pennsylvania, studies have indicated there is no known magnetic strength that has shown any biological effect on cells or chromosomes. MRI produces pictures of striking anatomical clarity, and images of things never seen before, such as changes in bone marrow and the stages of a hemorrhage. Tumors show up very clearly, along with ligaments, tendons and cartilage, which makes this an excellent tool for diagnosing sports injuries.

### ANGIOGRAPHY: JUST DYEING TO SEE YOU

Like any other heavily trafficked highway, the body's blood vessels frequently need repair. Our rich, fatty diets produce plaque that collects in certain spots and creates roadblocks to impede the smooth flow of blood. Moreover, as we age, the elasticity of the roadbed itself diminishes, vessels harden and narrow, and sometimes sections need replacing. With the development of angiography—a kind of X–ray photography of blood vessels—it's possible to do quite sophisticated medical roadwork.

The angiographer's tools include long, thin plastic catheters, guide wires that slide inside them, and a colorless solution—popularly referred to as dye—that mixes with the blood and blocks enough X–rays to create an image. Using these instruments, doctors can locate a clogged artery in the heart, pinpoint a blockage causing severe leg cramps, or check whether the brain is being sufficiently nourished with blood.

The procedure begins with a small puncture (in the groin, arm or neck) to insert the catheter. These pliable tubes come in a variety of lengths and widths, and often have special curves or hooks on the ends designed to pre–fit particular arteries. By twisting and turning the guide wire, an angiographer manipulates the catheter up one blood vessel and into another. He is directed by a fluoroscope, a device that uses a weak X-ray to picture the route the angiographer is following on a TV monitor. (Years ago, some shoe stores had fluoroscopy machines, so customers could check the fit by viewing their feet inside their new shoes.) When the angiographer reaches the spot he wants to examine, he withdraws the wire and injects the contrast solution through the catheter. It squirts out of the far end directly into the blood vessel, and a rapid series of X-ray pictures maps the solution's path.

Angiograms are performed without anesthesia, and patients generally experience little discomfort other than a warm flush from the contrast solution. But there are genuine concerns every time a doctor puts a catheter into a blood vessel, especially when these vessels are already weakened by disease. Excessive bleeding is one possible complication. An extreme example was the 83-year-old woman with unusually hard arterial walls that simply wouldn't seal when the catheter was removed. After several hours of continued bleeding, she had to be taken to the operating room, where the vessel was stitched shut. A more common risk is the chance a blood clot will dislodge, shut off the blood supply, and cause a stroke. Some people have reactions to the dye itself, ranging from an occasional severe allergic response to a milder stress reaction that slows the heartbeat and sends blood pressure plummeting.

At the University of Pennsylvania, angiography is one of the tools used at the Interventional Neuro-Center to study problems in the brain, such as aneurysms, tumors and AVMs. This center has refined the delicate catheterization technique to a level where it is used not only for diagnostic purposes, but also to seal off or radiate malformations in the brain that cannot be reached by traditional surgery. In other instances, interventional radiology becomes the vehicle for delivering treatment. One such procedure, called TIPSS, stops recurrent internal bleeding at hard-to-reach sites.

While life-threatening problems occur in about one-tenth of 1 percent of angiograms, medicine continues to explore diagnostic procedures with even better odds. One currently popular alternative for some patients is digital subtraction angiography. In this procedure, instead of using catheters, doctors inject contrast solution directly into the vein. The fluid's rapid course is tracked via fluoroscopy, and X-rays are taken the moment the "dyed" blood arrives at the suspicious spot. This kind of direct injection was impossible before computers, because the contrast solution became diluted en route and too faint to read on a normal X-ray. Now, digital radiography compares before-and-after X-rays and subtracts the numerical values of the original picture from those of the "dyed" version. The computations are then translated into a visual image that can be made lighter or darker, bigger or smaller. This technique is a fine screening device for patients whose advanced arterial disease makes angiograms too dangerous.

# ULTRASONOGRAPHY:
## FROM SUBMARINES TO PROBLEM PREGNANCIES

Submarines are tracked by sending sound waves through the ocean's depths. In medicine, the same principle allows doctors to monitor everything from a fetus developing in the womb to the degree of damage to a heart valve. Unique sound pictures are produced from harmless high–frequency sound waves passing over certain areas of the body. The returning signal varies with the density of the tissue it hits. A computer measures that variance—how long it takes the sound to bounce back, as well as how much of it returns. The digital information gleaned from the reflected sound gets translated into a shadowy image, somewhat like the pictures of the Earth's surface taken from a spacecraft.

This noninvasive screening device is widely used in perinatology, the care of unborn babies, since X–rays are far too dangerous to be used during pregnancy. Doctors are now able to study the fetus in its own little world. Is it the normal size for its stage of development? Is there any abnormal bleeding? Are all four chambers of the heart present? With the advent of ultrasound, doctors have reduced the number of stillbirths by diagnosing an absence of critical amniotic fluid and delivering early a baby who would otherwise starve to death. If ultrasound should reveal that a fetal bladder isn't emptying properly, doctors can insert a needle to drain the fetal urine and prevent damage to the unborn's kidney. Ultrasound has also cut the risk of amniocentesis, an important test for birth defects that requires drawing fluids from the womb. In the past, doctors occasionally harmed the fetus when they inserted the needle. With the help of the ultrasound, these accidents can be averted.

In adults, ultrasound routinely diagnoses certain heart problems that previously could be confirmed only with the riskier procedure of cardiac catheterization. Using a technique called Doppler echo cardiography, doctors can watch heart valves opening and closing, see the direction and speed of blood flowing from chamber to chamber, and determine whether there are any leaks or structural defects.

The test is painless. The patient lies on a table while an operator passes what looks like a small flashlight over the heart. The sound waves it emits produce an electrical signal that is translated by computer into moving images on a TV screen. A whooshing sound that accompanies the picture tells an experienced listener how much a valve has actually narrowed. Echo cardiography is particularly successful in diagnosing heart valve problems, the cause of one out of seven open–heart surgeries in America. Many surgeons use it in the operating room to make certain their valve repairs have completely plugged the leak.

## NUCLEAR MEDICINE: THE MAGIC BULLET APPROACH

Despite the ominous implications of its name, nuclear medicine is a relatively safe and inexpensive way to detect certain abnormalities that don't stand out on traditional X-ray pictures. Actually, it's just the reverse of standard X-ray technique. Instead of using machines outside the body to fire radiation through it, nuclear medicine works from the inside out, by sending off very low-level radiation generated by a solution injected into the body.

The field came to prominence after World War II, when research on atomic weapons yielded information about radioactivity that had applications beyond the military. From the men who made bombs, medicine learned how to combine chemicals with radioactive isotopes and study the effect these chemicals have on living tissue. In adapting radioactivity to mapping organs in action, the science of nuclear medicine was born.

First, a solution laced with radioactive isotopes is injected into the bloodstream. Then a special camera, equipped with a crystal that picks up these signals, translates them into an image. With this technique, doctors can see if a transplanted kidney is functioning properly, or whether a thyroid gland is behaving normally. The presence or absence of the tracer indicates whether there's a problem, and also determines the extent of any damage.

Currently, over 30 different kinds of nuclear scans are done routinely in most area hospitals, to diagnose problems such as blood clots in the lung or cirrhosis of the liver. A scan of the spine will tell if cancer has spread, since bones are a common secondary site for the disease. When doctors want to know how fast a stomach empties in a patient with gastric problems, they might feed that patient scrambled eggs seasoned with a tracer, and take a series of images to see how quickly the isotope disappears. A gallium scan, normally used to detect inflammation or infection, has been helpful in diagnosing AIDS through a characteristic lung infection. Another type of isotope that concentrates in dead heart tissue can identify where a heart attack took place, as well as the amount of tissue affected. Even blood flow can be measured radioactively.

Nuclear scans are commonly used in stress tests. The patient walks on a treadmill to build up his heart rate. Toward the end of the exercise period, he's injected with a radioactive isotope that immediately travels to the heart muscle and reveals whether a normal amount of blood is coursing through.

Except for the prick of the needle to inject the isotope solution, nuclear scans are no more painful than X-rays. Allergic reactions are rare; the isotopes are nontoxic, and the most commonly used isotopes have an average half-life of only six hours—which means they are gone from the body faster than the average meal.

## PET SCANS: WINDOWS ON THE BODY AT WORK

Most of the machines that peer into the body take what might be called architectural pictures, the kind that show the basic structure of human parts. The advent of positron emission tomography—the PET scan—made it possible to leap from anatomy to function, and see living organs in action. Want to know what happens in the brain when we smell a flower or read a book, when we get upset or have a seizure? Or what happens when our heart doesn't get enough oxygen? PET scans can supply answers like these without invading the body.

Traditionally, researchers who studied the living brain relied on tests done with electrodes, or on whatever was revealed before their eyes when they cut open the body's think tank. Now they can get a wealth of information by injecting nontoxic chemicals laced with radioactive tracers into the bloodstream, then measuring how and where these chemicals are absorbed. By pairing glucose (a chemical that acts in the brain like gas in a car) with a tracer that emits measurable gamma rays, doctors can map the way the brain metabolizes its various fuels. PET studies have shown with precision what parts of the brain process high and low sounds, what regions react to feelings of anxiety, and how memory loss of a stroke differs from that of Alzheimer's disease.

Fewer than 20 hospitals across the country are doing PET research, because the radioactive isotopes usually need to be manufactured in costly cyclotrons right on the hospital grounds. (Penn has one of them.) Some of the isotopes have a half–life of just 30 seconds, and can't be transported. PET scans pose relatively little danger to patients. Depending on the test, the chemical compounds are either injected or inhaled, and the pictures are taken by machinery that looks similar to that used in CAT scans.

# From Sunrise to Midnight *and free valet parking*

- **Magnetic Resonance Imaging** (G. E. High Field)
- **Computed Tomography**
- **Magnetic Resonance Angiography**
- **Ultrasound**
- **Mammography** (ACR accredited)
- **Radiography/Fluoroscopy**

Hours: Monday-Friday, 7:00 am to Midnight / Saturday & Sunday, 8:00 am to 10:00 pm
Valet parking available Monday-Friday, 7:00 am to 5:00 pm

*Call us: 215-893-0832*

**THE GRADUATE HOSPITAL**
**Imaging Center**
Tuttleman Center 1840 South Street Philadelphia, PA 19146
Graduate Health System

David P. Mayer, *M.D., Director*
Michael L. Brooks, *M.D., Associate Director*

PET scans are opening up all kinds of hidden secrets. For instance, we can now identify certain areas of damaged brain cells in stroke victims, because they do not absorb glucose or oxygen. By following whether these areas resume activity, doctors can chart the course of recovery. Such monitoring could eventually lead to an understanding of why some people recover from strokes, and perhaps make it possible to initiate recovery where it doesn't occur spontaneously. With patients suffering from seizures, PET scans can pinpoint the exact area in the brain responsible for triggering the attacks—a flaw not always revealed on standard brain–wave tests. Once identified, the abnormal tissue can sometimes be removed, and the seizures will disappear. PET studies of schizophrenics have shown a pattern of glucose metabolism markedly different from that in normal brains. These findings support the biochemical theory of mental illness, and could be instrumental in identifying its causes.

Another fruitful arena for the PET scan is in the diagnosis and treatment of cancer. It provides information useful in staging the disease, determining prognosis, and differentiating scar tissue from diseased tissue following chemotherapy. For example, because active tumors gobble up glucose, doctors can measure glucose intake with a PET scan and use that information to evaluate how effective chemotherapy is, and whether to step it up or stop it.

PET scans are also gaining a place in cardiac care, because they are able to show blood flow into the heart muscle with greater accuracy than traditional thallium scanning. This information is valuable is deciding whether or not to proceed with heart surgery.

For researchers, in particular, PET scans provide a priceless opportunity to bypass animal models and study a variety of human conditions as they occur in their natural settings. Their potential is virtually unlimited, because the number of available radioactive tracers has increased in a decade from a few to a few hundred. Compared to still photography, the PET scan is like a movie that will provide medicine with endless living studies of the way our marvelous engine works.

# Our Surgeons Get The Inside Picture.

Today, the surgeons who perform hernia and gallbladder operations at Roxborough Memorial Hospital can use a miniature camera to see inside your body, eliminating the stress and pain of major surgery.

RMH surgeons, who have been specially trained and certified to perform the procedures (known as laparoscopic surgery), claim that this innovative technique is one of the greatest advances of modern surgery. And, their patients agree. With this procedure, patients can be in and out of the hospital in 24 hours or less and feel fully recovered within days.

As part of the Roxborough family, we're proud to keep bringing innovative care and technology to our neighborhood. For more information about laparoscopic procedures for gallbladder or hernia surgery, ask your family doctor, or call our physician referral line at 487-4618.

## Roxborough Memorial Hospital

5800 Ridge Avenue • Philadelphia, PA 19128 • (215)487-4540

# I'll Help You Find a Jefferson Doctor.

"I know it can be hard to find a doctor and even harder to make an appointment. JEFF-NOW® helps you do all that with just one call.

"I'll answer your questions about Jefferson doctors and even set up an appointment. In other words, I can help."

Call **1-800-JEFF-NOW** (1-800-533-3669) to speak with a JEFF-NOW® representative. It's fast, free, and confidential.

## Call 1-800-JEFF-NOW

Thomas Jefferson University Hospital, 11th & Walnut Streets, Philadelphia, PA 19107

# 7 Check It Out Before You Check In

*A survey of hospitals in the Delaware Valley.*

♥ It's hard to turn on the television or pick up a magazine these days without being confronted with an advertisement for a hospital. In the competitive field of health care, hospital marketing has burgeoned into big business. Last year, Americans spent $256 billion for hospital care—roughly $1,000 for every man, woman and child in the country. No wonder hospitals are selling their services the way stores sell clothes and appliances. Since hospitals have entered the consumer marketplace, you, the buyer, need information to be a wise comparison shopper. That's why we compiled the following profiles for hospitals throughout the Delaware Valley. We did not rate or evaluate individual hospitals; rather, we let them present themselves as they'd like to be seen. Some hospitals chose not to answer everything we asked, particularly in regard to costs. If you want to know more, ask them directly.

Be aware that the more expensive hospitals do not necessarily provide better care. At times, the costliest hospitals are likely to be teaching institutions, because of the added expense of maintaining academic programs. In general, use the hospital charges listed in these profiles as benchmark figures, because what you see is usually not what you pay. Like the sticker price on an automobile, hospital costs wind up being discounted and negotiated, especially by insurers. Hospitals are frequently reimbursed at reduced rates by Independence Blue Cross, by various HMO, Medicaid and Medicare programs, by auto insurers, etc. And some people pay nothing at all. In 1990, area hospitals provided $160 million in free care.

Pennsylvanians are fortunate in that the state's Health Care Cost Containment Council gathers, analyzes and gives away, free of charge, an immense amount of information about area hospitals, ranging from mortality rates to costs to how many back operations a particular place has done. You can get copies of the council's Hospital Effectiveness Report by calling 717–232–6787, or by writing to the council at the Harrisburg Transportation Center, Suite 208, 4th and Chestnut streets, Harrisburg, PA 17101.

Not surprisingly, these reports have been criticized by doctors and hospitals. Both complain that the statistics don't reflect the difficulty of the cases they admit, or the severity of the patients' illnesses. Doctors says that publishing the mortality rates for particular surgeons might make some physicians stop operating on really sick patients, to improve their performance records. However, computer programs now make adjustments for these kinds of things, so the complaints may be more self–serving than justified. Bear in mind when you're interpreting these kinds of data that the success of any surgery depends on a variety of factors, including the patient's health, the surgeon's and anesthesiologist's skill, the cleanliness of the hospital, and the attention of the nursing care. Moreover, studies have shown that you're more likely to live, and less likely to have complications, when you undergo a given procedure at a hospital where that procedure is done with a frequency approaching 200 cases a year.

For additional information, you can call the Delaware Valley Hospital Council at 735–9695.

---

- 🛏 **OVERNIGHT FACILITIES FOR FAMILIES**
- 🙏 **PASTORAL CARE**
- 🏥 **HOSPICE CARE**
- 💈 **BARBER**
- ⚖ **PATIENT ADVOCATE**
- 🚭 **SMOKE-FREE ENVIRONMENT**
- 🎓 **TEACHING HOSPITAL**
- **E**  **EMERGENCY ROOM**
- ✉ **PREPAYMENT FOR DEDUCTIBLE REQUIRED**

---

**Abington Memorial Hospital** 🛏 🏥 💈 ⚖ 🚭 🎓 E ✉
*1200 Old York Rd., Abington, 576–2000, 576–MEDI (physician referral), 881-5750 (ElderHelp).* Doctors on active staff: 425 (90% board–certified); number of beds: 508; 1.61 RNs per bed. Semiprivate room cost: $735; private room cost: $755; gourmet food service: $15 per meal; accreditation: JCAHO, PTSF, ACGME, AMA, AABB, CAP, ACR.

Sample charges for surgical services: back and neck procedures with–

out complication, $4,249; vaginal delivery, $1,207; prostate removal, $2,348.72; hourly operating-room charge, $995. Special surgical units: neurosurgery, gynecology, plastic and reconstructive, vascular, fetal, ophthalmologic, dental, ambulatory surgery, mini–surgery, Surgical Trauma Unit, Abington Surgical Center. Base cost for an ER visit: $74. Additional ER services: Regional Trauma Center, Chest Pain Center.

Ob/gyn programs: family–centered maternity care, Level III neonatal ICU, high–risk pregnancy and obstetrics services, genetic counseling, infertility services including in–vitro fertilization, Mother/Infant Unit, prenatal testing, amniocentesis, PUBS, neonatology unit, maternity education, sibling orientation, postpartum depression support group.

Specialized treatment programs: cardiac telemetry, CHAMPS (Children's Hospital/Abington Memorial Pediatric Service), hemodialysis, neuroscience, psychiatry unit, sports medicine, Fitness Institute, cardiac rehab, sleep disorders, pain management, radiation oncology, occupational medicine.

Physical rehab services: 26–bed inpatient unit, Falls Prevention Clinic, geriatric rehab assessment, neuromuscular retraining, speech pathology and dysphagia, occupational, physical and recreation therapy, stroke program, prosthetic/orthotic clinic.

Outpatient health and wellness programs: childbirth/parenting classes, "Look Good, Feel Better" (for women with cancer), "Reach to Recovery" (for breast cancer), "I Can Cope" (for cancer patients and their families), CPR training, diabetes education, first aid training, smoking cessation, weight management center, nutrition counseling, Eat Heart–y Program, Time Out for Men/Women, Abington Fitness Institute, ElderMed, van service for outpatient transportation.

Abington Memorial Hospital, a community teaching hospital, considers its strengths to be in: ob/gyn, newborn care, cancer care, rehab medicine, emergency services, cardiology, surgery, geriatric medicine, family practice, primary care, internal medicine.

## Albert Einstein Medical Center

*York and Tabor rds., 456–7890, 800–EINSTEIN (hot line).*
Doctors on active staff: 603 (76% board–certified); number of beds: 600; 1.17 RNs per bed; semiprivate room cost: $720; private room cost; $870; accreditation: JCAHO, ACS, PTSF, ACR.

Sample charges for surgical services including ancillary and supplies: coronary bypass without cardiac cath, $64,159; back and neck procedures without complication, $16,880; vaginal delivery, $5,284; prostate removal, $10,300; standard local anesthesia, $225; hourly operating-room charge, $1,938; preadmission testing, $577. Special surgical units: heart surgery, transplants. Base cost for emergency room visit: $105. Also available in ER: Trauma Center, psychiatric emergency unit.

Ob/gyn programs: "Healthy Beginnings Plus," "A Better Start."

Specialized treatment programs: heart surgery unit, Cancer Center, kidney dialysis, Center for Orthopedic Sciences, endoscopy, pediatric ICU, neonatal ICU, psychiatric unit.

Physical rehab services: physical, occupational and speech therapy.

Outpatient programs: Premier Years (senior membership program), insurance and financial counseling, health screenings and lectures, CPR training, prenatal classes, various health screenings for cancer, hypertension, glaucoma.

Albert Einstein Medical Center considers its medical strengths to be in: cardiology, cardiac catheterization, cancer orthopedics, geriatrics, psychiatry, transplants; and its surgical strengths to be in: cardio-thoracic and orthopedic.

Affiliated with the Philadelphia Geriatric Center. Belmont Center for Comprehensive Treatment and Moss Rehabilitation Hospital are Einstein subsidiaries.

### Brandywine Hospital

*201 Reeceville Rd., Cain Township, 383–8581.* Doctors on active staff: 150 (87% board-certified); number of beds: 218; 1.4 RNs per bed; semiprivate room cost:$621; private room cost: $677; accreditation: JCAHO, AABB, CAP, PDH, PTCF.

Surgical charges not furnished. Special surgical units: Ambulatory Surgery Center, Short Procedure Unit. Base cost for ER visit: $113. Additional ER services: Regional Trauma Center, chest pain emergency unit, Sky Flightcare (a pre- and interhospital aeromedical helicopter based at the hospital).

Ob/gyn programs: Maternity Care Center, pre- and postnatal exercise classes, Resolve Through Sharing.

Specialized treatment programs: dialysis, mental health unit, physical and hand rehab, occupational health, Fitness and Wellness Center, Breast Care Center, Pain Control Center, sports medicine, industrial rehab, work-hardening.

Brandywine Hospital considers its strengths to be in: cardiology, trauma/emergency care.

### Bryn Mawr Hospital

*130 South Bryn Mawr Ave., Bryn Mawr.* Doctors on active staff: 383 (83% board-certified); 393 beds; accreditation: PDH, JCAHO, ACGME, ACR. Room costs, surgical and ER charges not furnished.

Special surgical units: open heart, surgical "greenhouses" (for total hip replacement), minimal access surgery, same-day surgery, SurgiCenter.

Ob/gyn programs: maternal/fetal medicine, labor/delivery/recovery unit, postpartum unit, newborn nursery, neonatal ICU, maternal and newborn transport, childbirth preparation classes, gynecologic surgery, infertility services.

Specialized treatment programs: drug and alcohol intervention unit, inpatient and outpatient dialysis, inpatient psychiatry unit, Dental Clinic, Eye Clinic, pediatrics inpatient unit, ICU, coronary care unit, cardiac catheterization labs, electrophysiology.

Physical rehab services: physical, occupational and speech therapy.

Outpatient health and wellness programs: monthly blood pressure screenings, StressSmart, adult/infant/child CPR, baby-sitting course, nutrition counseling, adult health fair, Life Without Diets, travelers' advisory service, diabetes screening and counseling, childbirth preparation, cancer and cholesterol screenings, children's health fair.

Bryn Mawr Hospital considers its strengths to be in: arthritis, orthopedics, cancer care, cardiovascular illness, pediatrics, neonatology, obstetrics, psychiatry, general surgery.

### The Chester County Hospital 🏥 ⚕ 🏢 🛏 ⚕ ⊘ 🚑 E
*701 East Marshall St., West Chester, 431–5000.* Doctors on staff: 250; number of beds: 250; 1.76 RNs per bed; accreditation: JCAHO, NLN, CAP, AABB. Room costs, surgical and ER charges not furnished.

Special surgical units: nine–room surgical suite, Ambulatory Care Center.

Ob/gyn programs: 27–bed obstetrics unit with specially designed suites, Level II nursery, prenatal clinic, postnatal childbirth classes, genetic counseling, sibling classes, Stork Alert (24–hour beeper service to notify fathers when mother is in labor), Childbirth Connection.

Specialized treatment programs: Occupational Health Center, coronary care/ICU.

Physical rehab services: Center for Health and Fitness, physical medicine department, Occupational Health Center.

Outpatient health and wellness programs: smoking cessation, weight control, CPR/first aid training, nutrition counseling, fitness evaluation, muscle flexibility, resting and exercise heart rate, oxygen uptake, strength testing, exercise/aerobics programs.

The 100–year old Chester County Hospital considers its strengths to be in: oncology, cardiology, ob/gyn (approximately 2,000 babies delivered annually), occupational medicine, fitness/ wellness programs.

### Chestnut Hill Rehabilitation Hospital ⚕ 🏢 🛏 ⚕ ⊘ 🚑 E
*8601 Stenton Ave., Wyndmoor, 233–6200, 248–8069 (physician referral).* Doctors on active staff: 8 (87% board-certified); number of beds: 83; 1.75 RNs per bed; gourmet food service: $10 per meal; accreditation: JCAHO, ACGME, CAP, PDH, AABB. Room costs and surgical charges not furnished.

Special surgical units: Outpatient Surgical Center.
Base cost for ER visit: $79.
Ob/gyn programs: antenatal testing.
Specialized treatment programs: dialysis, cardiac rehab, endoscopy, ICCU, CICU, ICU.

Physical rehab services: physical, occupational, speech and language therapy.

Outpatient health and wellness programs: Parent's Place, childbirth education, cardiac rehab, medical weight management, Eater's Choice, diabetes, Smoke Stoppers, CPR, Senior CHEC, blood pressure screening.

Chestnut Hill Rehabilitation Hospital considers its strengths to be in: general medicine and surgery, obstetrics, cardiac care.

### Children's Hospital of Philadelphia 🛏 🍴 🏥 💊 ⚖ ⓢ 🎓 E
*One Children's Center, 34th St. and Civic Center Blvd., 590–1000, 800–TRY–CHOP (for referrals).* Doctors on active staff: 216 (99% board-certified); number of beds: 294; 2.4 RNs per bed; semiprivate room cost: $700; private room cost: $750; accreditation: ABP.

Surgical charges not applicable. Special surgical units: transplants (heart/liver/kidney and bone marrow), cardio–thoracic, craniofacial, craniofacial reconstruction, neurosurgery, urology, orthopedics.

Base cost for an ER visit: $140. ER services: Level I trauma service, six isolation rooms for patients with infectious diseases, trauma resuscitation room, state–of–the–art radiology suite, decontamination room.

Specialized programs: diabetes, Growth and Development Center, pain management, sleep disorders, Diagnostic Center, attention deficit/hyperactivity disorders, communication disorders, rheumatology, hemangioma, lipid heart, obese clinic, cystic fibrosis, cerebral palsy, scoliosis, sports medicine, orthopedics, dyslexia testing, neurofibromatosis, sickle-cell, hemophilia, neuro–oncology, Pediatric Regional Epilepsy Program, electroencephalography, neuromuscular program, psychiatric unit.

Special treatment units: oncology, surgical (trauma/liver and short–stay), medical (diabetes and asthma, cardiology), cardiovascular surgery and neurosurgery, pediatric ICU (acute, intermediate and isolation), Infant Transitional Unit, infant ICU.

Provides physical rehab services through the Children's Seashore House.

Founded in 1855 as the country's first pediatric hospital, CHOP is currently listed as the number two pediatric hospital in the United States, according to *U.S. News and World Report*. It is affiliated with the University of Pennsylvania Medical Center and owns Children's Seashore House.

### Children's Seashore House 🛏 ⚖ ⓢ 🎓
*3405 Civic Center Blvd., 895–3600.* Doctors on active staff: 14 (100% board-certified); number of beds: 70; 1 RN per bed; semiprivate room cost: $950; accreditation: JCAHO.

Surgical charges not applicable.

Specialized treatment programs: respiratory rehab, neuro rehab, biobehavioral unit, pediatric feeding disorders unit.

Physical rehab services: physical and occupational therapy, communication disorders (speech/language pathology and audiology), rehab nursing, Child Life/therapeutic recreation, pediatric psychology.

Children's Seashore House considers its strengths to be in: child development and rehab. It is the fourth oldest pediatric hospital in the country, and the first to provide specialized care and rehab to children with physical and developmental disabilities or chronic illnesses.

### Cooper Hospital/University Medical Center 🛏 🍴 🏥 💊 ⚖ ⓢ 🎓 E ✉
*One Cooper Plaza, Camden, New Jersey, 609–342–2000.* Doctors on active staff: 456 (91% board–certified); number of beds: 552; 1.5 RNs per bed;

semiprivate room cost: $488; private room cost: $551; accreditation: AABB, ACS, AHA, CAP, JCAHO, MSNJ. ER charges not furnished. Sample charges for surgical services: coronary bypass without cardiac cath, $16,234; back and neck procedures without complication, $4,762; vaginal delivery, $2,142; prostate removal, $3,277. Special surgical units: endoscopic and laser surgery, cardio–thoracic, bone marrow transplantation, pediatrics surgery, neurosurgery, gynecologic oncology, colo–rectal, orthopedics, otolaryngology, plastic and reconstructive, cleft palate program, urology, ophthalmology, traumatology and emergency. Cooper is a Level I Regional Trauma Center.

Ob/gyn programs: antenatal testing, comprehensive breast care center, maternal/fetal medicine, perinatal center, gynecologic oncology, reproductive endocrinology, in–vitro fertilization, genetic counseling, maternal advanced care.

Specialized treatment programs: Comprehensive Cancer Center, Cardiovascular Center, Sleep Disorders Laboratory, Geriatric Assessment Program, Diabetes Care Center, epilepsy program, radiation therapy, high–risk pregnancy program, Colo–rectal Care Center, Perinatal Center, Special Care Nursery, Children's Epilepsy Center, Young Adult Care Center, maternal advanced and intermediate care, Comprehensive Breast Care Center, Institute for Systemic Radiation Therapy.

Specialized pediatric programs: Child Development Center, birth defects and genetic disorders, pediatric hematology/oncology, pediatric and neonatal intensive care, Regional Arthritis Center, sickle–cell anemia, speech pathology, spina bifida, SIDS and infant apnea evaluation, young adult care, play therapy program.

Physical rehab services: physical and occupational therapy, psychiatric evaluations, prosthetics and orthotics, speech pathology, comprehensive oncology rehab, swallowing evaluations, electromyography and nerve conduction studies, audiology, chronic pain, comprehensive lymphedema treatment, balance disorders, gait dysfunction, movement disorder therapy.

Health and wellness programs: Understanding Menopause, breast surgery, pregnancy after 35, heart disease, stress management, diabetes management, childhood nutrition, cancer prevention through nutrition, breast cancer screening.

In recent years, Cooper Hospital/University Medical Center has become a major South Jersey medical center. It considers its strengths to be in: cancer treatment, cardiology and cardio–thoracic surgery, pediatrics, maternal/fetal medicine, gastroenterology, liver diseases, trauma.

It has been designated as the Southern New Jersey Regional Children's Hospital for complicated cases that cannot be treated at regional community hospitals.

## Crozer–Chester Medical Center
*15th St. and Upland Ave., Chester, 447–2000.* Doctors on active staff: 475 (74% board-certified); number of beds: 480; gourmet food service:

between $15 and $20; accreditation: ACS, PTSF, JCAHO, ACR. Room costs and surgical charges not furnished.

Special surgical units: open–heart surgery, angioplasty, Nathan Speare Regional Burn Treatment Center, the Trauma Center. Base cost for an ER visit: $95.

Ob/gyn programs: Free outpatient care for the uninsured through the Pennsylvania State Department of Health; special supplemental food program for women, infants and children; prenatal care programs through A Better Start, Health Partners, Family Planning Service and Healthy Beginnings, 14–bed intensive care nursery.

Specialized treatment programs: drug and alcohol treatment programs (in– and outpatient), mental health programs, dialysis, specialized clinics for ear/nose/throat, orthopedics.

Physical rehab services: occupational and physical therapy, speech–language pathology, audiology and dysphagia services, Feeding and Swallowing Center, Sports Medicine Center.

Health and wellness programs: Nutrition Information Center, Emporiatrics Program, maternity fitness classes, childbirth education classes, sibling preparation classes, diabetes maintenance classes, cancer prevention through mobile mammography van program.

Crozer–Chester Medical Center considers its strengths to be in: burn treatment, trauma services, obstetrics, cancer care, general surgery.

It is a member of the Crozer–Keystone Health System, which owns Crozer–Chester, Delaware County Memorial and Springfield Hospitals.

### Delaware County Memorial Hospital

*501 North Lansdowne Ave., Drexel Hill, 284–8100.* Doctors on active staff: 278 (95% board–certified); number of beds: 303; 1.4 RNs per bed; room cost: $709; gourmet food service: $10 per meal; accreditation: JCAHO, PDH, NLN, PMS, CAP, ACS.

Sample charges for surgical services: vaginal delivery, $3,600 for a two–day stay; standard local anesthesia, $503; hourly operating-room charge between $520 and $944; preadmission testing, $125. Special surgical units: outpatient surgery, endoscopy, laparoscopic, obstetrics, a complete range of genito–urinary services. Base cost for ER visit: $44. Additional emergency room services include a paramedic unit.

Ob/gyn programs: prenatal, pregnancy, newborn, breast–feeding, birthing, parenting, exercise, child–care emergency classes.

Specialized treatment programs: alcohol and addiction treatment, dialysis, Sports Medicine Institute, respiratory therapy/pulmonary rehab, cardiac catheterization, physical medicine and rehab, Delaware County Regional Cancer Center (a cancer program affiliated with the Fox Chase Cancer Network), Hearing and Speech Center, Women's Diagnostic Center, intensive care nursery, perinatal testing.

Physical rehab services: the Stroke Club, amputee, activities of daily living, orthotics, prosthesis, occupational therapy, physical therapy, speech therapy, social work, hearing, specialized nursing.

Outpatient programs: smoking cessation, stress management, CPR training, baby-sitting courses, weight-loss program, nutrition, health and beauty seminar, ElderMed, screening programs.

Delaware County Memorial considers its medical strengths to be in: cardiology, oncology, geriatrics, women's health, pulmonary, gastroenterology, physical medicine; and its surgical strengths to be in: laparoscopic procedures, orthopedics, ophthalmology, colo-rectal, ear/nose/throat, thoracic-vascular. It is a member of Crozer-Keystone Health System.

### Deborah Heart and Lung Center

*200 Trenton Rd., Browns Mills, New Jersey, 609-893-5400.* Doctors on active staff: 56 (88% board-certified); number of beds: 155; 2.25 RNs per bed; accreditation: JCAHO, CAP, AABB, NJDH.

Using funds raised by the Deborah Hospital Foundation, this institution has for 70 years provided free care to people, regardless of race, religion, or income. However, it takes third- party reimbursement when available.

Specialized programs: Sleep Apnea Clinic.

Outpatient health and wellness programs: Speaker's Bureau.

Deborah considers its strengths to be in: adult and pediatric cardiology, cardiac surgery, adult pulmonary medicine.

Deborah is an internationally known speciality hospital with an important Research Institute. It provides diagnosis and treatment of adults with cardiac, pulmonary and vascular diseases, and of children with congenital and acquired heart defects.

In 1990 it performed more open-heart surgeries and cardiac catheterizations than any other hospital in the Delaware Valley.

### Doylestown Hospital

*Route 202 and 611 Bypass, Doylestown, 345-2200.* Doctors on active staff: 159 (84% board-certified); number of beds: 213; 5 RNs per bed; semi-private room cost: $625; private room cost: $665; accreditation: JCAHO, CARF, PDH.

Sample charges for surgical services: back and neck procedures without complication, $9,910; vaginal delivery, $3,022; prostate removal, $6,815; standard local anesthesia, $118 per unit; operating-room charge, $1,498 plus $125 per unit; preadmission testing, $443. Base cost for ER visit: $200. Additional ER services: crisis intervention for mental health emergencies, direct access to Poison Center (Lehigh Valley), ALS and PALS certified staff.

Ob/gyn programs: prenatal genetic screening (amniocentesis and CVS), educational programs, Babywell.

Specialized treatment units: mental health, telemetry, critical care, endoscopy, oncology nursing.

Physical rehab services: occupational, physical, speech therapy, EMG, nerve conduction studies, cyber evaluation, psychological services, hydrotherapy, video fluoroscopic swallowing exams, hand rehab, recreational therapy.

Outpatient health and wellness programs: Alzheimer's workshop, CPR, diabetes education, first aid, I Can Cope, Dialogue with a Doctor, parenting, smoking cessation, stress reduction, screenings for blood pressure, breast cancer, cholesterol, diabetes, skin cancer, prostate cancer, senior wellness, baby-sitting, stress.

Doylestown Hospital considers its strengths to be in: cardiology, emergency, surgery, primary care, rehab, gastroenterology, obstetrics. It is the only hospital in the country owned and operated by a federated Women's Club.

## Episcopal Hospital

*Front St. and Lehigh Ave., 427–7000.* Doctors on active staff: 154 (78% board–certified), number of beds: 275; 2.75 RNs per bed; semiprivate room cost: $710; private room cost: $731; accreditation: JCAHO, AABB, ACS, CAP.

Surgical charges not furnished. Special surgical units: laparoscopic cholecystectomy, neurosurgery, cardio–thoracic, colo–rectal, laser. Base cost for an ER visit: $70.

Ob/gyn programs: prepared childbirth classes, maternal infant care, Women, Infants and Children, cocaine outreach services.

Specialized treatment programs: substance abuse, dialysis, dental (pediatric and adult), industrial medicine, Beacon House (residential facility for female drug abusers).

Physical rehab services: physical and occupational therapy, work–hardening and Back School, Pain Management Center.

Outpatient health and wellness programs: prenatal classes, fitness/circuit training.

Episcopal Hospital considers its strengths to be in: cardiovascular diseases, neonatology/intensive care, ob/gyn, substance abuse treatment.

It has a School of Nursing and a School of Perfusion, as well as a Patient Liaison Program for those who need an interpreter. For patients who do not need acute nursing care but aren't ready to go home, Episcopal has a skilled nursing facility called Harrison House.

## Fox Chase Cancer Center

*7701 Burholme Ave., 728–6900.* Doctors on active staff: 54 (89% board–certified); number of beds: 100; 1.5 RNs per bed; semiprivate room cost: $755; private room cost: $860; suite cost: $1,355; accreditation: PDH, JCAHO, ACS, ACR, AHA.

Surgical costs not applicable. Hourly operating-room charge: $1,260. Special surgical units: Intraoperative Radiation Therapy.

Ob/gyn programs: gynecologic oncology.

Physical rehab services: physical, occupational and speech therapy.

Outpatient health and wellness programs: smoking cessation, mobile mammography, community education programs.

Fox Chase Cancer Center is one of 28 hospitals nationwide designated as Comprehensive Cancer Centers by the National Cancer Institute. It is renowned as a research facility dedicated to the diagnosis, treatment and prevention of cancer.

## Germantown Hospital and Medical Center
*One Penn Blvd., 951–8000.* Doctors on active staff: 226 (83% board–certified); number of beds: 226; 1.25 RNs per bed; room cost (all private): $672; accreditation: JCAHO, CAP, AABB, ACR.

Sample charges for surgical services: back and neck procedures without complication, $11,100; vaginal delivery, $3,300; prostate removal, $7,300; hourly operating-room charge, first half–hour, $1,035, each additional half-hour $596; preadmission testing, $332. Special surgical units: Custom Joint Center (Computer Laser Assisted Surgical System), Laser Center. Base cost for ER visit: $105.25.

Ob/gyn programs: Healthy Beginnings (a federally sponsored program providing prenatal care to Medicaid mothers), Childbirth Education Classes.

Specialized treatment programs: skilled nursing facility, Ambulatory Infusion Center, autologous blood donation program, Comprehensive Headache Center.

Physical rehab services: biodex, occupational, speech and TMJ therapy.

Outpatient health and wellness programs: free screenings for prostate, breast and colo–rectal cancer, glaucoma, cholesterol, blood pressure and hearing, childbirth education classes, Stop Smoking Clinic.

The Germantown Hospital and Medical Center considers its strengths to be in: neurosurgery, general surgery, neurology, orthopedics, medical and surgical oncology. Its Custom Joint Center is the first of its kind in the area and only the eighth in the country to offer CLASS Hip (Computed Laser Assisted Surgical System).

## The Graduate Hospital
*18th and Lombard sts., 893–2000, 800–654–GRAD (physician referral).*
Doctors on active staff: 287 (90.6% board–certified); number of beds: 334; 1.3 RNs per bed; semiprivate room cost: $949; private room cost: $978; suite cost: $1,038; gourmet food service: $16.20 per day; accreditation: JCAHO, ACR, PDH, AABB.

Surgical charges not furnished. Special surgical units: open–heart surgery, musculoskeletal tumor surgery, neurosurgery for epilepsy, gynecologic cancer surgery, same–day surgery. Base cost for ER visit: $98.67.

Gynecological services include a range of laparoscopic surgical procedures, including total laparoscopic hysterectomies, emphasizing organ preservation.

Specialized treatment programs: back program, cancer program, Cardiac Care Unit, Cerebral Blood Flow Laboratory, Comprehensive Epilepsy Center, Disk Treatment Center, Eating Disorders Program, kidney dialysis, Human Performance and Sports Medicine Center, Incontinence Center, Intra–Operative Radiation Therapy, medical intensive care unit, Memory Disorders Service, radiation therapy, Musculoskeletal Tumor Service, Neurological ICU, Parkinson's Disease and Movement Disorders Center, Surgical CCU, Nutritional Support Unit, TMJ service, Wound Care Center.

Its comprehensive rehab services include: physical, occupational and speech therapy, Phase 1 cardiac rehab, artificial airways, arthritis, articulation, athletic rehabilitation, aural rehabilitation, botulinin injection for spasmodic disorders, delayed language, diabetic care, dysphagia assessment and therapy, fractures, full–scale knee rehabilitation, general reconditioning, hand therapy, hearing aid evaluation, mastectomy protocol, neurological disorders, pain management, specialized back and neck care, splinting, sterile and nonsterile whirlpool including wound redressing, stroke rehabilitation, total knee and hip replacement, venous insuff circulator boot therapy/wound care, voice disorders.

Graduate operates a Health and Fitness Center (985–2205) and a Human Performance and Sports Medicine Center (688–6767).

The Graduate Hospital is part of Graduate Health System, a major regional health-care organization. It owns Mount Sinai Hospital, Rancocas and Zubrugg Hospitals, Community General Hospital (Reading), and Greater Atlantic Health Service.

### Hahnemann University Hospital

*Broad and Vine sts., 448–7000.* Doctors on active staff: 480 (92% board–certified); number of beds: 616; 1.5 RNs per bed; semiprivate room cost: $820; private room cost: $860; suite cost: $930; accreditation: JCAHO.

Sample charges for surgical services: coronary bypass without cardiac cath, $25,000; back and neck procedures without complication, $14,000 (back), $18,200 (neck); vaginal delivery, $5,100; prostate removal, $24,000; local anesthesia, $46 for each 15–minute period; operating-room cost, $1,875 per hour; preadmission testing, $250. Special surgical units: Dedicated Kidney and Pancreas Transplant Care Unit, Surgical Trauma ICU. Base cost for ER visit: $57. Additional emergency room services: Level I Regional Resource Trauma Center, university MedEvac helicopter, cardiac resuscitation area, self–contained radiology section, 24–hour triage, minor treatment area.

Ob/gyn programs: Women's Care Center, Reproductive Endocrinology and Infertility Clinic, Sports Gynecology and Women's Lifestyle Center, birthing rooms.

Specialized treatment programs: renal dialysis, Dental Center, Cardiovascular and Coronary Care ICU, Monty Hall–Variety Club Children's Pavilion, Child/Adolescent Psychiatric Inpatient Unit, Psychiatric Medical Care Unit, bone marrow transplant, Adult Psychiatry Unit.

Physical rehab services: interdisciplinary approach to physical, occupational and speech therapy, Cardiac Rehab Center, Prosthetics Clinic, ALS Clinic.

Outpatient health and wellness programs: vision screening, women's health seminars, physical fitness, smoking cessation, Executive Health and Wellness Center, CPR, stress management, weight management, nutrition seminars.

Hahnemann considers its strengths to be in: cardiology and cardiac catheterization, cardiac surgery, cancer and blood disease, radiation oncology, trauma, orthopedic surgery, transplantation, pediatric gastroenterology.

### Holy Redeemer Hospital and Medical Center
*1648 Huntingdon Pike, Meadowbrook, 947–3000.* Doctors on active staff: 307 (81.4% board–certified); 283 beds; 1.52 RNs per bed. Room cost: $728; gourmet food service: $12. Accreditation: JCAHO, ACR.

Sample charges for surgical services: back and neck procedures without complication, $9,514; vaginal delivery, $3,302; prostate removal, $6,441; standard local anesthesia, $43 per half hour; hourly operating-room charge, $995. Special surgical units: infertility (reproductive–endocrinology), corneal transplants, total joint replacements, reconstructive knee surgery, full endoscopic urology service. Base cost for ER visit: $91.

Ob/gyn programs: maternal/fetal medicine, oncology, perinatology, reproductive endocrinology (infertility), lactation consultation, antenatal testing.

Specialized treatment programs: medical oncology, renal dialysis, neonatology, telemetry, labor, delivery and recovery, sports medicine, ambulatory surgery and care, pediatrics, orthopedics, critical care.

Physical rehab services: physical therapy, occupational therapy, speech pathology, pediatric development clinic and rehab, EMG/NCU, psychological services, sports medicine.

Outpatient programs: Diabetes Educator, Speaker's Bureau, Nutrition Counseling, Freshstart Smoke Cessation, Fitness & Exercise, Education Series for Expectant Families, health screenings, enterostomal therapy.

Holy Redeemer considers its medical strengths to be in: orthopedics, obstetrics/gynecology, cardiology, pediatrics, ophthalmology. It is a member of the Holy Redeemer Health System, Inc., which also includes local organizations for home care, long–term health care, subsidized housing and single mothers with children.

### Jeanes Hospital
*7600 Central Ave., 728–2000, 728–2033 (Women's Healthline), 728–2100 (Senior's Healthline).* Doctors on active staff: 160 (81% board–certified); number of beds: 220; .91 RNs per bed; semiprivate room cost: $650; private room cost: $687; accreditation: JCAHO, PDH, CAP.

Sample charges for surgical services: back and neck procedures without complication, $11,156; vaginal delivery, $3,505; prostate removal, $9,208; standard local anesthesia, $34.75; hourly operating-room charge, $1,039; preadmission testing, $156.25. Special surgical units: orthopedics, cancer care. Base cost for ER visit: $45.50. Additional ER services: Level II general emergency department.

Ob/gyn programs: childbirth education, UNITE, women's health, sibling, infant care, refresher course.

Physical rehab services: occupational, physical and speech therapy, audiology, cardiac rehab, pulmonary rehab.

Outpatient health and wellness programs: diabetic teaching and counseling, Parkinson's Exercise Group, nutritional counseling, Healthy Back lectures, Lifestrides Senior Citizen Program for adults over 50, arthritis aquatics.

Jeanes considers its strengths to be in: internal medicine, orthopedics, infectious diseases, ob/gyn surgery, neonatology.

### Kennedy Memorial Hospitals

*Three divisions: CHERRY HILL DIVISION, Chapel Ave. and Cooper Landing Rd., Cherry Hill, New Jersey, 609–488–6500;* number of beds: 225; *STRATFORD DIVISION, 18 East Laurel Rd., Stratford, New Jersey, 609–346–6000;* number of beds: 236; *WASHINGTON TOWNSHIP DIVISION, Hurtville–Cross Keys Rd., Turnersville, New Jersey, 609–582–2500;* number of beds: 146. Kennedy operates one medical and nursing staff for all three divisions. Doctors on active staff: 390 (70% board–certified); 1.06 RNs per bed; accreditation: NJDH, AOA, and ACR (for mammography). Room costs and surgical charges not furnished.

Special surgical units: same–day surgery, laser surgery, (carbon dioxide, Yag, ophthalmologic Yag and argon, pulse dye laser), lithotripter. Base cost for ER visit: $41. Additional emergency room services: specialized trauma response teams, crisis intervention in affiliation with Steininger Center (at CHERRY HILL DIVISION).

Ob/gyn programs: perinatology, neonatology, family–centered childbirth, pelvoscopy, laser surgery, dads–on–call beepers, childbirth education classes, genetic counseling, sibling classes, breast–feeding classes, Motherwell maternity exercise and fitness program, Healthy Start, infertility diagnosis and treatment.

Specialized treatment programs: in– and outpatient dialysis, child and adolescent psychiatric unit, adult psychiatric unit, alcohol and drug detox programs, alcohol and drug rehab, cardiac, respiratory and surgical ICUs.

Physical rehab services: comprehensive physical therapy, Sports Medicine Program.

Outpatient health and wellness: CPR training, community education programs, ElderMed senior membership program, baby–sitter certification classes, CLASP (Child Life and Safety Program).

Kennedy Memorial considers its medical strengths to be in: cardiology, geriatrics, fetal–maternal/obstetrics, pulmonary, rheumatology, infectious diseases including HIV, hematology, oncology, nephrology; and its surgical strengths to be in: laser laparoscopy, gynecology, orthopedic, urology including laser lithotripsy.

Kennedy Memorial Hospitals is also the core teaching affiliate of the University of Medicine and Dentistry of New Jersey, School of Osteopathic Medicine.

### The Lankenau Hospital 🛏️ 🍴 🏥 🛋️ ⚕️ Ⓢ 🪑 **E**
*100 Lancaster Ave., Wynnewood, 645–2000.* Doctors on active staff: 307 (88% board–certified); number of beds: 475; 1.37 RNs per bed; accreditation: JCAHO, AABB, ACR, CAP. Room costs and surgical charges not furnished.

Special surgical units: ambulatory surgery, orthopedic, cardio–thoracic surgery, intensive care. Base cost for ER visit: $37.

Ob/gyn programs: reproductive endocrinology, gynecologic oncology, perinatology, midwifery, osteoporosis management, incontinence, family planning clinic, Norplant implantation, Level III intensive care nursery.

Specialized treatment programs: Sports Medicine Center, inpatient psychiatric unit, Sleep Disorders Center, Cancer Treatment Center.

Physical rehab services: physical and occupational therapy, speech therapy/pathology, hand therapy, sports medicine rehab.

Outpatient health and wellness programs: travelers' advisory service, dietary/nutrition counseling, fitness, exercise, diet, smoking cessation, free health screenings and lectures.

Lankenau considers its medical strengths to be in: cardiology, gynecological oncology, neonatal care, ophthalmology; and its surgical strengths to be in: cardiac, orthopedic surgery. It is home to the Lankenau Medical Research Center, which offers over 200 basic and clinical protocols including cancer and cardiology.

### The Lower Bucks Hospital 🛏️ 🍴 ⚕️ Ⓢ 🪑 **E**
*501 Bath Rd., Bristol, 785–9200;* Doctors on active staff: 260 (61% board–certified); number of beds: 320; 1.2 RNs per bed; semiprivate room cost: $620; private room cost: $685; accreditation: JCAHO, AABB, CAP.

Sample charges for surgical services: back and neck procedures without complication, $4,324; vaginal delivery, $1,113; prostate removal, $2,369; standard local anesthesia, $48 per unit; hourly operating-room charge, $713. Special surgical units: Regional Eye Center, endoscopy, orthopedic. Base cost for ER visit: $113. Additional ER services: advanced pediatric life support, Chest Pain Center.

Ob/gyn programs: labor whirlpool, totally private postpartum room, preparation for childbirth classes, sibling classes, VBAC classes, Level II neonatal intensive care unit, Motherwell fitness program.

Specialized treatment programs: Mental Health Unit, sports medicine, oncology, pediatrics.

Physical rehab services: speech, occupational, physical and hand therapy, Sports–Orthopedic Center, Athleticare.

Outpatient health and wellness programs: weight loss, stress, nutrition, cardiac rehab, senior health, diabetes, smoking cessation, childbirth classes, CPR, first aid, health screenings, women's services. The Wellness Center offers nutritional programs, cholesterol screenings, speakers and conferences on health–related issues (752–4300).

Lower Bucks considers its strengths to be in eye surgery and orthopedics. It has the only hospital–based primary care clinic in Bucks County.

### Medical College Hospitals, Bucks County Campus

*225 Newtown Rd., Warminster, 441–6600.* Doctors on active staff: 260; number of beds: 188; room cost: $660; gourmet food service: $14.30 per meal; accreditation: JCAHO, PDH, ACR, CAP.

Sample charges for surgical services: back and neck procedures without complication, $4,612; prostate removal, $4,570; standard local anesthesia, $814.75; hourly operating-room charge, $1,062.50; preadmission testing, $158.50; base cost for ER visit: $84.75. Detox available 24 hours.

Specialized treatment programs: drug and alcohol, psychiatry, dialysis, oncology.

Physical rehab services: the Achievement Center for cardiac rehab, physical therapy and adult fitness; inpatient rehab unit; speech pathology; audiology; occupational therapy.

Outpatient programs: Aqua Aerobics, Aquatic Exercise and Water Walking Programs, CPR, diabetes education, women's programs, senior dining, Slim–a–Weigh with exercise, Option, Slim Kids, Slim Teens.

Medical College, Bucks County Campus considers its medical strengths to be in: cardiology, gastroenterology, pulmonary; and its surgical strenths to be in: general, vascular, and orthopedics.

### Medical College Hospitals, Elkins Park Campus

*60 E. Township Line Rd., Elkins Park, 663–6000, 1–800–776–4325 (for physician referral).* Doctors on active staff: 278 (70% board–certified); number of beds: 266; semiprivate room cost: $651; private room cost: $676; accreditation: JCAHO, PDH.

Sample charges for surgical services: back and neck procedures without complication, $4,300; vaginal delivery, $4,000; prostate removal, $5,000; standard local anesthesia, $60; hourly operating-room charge, $650; preadmission testing, $150. Special surgical units: general surgery, laparoscopic surgical procedures, pain management, ophthalmological procedures, plastic surgery. Base cost for ER visit: $30.

Ob/gyn programs: high–risk prenatal care, antenatal testing, level III respiratory care nursery.

There is a detox and rehab unit.

Physical rehab services: physical, occupational and speech therapy (through the Achievement Center, on both an in– and outpatient basis).

Outpatient programs: Motherwell, Women's Diagnostic Center, Heart Saver Course, glaucoma/eye screenings.

Medical College, Elkins Park Campus considers its strengths to be in: rehab and maternity medicine, ob/gyn and general surgery.

### Medical College Hospitals, Main Clinical Campus

*3300 Henry Ave., 842–6000.* Doctors on active staff: 381 (86.3% board–certified); number of beds: 369; .96 RNs per bed; semiprivate room cost: $950; private room cost: $990; accreditation: JCAHO, CAP, AABB, ACGME, ACR.

Sample charges for surgical services: coronary bypass without cardiac cath, $58,633; back and neck procedures without complication, $13,104; vaginal delivery, $3,744; prostate removal, $8,076; hourly operating-room charge, $1,075. Special surgical units: critical care, coronary care, medical/surgical ICU, neuro special care. Base cost for ER visit: $93. Additional ER services: Level I trauma care, Chest Pain Emergency Center, hyperbaric medicine (wound care and decompression illness), toxicology program.

Ob/gyn programs: Comprehensive Women's Center, reproductive endocrinology/infertility, Mobile Mammography Unit, genetic counseling, perinatal obstetrics, gynecologic oncology, ambulatory clinic, incontinence care for older women, newborn and critical care.

Specialized treatment programs: neonatal ICU, Harbison Recovery Program (substance abuse), Dental Care Center, Dental Implant Center, oral microbiology testing service, Lyme disease service, dialysis unit.

Physical rehab services: speech, occupational and physical therapy, Sports Medicine Center.

Outpatient health and wellness programs: Center for Continuing Health (FITNESS for people over 50), Travel Health Center, skin cancer screening, Adolescent Outreach Program, Delaware Valley Sports Medicine Center.

It considers its medical strengths to be in: pediatrics, geriatrics, neurology, emergency/trauma care, psychiatry, oncology, obstetrics/gynecology; and its surgical strengths to be in: cardio-thoracic, orthopedic, neurosurgery.

Medical College, Main Clinical Campus, and the Medical College of Pennsylvania are members of Allegheny Health, Education and Research Foundation (AHERF). Other Delaware Valley members include: Medical College Hospitals, Elkins Park Campus; Medical College Hospitals, Bucks County Campus; St. Christopher's Hospital for Children.

### Memorial Hospital of Burlington County

*175 Madison Ave., Mount Holly, New Jersey, 609-267-0700.* Doctors on active staff: 220 (more than 90% board-certified); number of beds: 402; accreditation: JCAHO, ACR, ACS. Room costs not furnished.

Sample charges for surgical services: coronary bypass without cardiac cath, $28,953; vaginal delivery, $3,337; prostate removal, $5,788; standard local anesthesia, $101.25; hourly operating-room charge, $902.24. Base cost for ER visit: $100. Additional ER services: Chest Pain Clinic, Fast Track (quick service for minor problems).

Ob/gyn programs: a full range of neonatal, perinatal and parenting services through Women's Health Network (609-261-7482).

Specialized treatment programs: dialysis, psychiatry, pediatrics, Speech and Hearing Center, same-day surgery unit, geriatric assessment, incontinence program.

Physical rehab services: physical and occupational therapy.

Outpatient health and wellness programs: aerobics, Senior

Health–Link (a wellness program for those over 55; 265-7900).
The hospital considers its strengths to be in: cardiology, oncology (affiliated with Fox Chase Cancer Center), family practice, geriatrics.

### Mercy Catholic Medical Center, Fitzgerald Division

Lansdowne Ave. and Baily Rd., Darby, 237-4000, 800-227-2575 (physician referral). Doctors on active staff: 413 (78% board–certified); number of beds: 479; accreditation: AABB, CAP, JCAHO, PDH, PDW, ACGME. Room costs and surgical charges not furnished.

Special surgical units: surgical ICU. Base cost for ER visit: $68. Additional ER services: Fastcare (for non–life-threatening injuries), toxicology.

Ob/gyn programs: midwifery, perinatology, pre– and postpartum education, exercise classes, neonatology, Gamete Intra–Fallopian Transfer (GIFT) treatment for infertility.

Specialized treatment programs: dialysis, drug and alcohol rehab, pediatrics, cardiac rehab, psychiatry, psychiatry crisis, outpatient physical rehab.

Outpatient health and wellness programs: prenatal classes, Culinary Hearts Kitchen, cardiac rehab, weight management, CPR, speech, hearing and swallowing tests, monthly cancer screening, mobile van for community cholesterol, blood pressure, diabetes screenings, children's safety–wellness programs, occupational health.

Mercy Catholic Medical Center, Fitzgerald Division considers its strengths to be in: radiation oncology, head and neck cancers, lithotripsy, gallbladder laparoscopy, maternity, pediatrics.

### Mercy Catholic Medical Center, Haverford Division

2000 Old West Chester Pike, Havertown, 645-3600. Doctors on active staff: 180 (99% board-certified); number of beds: 107; accreditation: AABB, JCAHO, PDH, CAP. Room costs and surgical charges not furnished. Base cost for ER visit: $62.

No ob/gyn services.

Specialized treatment programs: Substance Abuse Center (inpatient detox), Retina and Diabetic Eye Institute.

Physical rehab services: general medical/surgical, orthopedic physical therapy, speech and occupational therapy, clinical lab, diagnostic radiology, respiratory therapy.

Outpatient health and wellness programs: Mercy Care Van, educational wellness, diabetic education.

Mercy Catholic Medical Center, Haverford Division considers its strengths to be in: cardiology, general surgery, orthopedics.

### Mercy Catholic Medical Center, Misericordia Division

5301 Cedar Ave., 748-9000, 748-8600 (cancer–screening hot line). Doctors on active staff: 413 (78% board–certified); number of beds: 276; accreditation: AABB, CAP, JCAHO, PDH, PDW. Room costs and surgical charges not furnished.

Special surgical units: surgical intensive care, surgical short procedure unit. Base cost for ER visit: $72. Additional ER services: hyperbaric oxygen therapy.

Ob/gyn programs: Women's Service, midwifery.

Specialized treatment programs: detox, dialysis, psychiatry, psychiatric crisis.

Outpatient health and wellness programs: weight loss, cancer, blood pressure, cholesterol, lung and glaucoma screenings, CPR, mobile health van, children's wellness and safety program, parenting series, women with HIV support group, Older Adult Club (nutrition support), cardiovascular risk reduction, breast cancer/low–cost mammography, smoking cessation.

Mercy Medical Center, Misericordia Division considers its strengths to be in: psychiatry, general surgery, emergency service.

### Methodist Hospital

*2301 South Broad St., 952–9000.* Doctors on active staff: 254 (77% board-certified); number of beds: 289; 1.1 RNs per bed; semiprivate room cost: $740; private room cost: $820; accreditation: JCAHO, PDH, DVHC.

Sample charges for surgical services: back and neck procedures without complication, $12,050; vaginal delivery, $3,600; prostate removal, $8,621. Special surgical units: Rapid Recovery Surgical Center, Short Procedure Unit. ER charges not furnished. ER services: Chest Pain Emergency Center, Fast Trac Emergency Program.

Ob/gyn programs: Family Birth Center, neonatal ICU, antenatal testing services, laparoscopic gyn surgery.

Physical rehab services: physical and occupational therapy, speech pathology, cardiac rehab.

Outpatient health and wellness programs: smoking cessation, weight loss, aerobics, nutrition counseling.

Methodist Hospital considers its strengths to be in: ob/gyn, cardiology, minimally invasive scope surgery, emergency medicine. It is a member of the Methodist Hospital Foundation and is affiliated with Thomas Jefferson University and Magee Rehabilitation Hospitals.

### Montgomery Hospital

*Powell and Fornance sts., Norristown, 270–2000.* Doctors on active staff: 265; number of beds: 269; .75 RNs per bed; semiprivate room cost: $535; private room cost: $635; accreditation: JCAHO, ACS, CAP. Room costs and surgical charges not furnished.

Special surgical units: cardiac catheterization. Base cost for ER visit: $53. Additional ER services: hospital–based ambulance and paramedics, cardiac, trauma room.

Specialized treatment programs: in– and outpatient psychiatry, dialysis, pediatrics, Cancer Center, obstetrics, Women's Imaging Center, Eye Laser Center.

Physical rehab services: cardiac, pulmonary, Back School, physical, occupational and speech therapy.

Outpatient health and wellness programs: cancer screenings, weight loss, stress management, nutrition, cholesterol evaluation.

Montgomery Hospital considers its strengths to be in: emergency, cardiology, cancer care, pediatrics, diabetes treatment.

### Nazareth Hospital 🛏 🚗 🏥 ⚕ ⚖ 🚭 E

*2601 Holme Ave., 335–6000.* Doctors on active staff: 240 (71% board–certified): number of beds: 347; semiprivate room cost: $600; private room cost; $650; gourmet food service: $10; accreditation: JCAHO, PDH, CAP, AABB, CAE, AMA.

Sample charges for surgical services: back and neck procedures without complication, $7,775; vaginal delivery, $3,105; prostate removal, $4,920; standard local anesthesia, $165 per procedure; hourly operating-room charge, $600. Special surgical units: short procedure unit. Base cost for ER visit: sliding scale.

Ob/gyn programs: Women's Health Center, neonatal ICU, rooming–in, childbirth classes, sibling and grandparent classes.

Specialized treatment programs: mental health, perinatal testing, heart station testing, Mustard Seed detox, high–risk pregnancy clinic, pediatrics, cardiac catheterization, psychiatric unit.

Physical rehab servics: Occupational Health Center, physical, respiratory and speech therapy.

Outpatient programs: nutritional counseling, cardiac rehab.

Nazareth Hospital is a 50–year–old hospital sponsored by the Sisters of the Holy Family of Nazareth. It considers its strengths to be in: cardiology, medical imaging, maternity, orthopedics, general medicine.

### Osteopathic Medical Center, City Avenue Campus 🚗 ⚕ ⚖ 🚭 🏥 E ✉

*4150 City Ave., 871–1000, 800–871–1999 (physician referral).* Doctors on active staff: 628 (63% board–certified): number of beds: 218; 1 RN per 6 beds; semiprivate room cost: $550; private room cost: $600; accreditation: AOA, CAP, AABB.

Sample charges for surgical services: back and neck procedures without complication, $17,844; vaginal delivery, $2,961; prostate removal, $7,482; standard local anesthesia, $74; hourly operating-room charge, $1,166. Special surgical units: surgical short procedure unit, carbon dioxide and Yag laser, laparoscopic procedures, sinus endoscopy with video capabilities. Base cost for ER visit: $70. Level II emergency services available for minor traumas and fractures.

Ob/gyn programs: family–centered maternity care with certified midwives and obstetricians, teen pregnancy, parenting, perinatology, infertility, advanced laparoscopic surgery, childbirth education, certified nurse-midwifery.

Specialized treatment programs: inpatient mental health, podiatry, pediatrics, TMJ clinic, medical short procedures unit for outpatient chemotherapy, pain management, autologous blood donations, ICU, CCU, telemetry.

Physical rehab services: in– and outpatient physical therapy, outpatient audiology and speech pathology, osteopathic manipulative therapy.

Outpatient programs: childbirth education, parent support, CPR, first aid, diabetes education, free health screenings.

Osteopathic, City Avenue Campus considers its medical strengths to be in: family medicine, ob/gyn, cardiology, nephrology, neonatology, pulmonary; and its surgical strengths to be in: orthopedics, urology, general, surgical laser applications.

### Osteopathic Medical Center, Park View Campus

*1331 East Wyoming Ave., 537-7400.* Doctors on active staff: 678 (63% board–certified); number of beds: 195; 1 RN per 6 beds; semiprivate room: $600; private room: $680; accreditation: AOA.

Sample charges for surgical services: back and neck procedures without complication, $12,018; vaginal delivery, $2,826; prostate removal, $6,689; standard local anesthesia, $77; hourly operating–room charge, $820. Special surgical units: laparoscopic procedures, sinus endoscopy with video capabilities. Base cost for ER visit: $79. ER services include fully equipped cast room with orthopedic specialists available 24 hours, cardiac treatment, trauma treatment, thromolytic therapy.

Ob/gyn programs: full–service ob with labor, postpartum and nursery on same floor, optional rooming–in, modified mother–infant care, classes in sibling and grandparent preparation, childbirth education, breast–feeding.

Specialized treatment programs: dialysis, psychiatry, skilled nursing, pediatrics, ICCU, CCU, pulmonary care unit, surgical and medical step–down, telemetry unit, short procedure unit, minor surgery, chemotherapy.

Physical rehab services: in– and outpatient occupational, physical and speech therapy, osteopathic manipulative therapy.

Outpatient programs: family and parenting courses, CPR, skin cancer screenings, blood pressure screenings.

Osteopathic, Parkview Campus considers its medical strengths to be in: ob/gyn, cardiology, nephrology, pulmonary; and its surgical strengths to be in: orthopedics, urology, general.

### Our Lady of Lourdes Medical Center

*1600 Haddon Ave., Camden, New Jersey, 609–757–3500.* Doctors on active staff: 296 (81.1% board-certified); number of beds: 375; 1.9 RNs per bed; semiprivate room cost: $451; private room cost: $565; accreditation: JCAHO, CARF, AABB, CAP, ACR.

Sample charges for surgical services: coronary bypass without cardiac cath, $14,786; vaginal delivery, $1,711; standard local anesthesia, $52; hourly operating–room charge, $538 (minor surgery), $806 (major surgery). Special surgical units: kidney transplantation program, open–heart surgery program. Base cost for ER visit: $90; additional ER services: psychiatric emergency service.

Ob/gyn programs: Level III Regional Perinatal Center, neonatal ICU, maternal transport services, Osborn Family Health Center, newborn nursery and transitional nursery, LDR rooms.

Specialized treatment programs: pediatric, mental health, in– and outpatient dialysis units.

Physical rehab services: physical, occupational, speech and recreational therapy, electromyography, hand rehab, prosthetic–orthotic evaluation, videofluoroscopic swallowing studies.

Outpatient health and wellness programs: prenatal classes; infant, child and adult CPR, asthma workshops, massage, weight loss program, stress reduction courses, Christian yoga, meditation, foot reflexology, dance instruction, nutritional counseling.

Our Lady of Lourdes Medical Center considers its strengths to be in: diagnostic cardiology, cardiac catheterization, cardiac surgery, high–risk obstetrics, neonatology, physical medicine and rehab, kidney dialysis/transplantation.

In June 1992, Our Lady of Lourdes was selected as one of four finalists nationwide for the Foster McGraw Prize, the AHA's award for excellence in community service.

### Paoli Memorial Hospital

*255 West Lancaster Ave., Paoli, 648–1000.* Doctors on active staff: 180 (90% board–certified); number of beds: 208; 1 RN per 5 beds; accreditation: JCAHO, CAP, PDH. Room costs, surgical and ER charges not furnished.

Special surgical units: Short Procedure Unit for minimally invasive surgery.

ER services: Advance Life Support Program (hospital–based paramedics who respond to emergencies).

Ob/gyn programs: perinatal testing center, genetic counseling.

Specialized treatment programs: Drug and Alcohol Detox Unit, Center for Addictive Diseases, STOP (intensive outpatient treatment for alcohol and drug abuse), psychiatric unit.

Physical rehab services: complete Physical Rehab Center, occupational therapy.

Outpatient health and wellness programs: Medical Weight Management Program; Travelers' Health Advisory Program; diabetes and blood pressure screenings, cholesterol testing, hearing and vision testing, CPR courses, Life Without Diets, StressSmart, smoking cessation; New Direction for Lasting Weight Control; Outlook, for weight loss of 20 to 40 pounds.

Paoli Memorial considers its strengths to be in: family practice, internal medicine, general surgery, psychiatry.

### Pennsylvania College of Optometry

*1200 West Godfrey Ave., 276–6210.* Outpatient only. Doctors on active staff: 37; accreditation: AOA. Room costs and surgical charges not applicable.

ER charges not furnished. ER services include: immediate eye care, 24–hour on–call ocular emergency service.

Specialized treatment programs: low vision, sports vision, corneal and speciality contact lens, neuro eye. Physical rehab services: low-vision rehab.

Pennsylvania College of Optometry has a clinical care facility, the Eye Institute, and is the only college of optometry in the state, as well as one of only 17 in the country.

## Pennsylvania Hospital 🛏 🖉 ⚕ 🛇 ⚕ E ✉

*800 Spruce St., 829–3000, 829–6800 (physician referral), 829–KIDS (pregnancy hot line).* Doctors on active staff: 310 (84% board–certified); number of beds: 480; semiprivate room cost: $874; private room cost: $1,019; suites available; accreditation: JCAHO.

Surgical charges not furnished. Special surgical units: Cardiac Surgery Suite, 14–room suite for general and speciality surgery such as colo–rectal, gynecologic oncology, neurosurgery, obstetrics and gynecology, ophthalmology, oral, orthopedics, otorlaryngology, plastic/reconstructive, urology and vascular surgery. Base cost for ER visit: $157.

Ob/gyn programs: antenatal testing unit, birthing suite (nurse–midwifery), childbirth education classes, genetic counseling, high–risk obstetrics, infertility treatment, perinatal cardiology, postpartum disorders project, pregnancy hot line, gynecologic oncology.

Specialized treatment programs: special care unit, intensive care nursery, CCU, neurointensive unit, ICU, Franklin Dialysis Center, Hall–Mercer Community Mental Health and Mental Retardation Center, Counseling Program (outpatient services for mental health and chemical dependency problems of contracted companies). Its psychiatric facility is the Institute of Pennsylvania Hospital, 111 N. 49th St.

Physical rehab services: physical therapy and rehab, occupational therapy, Back School (back care and injury prevention), cardiac rehab, Skilled Care Center (addresses needs of patients during transitional period between stay in an acute care hospital and return to daily living at home).

Outpatient health and wellness programs: Diabetes Education Program, Travel Medical Service, Society Hill Diet (food and nutrition services), free monthly community health seminars, Speakers Bureau, Child and Parent Center, childbirth education classes. Adult Day Health Center, the first hospital–based adult day care in Philadelphia, provides medically supervised care along with comprehensive rehab and recreational services for older adults.

Pennsylvania Hospital considers its medical strengths to be in: cardiology, neurology, gastroenterology, infectious diseases; and its surgical strengths to be in: gynecologic and abdominal laparoscopic, orthopedics, urology, neurosurgery, otolaryngology, vascular and pancreatic cancer.

Pennsylvania is the nation's first hospital, founded in 1751 by Benjamin Franklin and Dr. Thomas Bond. It has the largest obstetric service in Eastern Pennsylvania, with over 4,500 births annually, and is the third–largest surgical facility in Philadelphia. The Rothman Institute, one of the country's busiest orthopedic surgery centers, has performed more than 10,000 joint replacements since 1970.

### Phoenixville Hospital

*140 Nutt Rd., Phoenixville, 983–1000.* Doctors on active staff: 123 (93% board–certified); number of beds: 145; 1.83 RNs per bed; semiprivate room cost: $490; private room cost: $585; accreditation: JCAHO.

Sample charges for surgical services: back and neck procedures without complication, $5,871; vaginal delivery, $1,946; prostate removal, $4,867; hourly operating-room charge, $900. Base cost for ER visit: $90. Additional ER services: ALS–Medic 95 (physicians and staff certified in emergency care).

Ob/gyn programs: expectant parent course, early pregnancy, preconceptional care.

Specialized treatment programs: dialysis, pediatrics, oncology, Cancer Center, Maternity Pavilion.

Physical rehab services: physical therapy, cardiac rehab.

Outpatient health and wellness programs: community health education classes, Nutritional Resource Center, healthy birthing/healthy baby.

A community hospital founded in 1893, Phoenixville has a combined intensive care–coronary unit, a short procedure unit, a Maternity Pavilion, and a five–bed surgical suite.

### Pottstown Memorial Medical Center

*1600 East High St., Pottstown.* Doctors on active staff: 110 (100% board–certified); number of beds: 295; 1 RN per 5 beds; accreditation: JCAHO, ACR, CAP. Room costs, surgical and ER charges not furnished.

Special surgical units: lithotripsy, laparoscopic cholecystectomy, interventional radiology suite.

Ob/gyn programs: Maternity and Women's Health Center, women's health care seminars, Baby and Toddler Health Fair, single–room maternity health care.

Specialized treatment programs: Renal Care Center (dialysis), Center for Behavioral Medicine (psychiatry), pediatric unit, ICU/CCU, Cardiac Health Center.

Physical rehab services: Industrial Medicine Program—Work Recovery, ERGOS Work Simulator (to assess employees' physical condition).

Outpatient health and wellness programs: senior aerobics, TRIM classes (weight control), Fresh Start (smoking cessation), How to Read Food Labels, CPR, first aid, Lamaze classes, blood pressure and cholesterol screenings, stress management classes.

### Presbyterian Medical Center

*39th and Market sts., 662–9139.* Doctors on active staff: 356 (92% board–certified); number of beds: 344; 1 registered nurse per 2 beds; room cost: $715; suite: $825 to $860; accreditation: JCAHO, CAP.

Sample charges for surgical services: coronary bypass without cardiac cath, $40,994; back and neck procedures without complication, $15,270; prostate removal, $7,205; standard local anesthesia, $513 for the first hour; hourly operating–room charge, $1,409; preadmission testing, $389. Special surgical units: cardiothoracic, vascular. Base cost for ER visit: $62.

Presbyterian does not have an obstetrics department, but offers family planning services and operates a gynecology program through its Medical Clinic.

Specialized treatment programs: heart failure unit, Heart Disease Prevention Center, cardiac rehab (in– and outpatient), alcohol/drug abuse program, addiction treatment, detox unit and rehab unit, Neck and Back Institute.

Outpatient programs: cardiac evaluation and fitness, weight management, nutrition classes and consultation, stress management, National Heart Attack Risk Study, healthy heart forum seminars, cholesterol screenings, community outreach programs on breast cancer prevention.

Presbyterian considers its medical strengths to be in: cardiology, oncology, rheumatology, ophthalmology, gastroenterology, circulatory disease, chronic and acute psychiatric illnesses; and its surgical strengths to be in: cardio–thoracic, oncologic, vascular.

It is home to the Scheie Eye Institute as well as the Philadelphia Heart Institute, a comprehensive center for the diagnosis, treatment and prevention of heart disease. The first of its kind in the region, the heart center houses all outpatient services and programs, including noninvasive imaging, ambulatory catheterization, cardiac rehab and heart disease prevention.

At the Presbyterian Cancer Center, physicians from several medical specialties meet as a team with cancer patients to determine treatment options. Presbyterian also has the nation's first HOTELHOSPITAL, designed for those who require medical care but are well enough to leave the hospital.

## Quakertown Community Hospital

*11th St. and Park Ave., Quakertown, 538–4500.* Doctors on active staff: 165 (95% board–certified); number of beds: 89; semiprivate room cost: $750; private room cost: $770; suite cost: $790; gourmet food service: $12.71 per meal; accreditation: JCAHO, CAP.

Sample charges for surgical services: back and neck procedures without complication, $14,874; prostate removal, $9,944; hourly operating-room charge: $1,611; preadmission testing: $399. Special surgical units: ambulatory procedure unit.

Ob/gyn programs: Healthy Beginnings, Women's Center, Upward Bound.

Specialized treatment programs: psychiatry, dialysis, podiatry/sports medicine.

Physical rehab services: outpatient rehab program, therapy pool.

Outpatient health and wellness programs: Optifast, smoking cessation, EASE, diabetes education.

Quakertown Community Hospital considers its strengths to be in: orthopedics, vascular, gynecology, podiatry.

### Riddle Memorial Hospital

*1068 West Baltimore Pike, Media, 566–9400.* Doctors on active staff: 246 (66.6% board– certified); number of beds: 251; 1.02 RNs per bed; semiprivate room cost: $740; private room cost: $825: accreditation: JCAHO, PDH.

Surgical and ER charges not furnished. ER services include: Fast Track, a specially trained team of physicians, nurses and paramedics serving minor ER patients.

Ob/gyn programs: Birthplace (labor, delivery, recovery, postpartum in one room), Level II neonatal ICU, Women's Imaging Center.

Specialized treatment programs: oncology, pediatrics, orthopedics, Skilled Nursing Facility.

Physical rehab services: Back Rehab and Work–Hardening Center, Riddle Hand Rehabilitation Center, inpatient rehab services.

Outpatient health and wellness programs: nutrition and weight management, specialty screenings, grief counseling, cancer screenings, back seminars.

Riddle Memorial Hospital considers its strengths to be in: maternity, oncology, ophthalmology, emergency services.

### Roxborough Memorial Hospital

*5800 Ridge Ave., 483–9900.* Doctors on active staff: 146 (73% board–certified); number of beds: 151; ratio of RNs to beds varies from 1:1 for intensive care to 1:10 for medical/surgery; semiprivate room cost: $564; private room cost: $599; gourmet food service: $11 per meal; accreditation: JCAHO, CAP, PDH, AABB, DPW, NBCT, USNRC, State Board of Medical Education and Licensure.

Sample charges for surgical services: back and neck procedures without complication, $4,440; vaginal delivery, $3,280; prostate removal, $5,700; standard local anesthesia, $337; hourly operating–room charge, $779 for first hour; preadmission testing, $369. Base cost for ER visit: $50. Air Medevac to Hahnemann available.

Offers family planning services as well as prenatal and sibling classes.

Specialized treatment programs: HMR Weight Management Program, enterostomal therapy, cardiac rehab, Breast Prosthesis Program.

Physical rehab services: work–hardening, Industrial Health Network.

Outpatient programs: weight management, nutrition counseling, screenings for breast, prostate and colo–rectal cancer, CPR classes, cardiac risk factor modification program, aerobics. Acute occupational medicine is provided through the Industrial Care Network, run by the physical therapy department.

Roxborough Memorial considers its strengths to be in: otolaryngology, general surgery, pulmonary, urology, primary care. It has a longstanding commitment to the community, dating back to its opening in 1890, when it was called St. Timothy's Memorial Hospital and House of Mercy.

### Sacred Heart Hospital and Rehabilitation Center

*1430 DeKalb St., Norristown, 278–8200.* Doctors on active staff: 280; number of beds: 256; 1.26 RNs per bed; accreditation: JCAHO, CARF, CAP, AABB, PDH. Base cost for ER visit: $84. Room costs and surgical charges not furnished.

Ob/gyn programs: expectant parent classes, Lamaze instruction, OB Clinic.

Specialized treatment programs: pediatrics, rehab center, diabetes unit, orthopedics unit, oncology, pulmonary progressive care, cardiac progressive care.

Physical rehab services: physical and occupational therapy, speech/language pathology, psychological counseling, social services, pastoral care, pediatric rehab.

Outpatient health and wellness programs: Diabetes Teaching Program, cardiac rehab.

Sacred Heart Hospital and Rehabilitation Center considers its strengths to be in rehab and obstetrics services.

### Scheie Eye Institute

*(Department of Ophthalmology/ University of Pennsylvania Medical School) Myrin Circle, 51 North 39th St., Philadelphia, 662–8119.* Shares services with Presbyterian Medical Center and Hospital of the University of Pennsylvania. Doctors on active staff: 14 (100% board–certified); room and gourmet food costs: refer to Presbyterian Medical Center and HUP; accreditation: JCAHO.

Sample charges for surgical services: hourly operating-room charge, $1,267 for first hour; preadmission testing, $92–$167 (under 40 years of age), $451–$526 (over 40). Special surgical units: cornea transplants, trauma, retina/vitreous, cataract and lens implants, glaucoma, oculoplastics, strabismus. Base cost for ER visit: $40–$85. ER services run through Presbyterian Medical Center and HUP.

Specialized treatment programs: primary and tertiary ophthalmological services, neuro–ophthalmology, ocular genetics, pediatrics, diabetic retinopathy, macular degeneration.

Outpatient health and wellness programs: low–vision services provides referrals for social service and rehab for low–vision and legally blind patients.

Scheie Eye Institute considers its strengths to be in: cataract and lens implantation, glaucoma, oculoplastic/orbital surgery, retina and vitreous surgery, strabismus surgery, laser surgery treatments.

### St. Agnes Medical Center

*1900 South Broad St., 339–4100.* Doctors on active staff: 257 (66% board–certified); number of beds: 259; 1 RN per bed; accreditation: JCAHO, AOA, CAP. Room costs and surgical charges not furnished.

Special surgical units: orthopedic.

Gynecologic services only.

Specialized treatment programs: Burn Center, Renal Dialysis Center, cardiac telemetry units, comprehensive physical rehabilitation unit.

Physical rehab services: comprehensive inpatient rehabilitation unit, comprehensive outpatient rehabilitation unit, physical capacity evaluations, speech and hearing program, comprehensive industrial health program, cardiac rehab program, electrodiagnostic laboratory.

Outpatient health and wellness programs: cardiac rehab, medically supervised/monitored exercise, adult fitness, aerobics, muscular conditioning, weight management, yoga, stress reduction, nutritional counseling, exercise classes, smoke cessation, adult day care, home health care.

St. Agnes Medical Center considers its strengths to be in: cardiology, nephrology, pulmonary, gastroenterology, physical rehabilitation.

### St. Christopher's Hospital for Children

*Erie Ave. at Front St., 427–5000.* Doctors on active staff: 305 (80% board–certified); number of beds: 183; 2 RNs per bed; semiprivate room cost: $750; private room cost: $850; suite cost: $1,650; accreditation: JCAHO, ACGME.

Charges not applicable.

Special surgical units: cardio–thoracic, neurosurgery, ophthalmology, orthopedics, otolaryngology, plastic surgery, short procedure, kidney/heart, lung/liver transplantation, burn surgery. Base cost for ER visit: $75. Additional ER services: trauma capabilities, 24–hour staffing, helipad.

Specialized treatment programs: Burn Center, cardiac ICU, End–Stage Renal Disease Center, neonatal ICU, cardiac catheterization lab, child psychiatry, short procedure unit, gastroenterology, orthopedics, ophthalmology, urology, Center for Genetic Diseases.

Physical rehab services: physical, occupational and speech therapy, audiology.

St. Christopher's Hospital for Children considers its strengths to be in: end–stage renal disease care, transplant surgery, cardiology/cardio–thoracic surgery, pediatric general surgery, pulmonary diseases, hematology/oncology, neurology/neurosurgery, neonatology, ear/nose/throat, burn care. The new state–of–the–art facility, which treats 160,000 children annually, has an acute care center, an ambulatory care pavilion, a teaching and education center and research laboratories. St. Christopher's is also a major teaching affiliate of Medical College of Pennsylvania.

### St. Mary Hospital

*Langhorne–Newtown Road, Langhorne, 750–2000, 750–5888 (physician referral).* Doctors on active staff: 357 (80% board-certified); number of beds: 277; 2 RNs per bed; accreditation: JCAHO, ACR. Room costs, surgical and ER charges not furnished.

Special surgical units: cornea transplant, ambulatory surgery, cardiac cath laboratory, cosmetic/plastic, laser, orthopedic, oral–maxillofacial, Eye Institute. ER services: urgent care/minor ER care, Regional Level II Trauma Center.

Ob/gyn programs: LDR/birthing suites, neonatal ICU, Prenatal Center, certified nurse midwifery service, expectant parent classes, car–seat loaner program, Mother Bachman Maternity Center.

Physical rehab services: occupational, physical, recreational, respiratory and speech therapy, clinical psychology, social services, pediatric rehab, work–hardening program, Back School.

Outpatient health and wellness programs: Wellness Workshop, Industricare (worksite health promotion), CPR classes, monthly senior seminar programs, Regional Cancer Center, cardiac and pulmonary rehab, Outpatient Diagnostic Center offering laboratory, CAT scan, ultrasound and X–ray service.

St. Mary has home health services and a van service for patients requiring transportation to the hospital.

### Taylor Hospital

175 E. Chester Pike, Ridley Park, 595–6000. Doctors on active staff: 280 (64% board–certified); number of beds: 203; .86 registered nurses per bed; private room cost: $750; accreditation: JCAHO, CAP.

Surgical charges not furnished.

Specialized treatment programs: oncology unit, outpatient chemotherapy service, podiatry, sports medicine, Chest Pain Center.

Physical rehab services: physical, occupational and recreational therapy, speech pathology and audiology.

Outpatient health and wellness programs: The Women's Source, Home Health Agency, Breast Care Center.

Taylor Hospital considers its strengths to be in: oncology, orthopedics, cardiology, emergency care.

### Temple University Hospital

Broad and Ontario sts., 221–2000, 800–TEMPLE–MD (physician referral), 221–3600 (Comprehensive Breast Center), 221–4000 (Comprehensive Cancer Center). Doctors on active staff: 380 (87% board–certified); number of beds: 504; 1 RN per bed; semiprivate room cost: $925; private room cost: $970; gourmet food service: $23 per dinner; accreditation: JCAHO, CAP, PDH, PTCF, HCFA Renal Dialysis Survey.

Sample charges for surgical services: coronary bypass without cardiac cath, $48,000; back and neck procedures without complication, $15,000; vaginal delivery, $5,000; prostate removal, $9,700; standard local anesthesia, $150; hourly operating-room charge, $1,000; preadmission testing, $200. Special surgical units: heart transplants, bone marrow transplants, kidney transplants, stereotactic radiosurgery, neurosurgical intensive care unit, oncologic cryosurgery. Base cost for ER visit: $130. Temple is a Level I Trauma Center and has a Psychiatric Emergency Center.

Ob/gyn programs: maternal–fetal medicine, gynecologic oncology, reproductive endocrinology, nurse midwifery, Center for Women's Health, fetal testing, genetic counseling, perinatal cardiology, diabetes in pregnancy.

Specialized treatment programs: psychiatry, dialysis, oral surgery, sports medicine, Multiple Sclerosis Center, Ventilator Rehabilitation Center.

There is a 20–bed physical medicine and rehab unit.

Outpatient programs: The Nutrition Center, weight loss program, stress management, SeniorCARE.

Temple University Hospital is a major regional academic medical center and the teaching hospital of the Temple University School of Medicine. It considers its medical strengths to be in: cardiology, gastroenterology, pulmonary medicine, neurology, neurosurgery, high–risk pregnancy; and its surgical strengths to be in: orthopedic, oncology, cardio–thoracic, vascula, trauma, gastrointestinal.

Temple's Cardiac Transplantation Center, the largest in the Delaware Valley, is the only one to offer the Ventricular Assist Device (VAD), which serves as a bridge to transplantation; the Comprehensive Cancer Center is one of the first investigative centers for stereotactic radiosurgery in the country; the Comprehensive Breast Center is a full–service breast center offering bone marrow transplantation for treatment of breast cancer; and the Ventilator Rehabilitation Unit is one of five such units in the country.

### Thomas Jefferson University Hospital

*111 South 11th St., 955–6000, 800–JEFF–NOW (hot line).* Doctors on active staff: 678; number of beds: 717; accreditation: JCAHO. Room costs, surgical and ER charges not furnished.

Special surgical units: cardio–thoracic, colo–rectal, Jefferson Surgical Center, short procedure unit, kidney and liver transplantation. ER services: Level I Regional Resource Trauma Center, Spinal Cord Injury Center, access through helicopter and JeffSTAT ambulance retrieval teams, on–site operating room, X–ray room, three trauma bays, patient testing lab, separate acute and intermediate care areas.

Ob/gyn programs: in–vitro fertilization, gynecologic oncology, high–risk pregnancy, reproductive endocrinology/fertility, ultrasound, Teenagers in Touch.

Physical rehab services: Regional Spinal Cord Injury Center, physical, occupational and speech therapy, Jefferson Comprehensive Rehabilitation Center, Work Evaluation/Work–Hardening Program.

Outpatient health and wellness programs: Alzheimer's disease, Amputee Program, Antenatal Evaluation Center, arts medicine, asthma, Back Center, biofeedback, Bodine Center for Cancer Treatment, Cardeza Foundation (hemophilia and sickle–cell centers), Children's Center for Cerebral Palsy and Neuromuscular Disorders, Weigh to Go, Smokestoppers, aerobics, cancer test, Dining With Heart, free screening programs, seizure disorders, colo–rectal, Cancer Genetics Center, Comprehensive Rectal Cancer, corporate health, dementia evaluation, dietetics, drug and alcohol, dialysis, extracorporeal membrane oxygenation (for newborns), Enuresis Program, Familial Polyposis Registry, foot and ankle surgery, geriatric assessment, hand rehab, infant apnea, Jefferson Center for International Dermatology, medical genetics,

# Need an eye doctor?

2 1 5
9 2 8
EYES

## Put Wills Eye's Sightline to the test.

Just one call to the Sightline puts you in touch with a Wills Eye doctor. It's a hotline for scheduling routine eye exams at Wills Eye Hospital or with a Wills ophthalmologist in your area.

In addition to basic eye care, you can arrange to see a Wills expert for special needs such as cataract evaluation, children's eye care, retinal problems or glaucoma. A Wills doctor can diagnose what's wrong – and recommend the best treatment.

It's what you'd expect from America's oldest and largest eye hospital.

Of course, you can have your eyes checked where you buy your glasses. But at Wills, you're examined by an ophthalmologist – a doctor with advanced training and qualifications.

Call the Sightline today. Find a Wills Eye doctor and see what you've been missing.

## 215-928-EYES
215-928-3937

## ))) Wills Eye Hospital
900 Walnut Street, Philadelphia, PA 19107

Monell–Jefferson Taste and Smell, Multiple Sclerosis Comprehensive Clinical Center, NeuroMuscular Disease Clinic, Occupational and Environmental Medicine Clinic, Pain Center, perinatal addiction services, pigmented lesion, pregnancy loss, psychiatric clinic, psychosomatic treatment, Rape Center, scleroderma, sexual function, sleep disorders, sperm bank, SIDS, Tay–Sachs prevention.

One of only four facilities in the country to be both a Level I Regional Trauma Center and a federally designated Spinal Cord Injury Center, Thomas Jefferson University Hospital also operates Jefferson Park Hospital and Children's Rehabilitation Hospital, and manages Methodist Hospital.

### The University of Pennsylvania Medical Center

*3400 Spruce St., 662–4000, 662–PENN (Penn Physician Referral), 800–777–8176 (Penn Cancer Care).* Doctors on active staff: 850 (97% board–certified); 722 beds; 1.18 RNs per bed; double–bed room cost: $850; single–bed room cost: $960; accreditation: JCAHO, AABB. ACR, CAP, PDH.

Surgical and ER charges not furnished. Special surgical units: Center for Minimally Invasive Surgery (specializing in laparoscopic, endoscopic and thoroscopic techniques); multi–organ transplant center.

Additional ER services: Level I Trauma Center, Head Trauma Center, Radiation Emergency Center, Work Injury Evaluation Center.

Ob/gyn programs: infertility and in–vitro fertilization (one of six programs nationwide designated by NIH for research and state–of–the–art treatment); high–risk pregnancy; reproductive genetics; reproductive surgery including laparoscopic procedures; Premenstrual Syndrome Program; Penn Center for Women's Health, a gynecologic clinic specializing in menopause, located in King of Prussia.

Specialized treatment programs: HUP has over 200 speciality programs, clinics and laboratories. Among them are: University of Pennsylvania Cancer Center, one of 28 nationwide designated by the National Cancer Institute, and including 200 cancer specialists; Joint Reconstruction Center; Sports Medicine Center; shoulder service; bone tumor service; Bone and Tissue Bank; Interventional Neuro–Center; neurogenetics; Addictions Research/Treatment Center; Center for Cognitive Therapy; Center for Human Appearance; affective disorders program (manic depression), facial pain/headache/TMJ program; Mood and Memory Disorders Clinic; Cutaneous Ulcer Center; hypertension and clinical pharmacology program; male sexual dysfunction program; male fertility program.

Physical rehab services: Amputee Clinic, Back and Spine Center, stroke rehab, physical, hand and occupational therapy, trauma and transplant rehab, TMJ physical therapy.

Outpatient programs: Penn Physician Referral provides information about medical services and physicians; Penn Cancer Care—nurses and referral counselors on hand weekdays from 8:30 to 5:30; Ralston Penn Center—comprehensive outpatient health evaluation for adults.

The University of Pennsylvania Medical Center, which consists of the University of Pennsylvania School of Medicine and the Hospital of the University of Pennsylvania, considers its strengths to be in: cancer care, musculoskeletal, transplantation, neurosciences, cardiac care, gastrointestinal disorders and radiology. It has one of the most comprehensive diagnostic and interventional radiology departments in the city, and a separate department of radiation oncology. Renowned as a teaching, research and clinical institution, it offers cutting–edge treatment and technology not always available in other facilities. The 1992 edition of the Best Doctors in America (Woodward/White) includes 82 Penn Medical Center faculty physicians. Also affiliated with the Scheie Eye Institute, one of the leading eye–care institutions in the country.

## Wills Eye Hospital 🛏 🏥 ⚕ 🚫 🐕 E
*9th and Walnut sts., 928–3000.* Doctors on active staff: 417 (84% board–certified); number of beds: 115; .7 RNs per bed; semiprivate room cost: $750; private room cost: $855; accreditation: JCAHO, PDH, ACGME, AMA, CAP.

Sample charges for surgical services: standard local anesthesia, $173; hourly operating-room charge: $826. Base cost for ER visit: $120.

Specialized treatment programs: contact lens service, cornea service, cataract and primary eye–care service, Foerdere Center for the Study of Eye Movement Disorders in Children, glaucoma service, neuro–ophthalmology service, oculoplastics service, oncology service, pediatric ophthalmology service, retina service, low–vision service, oncology service, Center for Sports Vision, social services.

The Wills Geriatric Psychiatry Program is a 30–bed inpatient unit dedicated exclusively to caring for the psychiatric and neurological disorders of the elderly.

Outpatient health and wellness programs: free public eye screenings to test for various eye problems.

Founded in 1832, Wills Eye was the nation's first eye hospital. In 1839 it established the first ophthalmology residency program in the country, which is to this day one of the nation's most desired training programs. In a 1991 article, *U.S. News and World Reports* rated Wills Eye one of the top hospitals in the nation for ophthalmology.

Systems Foundation.
*Abbreviations have been used for the following hospital accreditations: AABB*—American Association of Blood Banks; *ABP*—American Board of Pediatrics; *ACR*—American College of Radiology; *ACS*—American College of Surgeons; *ADA*—American Dental Association; *AHA*—American Hospital Association; *AMA*—American Medical Association; *ACGME*—Accreditation Council for Graduate Medical Education; *AOA*—American Osteopathic Association; *BCP*—Blue Cross of Pennsylvania; *BCNJ*—Blue Cross of New Jersey; *CAP*—College of American Pathologists; *CARF*—Commission on Accreditation of Rehabilitation Facilities; *DPW*—Department of Public Welfare; *DVCH*—Delaware Valley Hospital Council; *JCAHO*—Joint Commission on Accreditation of Health Care Organizations; *NJDH*—New Jersey Department of Health; *PDW*—Pennsylvania Department of Welfare; *PTSF*—Pennsylvania Trauma

# SCHEIE EYE INSTITUTE

The ophthalmologists of the Scheie Eye Institute are world renowned for advancing knowledge about vision, eye diseases, and the prevention of blindness. As faculty members of the **University of Pennsylvania School of Medicine,** they have developed many new treatment methods that dramatically improve sight, as well as new methods for the preservation of sight.

Scheie Eye Institute's ophthalmologists often use a team approach to provide comprehensive diagnosis and treatment for all eye conditions, including:

- General ophthalmology
- Cataract and lens implant surgery
- Contact lenses
- Cornea transplants
- Diabetic retinopathy
- Glaucoma
- Infections
- Low vision
- Macular degeneration
- Muscle and eye movement surgery
- Neuro-ophthalmology
- Ocular genetics
- Plastic surgery
- Pediatric ophthalmology
- Retina and vitreous diseases
- Tumors of the eye
- Vision impairments of aging

## Diagnostic Technology

State-of-the-art technology includes fluorescein and ICG angiography, laser surgery, ultrasound, CT scanning, MRI, visual fields and electro-diagnostic testing.

For information about our services, physicians, or to schedule an appointment, please call:

**Scheie Eye Institute**
**215-662-8121**

**Universtiy of Pennsylvania Medical Center**

**Presbyterian Medical Center Of Philadelphia**

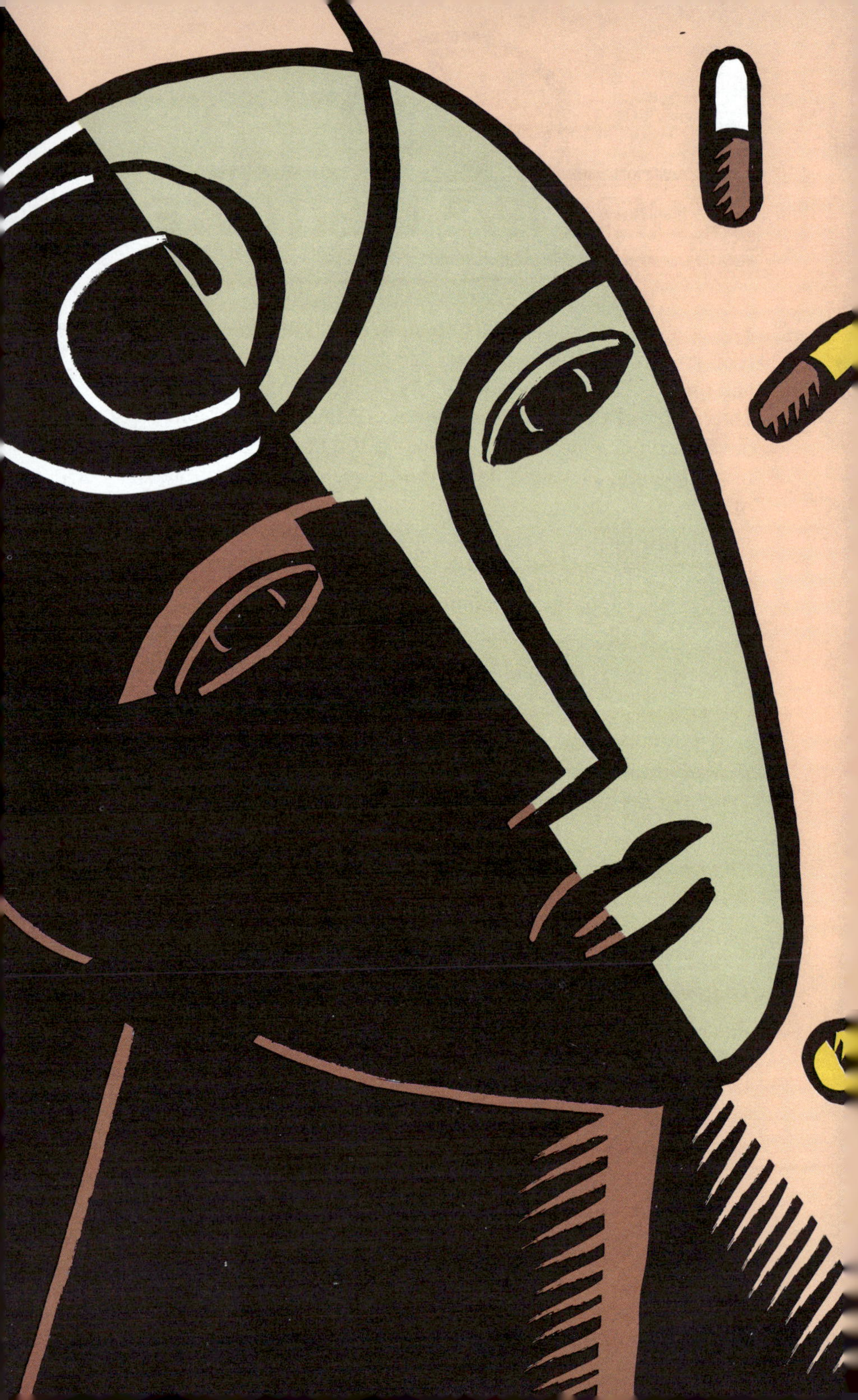

## SECTION THREE

# MENTAL HEALTH

# How a specialty hospital in Malvern earned national distinction.

Of the 2,453 hospitals surveyed nationwide by the *Joint Commission on Accreditation of Healthcare Organizations*, only 5.9% received Accreditation with Commendation.* Bryn Mawr Rehab was one of them.

Receiving this recognition is no simple task. To be judged among the finest, a hospital must receive outstanding "grades" in numerous categories for providing the highest level of health care services to its patients.

Over the past 20 years, Bryn Mawr Rehab has pioneered many advances in the treatment of individuals with head injury, stroke, arthritis, spinal cord injury, multiple sclerosis, and orthopedic conditions, helping them to return to as independent a life as possible.

For more information on our rehabilitation programs, please call us at 251-5658. We think you will find our treatment programs to be quite rewarding.

*Includes those surveyed from January 1, 1991 through July 14, 1992.*

## Bryn Mawr Rehab
*The Specialty Hospital For Physical Medicine and Rehabilitation*
414 Paoli Pike, Malvern, PA 19355

# 8

# Matter Over Mind

*Using drugs to treat depression, anxiety, and other problems once reserved for the shrink's couch.*

♥ One out of every eight prescriptions written in the United States is for a drug that affects our moods or how we think or behave. Problems like these used to be taken to a therapist's couch, when it was widely believed that things like depression and anxiety stemmed from deep-rooted conflicts best treated with psychotherapy. Now it's generally accepted that hating your mother or flunking out of college may be only part of the picture, and that mental disorders as diverse as panic attacks, bulimia and chronic depression actually can be triggered by chemical imbalances.

New technology makes it possible to see actual chemical changes taking place in the brain during a panic attack. And we now know the brain isn't really much like a computer; it's more like the hurly-burly floor of the stock exchange, with neurons shooting electrochemical messages to one another hither and yon. Scientists have established that psychotropic drugs work by affecting either the chemistry of these messages (the neurotransmissions) or the sites where the messages are received (the receptors).

The earliest psychotropic drugs arrived on the scene when very little was known about the brain; their discovery owes as much to accident as to design. The first antidepressant, for example, was stumbled upon back in the '50s, when doctors noticed that tuberculosis patients treated with a drug called iproniazid became unexplainedly cheerful. Someone shrewdly deduced that their exuberance might be drug-related, and that launched the use of one of the first mood elevators, the MAO inhibitors.

These were followed by a larger group of antidepressants known as the tricyclates—drugs like Elavil and Tofranil, which, while effective for relieving depression, had a variety of unpleasant side effects ranging from dry mouth to constipation. The latest antidepressants, a group of drugs call SRIs (which in pharmacological jargon means seroronin re–uptake inhibitors), are cousins to the tricyclates. However, they produce fewer side effects, because they act on fewer chemical systems. As many as 30 percent of the patients who did not respond to the older drugs—or wouldn't take them—seem to benefit from these second–generation antidepressants.

The most successful of these to date is a drug called Prozac, which has generated far more controversy than it deserves. Some 3.5 million people are taking Prozac, and a statistically small number of them have killed themselves—an act that, unfortunately, is not uncommon among the depressed—while on the drug. A few have even killed other people. Nonetheless, the cause-and-effect evidence linking Prozac to these aberrant behaviors is quite sketchy. It appears the attack on Prozac has been orchestrated by the Church of Scientology as part of its campaign to discredit psychiatry. Despite the horror stories trotted out on TV talk shows like *Donahue*, most of the psychiatric community steadfastly supports the safety and efficacy of Prozac. Dr. Myer Mendelson, a depression specialist at the Institute of Pennsylvania Hospital, says, "Even though many of my patients are now afraid of Prozac, I try to reassure them. While some experience jitters and restlessness as a side effect, that is quite different from violent behavior." Recently it's been found that patients will complain less of "feeling wired" when their dosage is reduced from the standard 20 milligrams a day to ten. The Prozac brouhaha might soon become academic with the introduction of Zoloft, a new member of the family with a shorter half-life than Prozac and even milder side effects.

How do you know if you're a candidate for antidepressants? You can make an assessment by asking yourself the following questions: Do I feel sad, blue, hopeless, down in the dumps or irritable, and am I enjoying *less* the things that normally give me pleasure? If the answer is yes, then look at whether you have had any four of the following symptoms for at least two weeks:

1. Poor appetite and weight loss, or increased appetite and weight gain.
2. Sleep disturbance, especially early-morning wakefulness.
3. Thoughts and actions slowed down or speeded up.
4. Loss of interest in normal activities, and decreased sex drive.
5. Loss of energy; fatigue.
6. Diminished ability to think and concentrate; difficulty making decisions.
7. Feelings of worthlessness, self–reproach or inappropriate guilt.

Dr. Joseph Mendels, a nationally known psychiatrist who specializes in psychopharmacology, says, "It's my view that someone who has suffered from a depression that persists for more than several weeks, one that is present more than half the time and interferes with general living, ought to be evaluated—preferably by a psychiatrist."

Today, all kinds of emotional disorders are being studied in the laboratory. Anxiety may in some cases be due to a problem in a part of the brain that secretes a tranquilizer–like chemical. Genetic studies have traced an inherited predisposition to anxiety—like those to diabetes or cancer—and physiological research has identified an area in the midbrain, no bigger than a pinhead, that actually controls anxiety.

Armed with this information, researchers have actively embarked on a search to find new substances to treat anxiety, in particular a drug that has the relaxing effect of Valium without the sedation and dependency that creates Valium abuse. The most promising of these new drugs is called Buspirone. It's part of a group referred to in the trade as non–benzodiazepines, to distinguish them from traditional tranquilizers.

While these newer antianxiety medications have the advantage of being nonaddicting, they have the disadvantage of a delayed response. Unlike Valium, they don't create an immediate feeling of relaxation. Where most tranquilizers are prescribed on an as–needed basis—take one when you feel anxious—Buspirone must be taken on a regimented program of so many pills every day, and two or three weeks might pass before the results occur. Consequently, the non–benzodiazepines have had a rough time gaining popular acceptance, despite the fact that they're much less dangerous. Dr. Karl Rickels, a professor of psychiatry at the University of Pennsylvania Medical School, says, "We have to re–educate people to be patient with these new drugs that work more slowly and may even cause agitation the first few days. But they have fewer side effects. After four weeks, patients do as well as on Valium, and after six months they show no dependency problems."

In the past there was a tendency to lump all anxieties under one label. Actually, there are three major categories of anxiety disorders. First are the phobias, such as fear of flying, fear of cats, fear of closed spaces, etc. Phobias do not respond particularly well to drugs. Second are panic disorders—the sudden onset of explosive, overwhelming feelings of terror, as if the body's alarm system is ringing for no apparent reason. The third and most common category is generalized anxiety. Someone with this condition may be treated with tranquilizers in concert with therapy if three of the four following signs persist for at least one month:

1. Motor tension: shakiness, tension, aching muscles, inability to relax, jumpiness, fatigue.
2. Uncontrollable body sensations: sweating, heart pounding, clammy hands, dry mouth, dizziness, light-headedness, hot and cold flashes, upset stomach, lump in the throat, diarrhea, pallor or flushed face.
3. Apprehensive expectation: fear, worry, rumination, anticipation of misfortune to self or others.
4. Vigilance and scanning: constant hyper–attention that makes it diffcult to concentrate and leads to irritability, impatience, insomnia

and always feeling on edge.

While not as easily treated as depression, anxiety disorders are significantly improved by drugs and/or psychotherapy 75 percent of the time.

By and large, the new psychotropics represent a decade of scientific refinement rather than discovery. The really exciting work in psychopharmacology is a good five to ten years away from appearing on prescription pads. The only way the public can get its hands on the wonder drugs of tomorrow now is by participating in the investigational drug studies that precede FDA approval. This isn't nearly as dangerous as it sounds. Some 500,000 people nationwide participate in these trials. The drugs involved have all passed extensive safety testing and are being examined chiefly to see if they perform as promised. The Philadelphia Medical Institute, one of a handful of private organizations around the country that evaluate and develop medical treatment for psychological disorders, has conducted trials involving more than 10,000 people, and only once has there been a serious side effect from an investigational drug.

Often the drugs in these trials are already marketed in other countries, or available here for a different purpose. For instance, a drug under investigation at PMI for its potential to improve memory function is already used by millions as a high-blood-pressure medication. And several studies are exploring new possibilities for existing antidepressants. Bulimics have shown substantial improvement when treated with an antidepressant, although the drug has no effect on anorexics, which suggests that these eating disorders may not be opposite sides of the same coin. People suffering from unmanageable cravings—foodaholics, alcoholics, cocaine abusers, chain-smokers—who are highly motivated to kick their habits also have been aided significantly by antidepressants.

Panic disorders, too, are now being successfully controlled by drugs. Once considered severe forms of anxiety, these attacks now appear to be something quite different, with a separate trigger that responds to chemical manipulation. The jury is still out on whether drugs are the best way to treat panic disorders, because many well-respected studies have shown that cognitive therapy (see "High Anxiety," page 125) is as effective in conquering panic as drug therapy.

There's also a good bit of evidence that obsessive–compulsive disorders respond to drugs. These illnesses can actually be observed in PET–scan pictures, where they show up as markedly different from normal brain activity—an indication that the problem can be helped by drugs. A case in point is Jim, a married man in his 40s who participated in one of the drug trials at PMI. He'd gone from being a neat, orderly young man to someone so obsessed with cleanliness that he spent two hours each morning and three each night cleaning himself. It got so bad that he made his children wear gloves to touch him. He knew his behavior was crazy, but he couldn't stop. After ten weeks on chlorimipramine, an antidepressant sold in Canada and Europe, he was back to being bearably meticulous. Dr. Mendels, the director of PMI, admits that nobody understands why many of these drugs work, although it's speculated that they have something to do with regulating serotonin, the chemical that plays a role in behaviors as diverse as appetite, sleep and sex.

Will psychotropic drugs someday put psychologists out of business? Absolutely not. There are still all kinds of emotional problems that can't be treated with medication, and a strong argument to be made in support of another approach to curing mood disorders. The man who makes that argument best is Dr. Aaron Beck, the avuncular University of Pennsylvania psychiatrist and father of cognitive therapy. Beck believes people get depressed because they view themselves negatively and magnify the extent of their problems. Cognitive therapy adjusts negative thinking to fit a more positive reality. Similarly, Beck says, the severely anxious person overestimates his fears and underestimates his ability to cope. The persistent nail–biting nervousness that produces chronic anxiety can often be corrected by changing thought patterns—which is what cognitive therapy seeks to do, in 12 to 15 sessions in which the therapist plays an active role.

The psychological and biological approaches are not mutually exclusive; there are plenty of data to support both. As we move forward into the 21st century with an increased understanding of the brain and behavior, the line between psychology and biology will shift and blur even more.

*If you need help:* Most investigational drug trials are free, because the research is funded by either the FDA or a pharmaceutical company. The University of Pennsylvania conducts a number of studies through its department of psychiatry. But the biggest free program in the city is at the Philadelphia Medical Institute, a for–profit organization whose sole purpose is conducting drug studies. It is medically managed with great care, and all patients undergo complete medical examinations before becoming part of any research program. PMI is located at 1015 Chestnut St; phone 923–2583.

Philadelphia also has a number of other excellent clinics specifically geared to treating both anxiety and depression, often at low or no cost.

**The University of Pennsylvania Anxiety Control Program,**
University Science Center, 3600 Market Street, Suite 872, 898–4301. Under the direction of the University of Pennsylvania Pharmacological Research Unit, each patient gets a complete psychiatric and medical evaluation. Treatment is then tailored to meet individual needs, using either standard or newly developed medications for depression, panic/anxiety disorders and social phobias. Of the 500 or so patients who come to the clinic in a given year, about half are referred elsewhere or refused because their stress seems to be situationally based. Of those

who are selected, about 70 percent improve significantly on drugs. This unit also has a program to wean people from long-term tranquilizer use, called "Life Without Tranquilizers." Because of federal funding, the programs here are free.

**Freedom From Depression,** HUP, 3600 Market Street, 8th Floor, 662-3462. This clinic is devoted to the treatment and investigation of biological depression. Each patient goes through a thorough psychiatric and medical evaluation, and those not considered appropriate are referred elsewhere. Treatment may combine antidepressant medication with supportive psychotherapy. A donation of $50 is requested for the Jack Warsaw Fund (founder of the program); the rest is free.

**Center for Cognitive Therapy**, HUP, 3600 Market Street, 7th Floor, 898-4100. This program uses the behavioral concepts pioneered by Dr. Aaron Beck, which are based on the premise that anxiety and depression come from distorted ways of thinking. The therapy uses no drugs, relying instead on teaching patients tools to recognize distorted thinking and change it. It has an excellent reputation and a high success rate. The sliding-scale fee is based on income.

**Panic Disorder and Depression Clinic**, Medical College of Pennsylvania/EPPI, 3200 Henry Avenue, 842-4242. Working in conjunction with the behavioral therapy clinic and the psychopharmacological therapy clinic at MCP, this program combines psychotherapeutic, behavioral and pharmacological modalities for people experiencing spontaneous recurrent panic in normal, everyday life situations. It also uses drug therapy in the treatment of biological depressions. The sliding-scale fee is based on income.

**The Belmont Center for Comprehensive Treatment**, 4200 Monument Road, 581-3720. This program treats patients in either a day program or a partial hospital program. The emphasis eschews drugs for cognitive therapy, and teaches participants to cope with daily challenges. Initially, patients are encouraged to attend three sessions per week. The fee may be covered by insurance.

# STILL MAKING HISTORY AFTER MORE THAN 125 YEARS

**AT THE GERMANTOWN HOSPITAL AND MEDICAL CENTER,** we continue to push ourselves to offer Philadelphians the most recent and innovative medical technologies available, including:

### OUR COMPREHENSIVE HEADACHE CENTER

Let our team of neurologists, psychologists and psychiatrists work with you to develop a treatment program for your headaches. We're one of the few centers in the nation dedicated exclusively to the study of headache.

### OUR CUSTOM JOINT CENTER

The only place in the Delaware Valley to offer you a custom-cratfed hip replacement--the CLASS Hip. Computer technology and laser scanners craft a hip implant to match your bone structure with an almost identical fit, which may allow you to avoid the revision surgery that is sometimes necessary years down the road.

**For more information** on these and our many other services, please call 215-951-8187.

THE GERMANTOWN HOSPITAL AND MEDICAL CENTER
1863

ONE PENN BOULEVARD
PHILADELPHIA, PA 19144

*All our rooms are private and offered at the semi-private rate.*

# Psychiatry at PENN

Specialists in **Penn's Department of Psychiatry** have developed many of today's most advanced treatments for a wide variety of psychiatric diseases. Their research has led to advances in our knowledge of disorders such as depression, Alzheimer's disease and schizophrenia.

In our special programs and centers, board-certified psychiatrists and licensed psychologists provide comprehensive evaluation and treatment.

- **Addictions Treatment Program**
- **Bipolar and Rapid Cycling Program**
  Including manic depression and other affective disorders
- **Center for Cognitive Therapy**
- **Child, Adolescent, and Young Adult Psychiatry**
- **Depression Program**
- **Geriatric Psychiatry**
  Including the Mood and Memory Disorders Clinic
- **Neuropsychiatry Program**
- **Psychopharmacology Program**
- **Psychotherapy Center**
- **Sleep Disorders Program**
- **Schizophrenia Center**

**Evaluation, Management and Research**
State-of-the-art imaging technology, such as MRI, PET and SPECT, in addition to innovative drug therapies, are used to provide evaluation and management for patients, including those with Alzheimer's disease, schizophrenia, affective disorders (including depression), and brain injuries that result in various behavioral disorders.

For information or to schedule an appointment, call **Penn's referral counselors, 215-662-PENN (7366)** or **215-349-5220**.

**UNIVERSITY OF PENNSYLVANIA MEDICAL CENTER**
University of Pennsylvania School of Medicine
Hospital of the University of Pennsylvania

# 9

# High Anxiety

*While you're reading this, some 20 million Americans may be having anxiety attacks. Makes you nervous, doesn't it?*

♥ The attack—the Big One, as Bob now calls it—arose out of nowhere. True, he'd been wrestling with scattered episodes of anxiety for nearly five years, but the others had been minor by comparison. A wave of fear would wash over him briefly in class, and his hand would shake so hard he couldn't take attendance. Or he'd walk down the street, bump into an acquaintance, and his mind would click off. He'd make a fast excuse that he had an appointment and dash away, absolutely certain that he could no more carry on a simple conversation than play quarterback for the Eagles. This time, though, it was different. This time he was sure he was going to die.

It happened on the Pennsylvania Turnpike, when he was coming back from a visit to his parents. He was feeling guilty because he'd given in to his sick mother's insistence that she didn't need a doctor. Suddenly he felt like he was sucking in too much air and couldn't catch his breath. He began to pant like an overheated dog on a 100° day. His hand shook so violently that he could barely steer. And he couldn't stop, because his right foot froze on the pedal. The speedometer read 55.

"I knew it was the end," he says. "I thought to myself, 'This is it.' In my mind's eye, I had this image of an awful wreck. I saw the car hitting the guardrail at the right front end, swerving, and then fishtailing so that my side would get smashed."

"I can't stop the car!" he yelled to his wife, who did not know how to drive. "I can't move my foot!"

Somehow he managed to slide his left foot onto the brake while she pried his right foot off the gas pedal. Providentially, they were near an exit and able to inch into the service area. There they sat for two hours, until he calmed down.

What happened to this high school teacher was neither rare nor inexplicable. He had an anxiety attack, a horrifying experience that will strike an estimated one in 12 Americans sometime in their lives. While most anxiety attacks are not so life–threatening, they can make life a horrible ordeal.

The symptoms of anxiety sufferers run the gamut from ongoing states of low–level jumpiness and hypervigilance to periodic panic attacks that hit with hurricane force. Some have phobias that compel them to avoid anything from cats to airplanes. Others (agoraphobics) live as prisoners in the only safe havens they can tolerate: their own homes.

The problem of anxiety is nothing new; it harks back to a prehistoric era, when the anxiety mechanism was a crucial factor in survival. What we label anxiety today was originally a primitive alert system that warned early man (and probably animals) of impending danger. Built into our subconscious is something that takes over our bodies and drives us to fight back, flee, freeze in our tracks or faint until danger passes. This "fight or flight" response, protected by evolution, always tended to err on the side of over–vigilance—which was certainly preferable to an alert system that in an ambiguous situation missed the danger entirely. "Nature," says University of Pennsylvania psychiatrist Dr. Aaron Beck, "favors anxious genes."

Even today, as we live in the 20th century, our bodies are still roaming the savanna. "Our environment has changed," says Beck, "but we haven't." In many ways, that's good. Anxiety is still a valuable survival tool, one that helps us assess situations and react quickly to potential dangers. Like pain, anxiety is an attention–getter that screams, *Something is wrong; correct it.* A primitive reaction like the suspicion of the unknown or unfamiliar is an important checking system.

If anxiety were triggered only in the face of real danger, as intended by nature, it would pose no problem. Instead, it's become a double–edged sword. The sense of insecurity that worked so beautifully to keep our ancestors from taking risks in the wild becomes an impediment rather than an aid when it's activated at the wrong time in contemporary life. It's no help at all when it blocks normal performance.

Sometimes anxious feelings are caused by a real "danger," and abate when the danger passes. Why is it that one person reacts to anxiety–producing situations with this normal response, while another loses hold of reality? Over the years, several theories have emerged for what's behind "free–floating anxiety." Psychoanalysts tend to follow Freud's lead, and say that anxiety is aroused by the threat of a forbidden unconscious impulse breaking into conscious awareness. The treatment mode in this model focuses on gaining insight into the fear, which should lead to controlling it. Behaviorists take another view. They believe anxiety is a conditioned reflex that occurs when a particular place or thing is paired with some real or imagined threat. Their cure involves desensitizing the patient through repeated visits to the feared place. Then there are the medical researchers who are convinced that anxiety (panic attacks, in particular) is caused by an imbalance in the body chemisty.

    Dr. Aaron Beck disagrees with all the traditional explanations. His theory, simplistic as it may sound, is quite revolutionary, although Beck himself hardly fits the stereotype of an iconoclast. An affable man with short, thick hair the color of whipped cream, a slightly bent posture and a shuffling gait, the 70ish Beck is a giant in the field he pioneered: cognitive therapy.

    "Cognition" means "thinking." Beck says anxiety is the result of thinking we are in danger, and the key to treating it is to unlock the automatic thoughts and spontaneous visual images that accompany an anxiety attack. Forget probing into childhood memories; forget that the dizzy feeling triggering a fear of fainting may be due to low blood sugar. What's more important in controlling anxiety, Beck says, is to understand how the anxious distort reality by *misreading* signals. Thus the anxious think that the wind rustling the blinds is an intruder breaking in, or that a salesclerk who is preoccupied with a headache is intentionally ignoring them. The leap from the distorted thought to the visual image to the first stir of panic takes but a split second. A graduate student prone to anxiety attacks described how she could be crossing the street and the light would change: Suddenly she'd imagine all the cars rushing at her; she'd be trapped, and she'd think, "I'm going to die without anyone to help me."

    These mental pictures are so powerful that they become reality. Anxiety patients believe that their fantasies are actually happening; no matter how preposterous the images may be, they can't turn them off. While the mind races with fearful thoughts and images, the body simultaneously begins sending its ancient defense signals. A nervous boy rings the doorbell for a blind date. He visualizes the girl looking at him contemptuously, and his palms begin to sweat; his heart feels like it's exploding in his chest. His mind goes blank, and when she opens the door he can't even say hello.

    Once Aaron Beck understood the role of automatic thoughts and images in producing anxiety, he had no trouble getting patients to describe the attacks in great detail. A male patient who falls apart when he has to make a speech describes how he actually sees himself crumbling on the podium and collapsing in a heap. Soon all his colleagues are standing over him, asking how this could have happened to such a top guy. Another sees himself, at a meeting where he is about to speak, bursting into tears and running from the room. He is mortified and thinks, "It's all over. I blew the job. My career is dead."

    Armed with these insights, Beck declared the old notion of free–floating anxiety to be nonsense. Anxiety, he claims, is an emotional response to the fearful thought that something awful is going to happen. That thought could be the fear of an internal physical disaster, the fear of a mental breakdown, or the fear of some social disgrace. The anxious overestimate the degree of real danger (which increases fear) while underestimating their ability to cope (which increases anxiety).

    It's typical for the anxious to focus on the signals that possibly indicate danger (a stomachache, for instance) while ignoring the possible cause of the signal (having just wolfed down a huge meal). Regardless of how distorted the anxious person's perceptions are, they seem perfectly reasonable—and terrifying—to him or her. In cognitive therapy, the anxious are taught to zero in on their fear–producing thoughts, test them against reality, and look for reasonable alternative explanations. In short, they learn to think the way the rest of us do when we get a stomachache.

Beck has found that the anxious among us share a number of characteristic thought patterns. Taken one at a time, these misperceptions are not all that uncommon. But together, they create a twisted view of life's perils. A core problem of anxiety sufferers is the need to be perfect at everything. While perfectionism is generally an asset on the job and a positive factor in career advancement, it also creates a special vulnerability to anxiety attacks. The anxious feel insecure about one area of their lives, and dramatize that particular flaw. Perhaps they are competent in business but fall apart on dates. Or they're great in one–to–one relationships but duds at parties. Whatever the weak link is, they'll dwell on it, magnify its importance, and minimize the strengths they do have. This makes them particularly anxiety–prone, because each error is seen as a harbinger of impending disaster, a catastrophe waiting to happen.

Although anxiety has many faces, general anxiety victims fall into two categories. Either they dread some kind of physical harm—an attack, an accident, a disease—or they are threatened by their social environment. Social anxiety is the harder of the two to conceptualize. While it may relate to personal encounters or career concerns, Beck says that all social anxiety stems from an underlying fear of negative evaluation. "People are universally afraid of being judged poorly by others," he says. "They're worried about measuring up." Social anxiety is extremely widespread, but not always crippling. At a recent workshop he conducted for 500 therapists, Beck asked how many had ever experienced some anxiety based on negative evaluation. Every single person raised his hand. "The pros worry they won't be good enough," Beck says, "and the amateurs worry they'll look as inexperienced as they really are."

The burden of keeping anxiety in check is exhausting for those who suffer from it. Unlike depression victims, who are often immobilized, people with generalized anxiety are out there struggling from moment to moment to keep a grip on their lives. For many of them, cognitive therapy, as practiced by Beck's disciples, holds great promise, because it seems to succeed when all else fails by teaching people to give everything a second thought.

# The Interventional Neuro-Center

The multidisciplinary specialists in the Interventional Neuro-Center combine the latest **microneurosurgical techniques** with **interventional neuroradiology** and **stereotactic radiosurgery.**

Our internationally recognized specialists in neurosurgery, neuroradiology, and radiation oncology are board-certified. They provide team evaluation for each patient and recommend the most appropriate course of treatment, utilizing these state-of-the-art techniques.

Examples of conditions treated include patients with arteriovenous malformations, cerebral aneurysms, brain tumors, skull base tumors, vascular tumors, and other complex vascular lesions and tumors of the central nervous system.

For more information, please call our referral counselors at 215-662-PENN (7366) or Neurosurgery at 215-662-3487.

**UNIVERSITY OF PENNSYLVANIA MEDICAL CENTER**

University of Pennsylvania School of Medicine
Hospital of the University of Pennsylvania

# Call for a list of your friends.

When you're struggling with a mental or emotional problem, where do you turn? Those close to you can provide compassion and understanding, but sometimes you need more — the help of an expert trained to understand problems like yours.

This is when Friends of a different sort can help. Friends Hospital has only one purpose: to treat mental and emotional illnesses.

We'd like to send you our free "Guide to Staff." It's a list of our people, programs and philosophy. You'll see the depth of knowledge we have here. And you can use it to call any one of our physicians.

Keep it handy. Mental and emotional problems affect millions of people. You never know when you might need Friends.

## FRIENDS
HOSPITAL

4641 Roosevelt Boulevard
Philadelphia, PA 19124-2399
**215-831-4600**

# 10
# Where To Go For Help

*A list of psychiatric hospitals and mental health centers.*

♥ When emotional problems require more attention than regular visits to a therapist's office, it may be necessary to check into a hospital or enroll in some kind of daily or weekly outpatient program. As these listings show, there are treatment programs tailored to every kind of psychological disturbance, from stress to incest to obsessive–compulsive disorders to schizophrenia. Options range from long– or short–term inpatient care in a specialized hospital setting to drop–in neighborhood centers that may provide outpatient day care and or simply dispense medication.

- 🛏 **OVERNIGHT FACILITIES FOR FAMILIES**
- 🙏 **PASTORAL CARE**
- 🏛 **HOSPICE CARE**
- ✂ **BARBER**
- ⚖ **PATIENT ADVOCATE**
- 🚭 **SMOKE-FREE ENVIRONMENT**
- 🎓 **TEACHING HOSPITAL**
- **E** **EMERGENCY ROOM**
- ✉ **PREPAYMENT FOR DEDUCTIBLE REQUIRED**

This chapter lists both private psychiatric hospitals and community mental health centers. Some of the places treat mental retardation as well as mental illness. In addition to the speciality hospitals included in this section, many local hospitals have psychiatric departments offering both in–and outpatient care. Check Chapter 7 for that information.

## PSYCHIATRIC HOSPITALS

### Belmont Center for Comprehensive Treatment

*4200 Monument Rd., 877–2000, 456–8000 (program information), 581–3774 (admission), 581-3757 (Woodside Hall Addiction Treatment Program).* Doctors on active staff: 254 (77% board–certified); number of beds: 146; 6.2 RNs per bed. Cost for room and board: $750; accreditation: JCAHO, National Association of Private Psychiatric Hospitals.

Emergency room services: access to psychiatric emergency at Albert Einstein Medical Center.

Special treatment units: in– and outpatient addictions (drug, alcohol, gambling), Eating Disorders Unit, Anxiety/Affective Disorders Unit, dual-diagnosis for adults and adolescents.

Physical rehab services: physical medicine and rehab; physical therapy.

Belmont Center for Comprehensive Treatment is a private, nonprofit psychiatric hospital and a subsidiary of Albert Einstein Healthcare Foundation. It was formerly known as the Philadelphia Psychiatric Center. The Woodside Hall Addiction Treatment Program offers services for substance abuse patients on an inpatient, outpatient, and intensive outpatient basis.

### The Charter Fairmount Institute

*561 Fairthorn Ave., Roxborough, 487–4000.* Staff comprised of 14 psychologists, 11 social workers and 18 psychiatrists; number of beds: 17; 3.23 RNs per bed; accreditation: JCAHO; accepts most insurance.

Specialized treatment programs: geriatric unit, dual-diagnosis program, Special Care Unit, separate adolescent units for teens 12–18.

Outpatient health and wellness programs: drug and alcohol education, stress management, mental health lectures, partial hospitalization, Bucks County Outpatient Center (638–7692).

Established in 1926 as a private psychiatric hospital, Charter Fairmount specializes in dual-diagnosis problems. It provides a variety of therapy programs, including music, art, occupational, recreational, psychodrama, group and family.

### Friends Hospital

*4641 Roosevelt Blvd., 832–4600.* Staff comprised of 25 psychiatrists (90% board–certified) and 12 social workers; number of beds: 192; 1 RN per 2.5 beds; accreditation: JCAHO.

Specialized treatment programs: geropsychiatry, adolescent dual diagnosis and evaluation, supportive care unit, day program, residential services, pain/stress management, addictions recovery.

Outpatient programs: partial hospitalization for adolescents, day program, Clark Clinic (where uninsured patients can meet with a psychiatrist on a sliding fee scale), horticultural, recreational, expressive, therapeutic and occupational therapy.

Founded in 1813, Friends is the oldest private psychiatric institution in the country. Located on a beautifully landscaped 100-acre site, it offers a full range of in-and-outpatient services for adults, adolescents and the elderly.

### Hampton Hospital
*Rancocas Rd., Rancocas, New Jersey, 609- 267-7000, 800-345-7345* (referral and assessment). Staff comprised of 7 psychiatrists, 5 psychologists and 12 social workers; number of beds: 100; 1.25 RNs per bed; accepts all types of major insurance; detox available.

A private psychiatric hospital offering treatment, research, education and diagnosis for adults and adolescents with emotional problems. Comprised of five independent speciality units: the Neuropsychiatric Evaluation Unit, the Adolescent Psychiatric Treatment Program, the Adolescent Substance Abuse Program, the Adult Psychiatric Treatment Program and the Psychiatric Substance Abuse Program.

Concentrates on dual-diagnosis patients (those who are diagnosed with both a mental disorder and a substance abuse problem). Offers outpatient services at Hampton Counseling Clinic sites at Greentree Commons, Suite 8001 B, Rte. 73, Marlton, New Jersey, 609-596-3222, and 368 Lakehurst Rd., Suite 205, Toms River, New Jersey, 908-914-9036.

Services include intensive drug and alcohol programs, short-term therapy, co-dependency programs, early intervention programs for adolescents, after-care programs, neuropsychiatric evaluations, medication management, employee assistance programs, intervention programs, family and marital counseling.

### The Institute of Pennsylvania Hospital
*111 North 49th St., Philadelphia, 471-2000.* Staff comprised of 24 licensed psychiatrists; number of beds: 234; 1 RN per 2 beds; room cost: $828; gourmet food service: $16 per day; accreditation: JCAHO, ACGME, DPW.

Specialized treatment programs: substance abuse, adolescents, evaluating series, anxiety disorders, dissociative disorders program, young adult program, geriatric psychiatry.

Physical rehab services: occupational therapy, therapeutic, leisure and recreational activities.

Outpatient health and wellness programs: Speaker's Bureau, Coping Skills Workshop (for families of the mentally ill).

The Institute of Pennsylvania Hospital is a highly respected, attractively furnished psychiatric hospital established in 1841, with strengths in drug and alcohol abuse, geriatric psychiatry and dissociative and multiple-personality disorders.

**Mount Sinai Hospital**
*See Chapter 34.*

**Northwestern Institute**
*450 Bethlehem Pike, P.O. Box 209, Fort Washington, 641–5300.* Staff comprised of 45 psychiatrists (90% board–certified), 4 psychologists and 20 social workers; number of beds: 146; 2.24 RNs per bed; semiprivate room costs: $775–$1,000; accreditation: JCAHO; for more information, call 800–344–NWIP.

A private psychiatric hospital offering in– and outpatient treatment as well as a partial hospitalization program, for those who need inpatient services without overnight hospital stays.

Specialized adult programs: dissociative disorders; older adult program (for dealing with the loss of a spouse or longtime friend or emotional problems resulting from retirement); adolescent program (for youngsters 13–18 with emotional or behavioral problems); children's program (for 6–to–12–year–olds suffering from hyperactivity, depression, psychosis, trauma or abuse); Women's Unit (to help women over 18 cope with depression, sexual, physical or emotional abuse, co–dependency, and sexual dysfunction).

Unique treatment unit: the Sanctuary Program, a 22–bed voluntary inpatient protected environment organized for adults who've experienced abuse or psychological trauma as children and as a result find themselves suffering from depression or self–destructive, obsessive behavior. The treatment uses a multidisciplinary staff of psychiatrists, social workers, dance and art therapists and nurses in an integrated approach to healing.

Outpatient health and wellness programs: a broad spectrum of community education seminars.

**Philadelphia Child Guidance Clinic**
*34th St. and Civic Center Blvd., 243–2600 (evening crisis hot line: 243–2888); Child Assist Network: 243–2702.* Staff comprised of 11 psychiatrists (91% board–certified), 20 psychologists and 21 social workers; number of beds: 38; 1 RN per 3 beds; room cost: $800; accreditation: JCAHO.

A comprehensive mental health organization serving children and adolescents with emotional/behavioral problems.

Specialized treatment programs: two residential apartment buildings for families undergoing intensive inpatient treatment.

Outpatient programs: assessment; individual, group and family therapy; medication clinic; intensive family/home–based program; preschoolers; therapeutic foster homes; drug and alcohol treatment.

PCGC is one of the country's foremost clinics for troubled youths, with particular strengths in family therapy, eating disorders and psychosomatic illness. It is a teaching hospital, affiliated with the University of Pennsylvania School of Medicine and CHOP.

# COMMUNITY MENTAL HEALTH SERVICES, PUBLIC AND PRIVATE

**Philadelphia County:**

The following are mental health/mental retardation centers run by the City of Philadelphia. Most offer case management services that provide each patient with a therapist, evaluate the individual's needs, advocate for services, and monitor follow–ups. Social rehabilitation and partial hospitalization programs are also available. Call for more information.

**John F. Kennedy Mental Health/Mental Retardation Center,** 112 North Broad St., 568–0860.

**Hall–Mercer Mental Health/Mental Retardation Center,** 8th and Locust sts., 829–5249.

**CATCH, Inc.,** 1409 Lombard St., 735–7447.

**The Consortium,** 451 University Ave., 596–8000. See Chapter 34 for more information.

**Community Council for Mental Health/Retardation, Inc.,** 4900 Wyalusing Ave., 473–7033.

**CO–MHAR, Inc.,** 100 West Lehigh Ave., 427–5800.

**Cora Services,** 733 Susquehanna Rd., 342–2660. See Chapter 34 for more information.

**The Northwest Center,** 27 East Mount Airy Ave., 248–6700.

**Charles R. Drew Community Mental Health/Mental Retardation Center,** 1351 Tabor Rd., 276–9101.

**Northeast Community Center for Mental Health/Mental Retardation,** Roosevelt Blvd. and Adams Ave., 831–2863.

**PATH, Inc.,** 8220 Castor Ave., 728–4560.

**Benjamin Rush Mental Health/Retardation Center,** 10125 Verree Rd., 698–4200.

**Southeast Asian Mutual Assistance Coalition,** 4601 Market St., 476–9640.

In addition to mental health services provided by the hospitals and city agencies, there are a number of social service organizations offering a variety of programs. Here are some of them:

**A.P. Orleans Industries, A.P. Orleans Vocational Center, Division of Jewish Employment/Vocational Service,** 1330 Rhawn St., 728–4400. Has partial hospitalization programs, vocational rehabilitation programs, and a vocational after–care program for emotionally disabled consumers over 18.

**Asociacion de Puertorriquenos en Marcha, Inc.,** 2147 North 6th St., 235–6788. Offers psychiatric and psychological evaluations, short–term supportive therapy and long–term individual therapy.

**Catholic Social Services,** 222 North 17th St., 587–3900. Has individual, family, marital and premarital counseling.

*Delaware Valley Psychological Clinics*, 1536 Pratt St., 744–4777. Full service outpatient care. Referrals available.

*Mental Health Services at Philadelphia Elwyn*, 4040 Market St., 895–5536. Offers a vocational rehabilitation program with three sections: pre–vocational training in job attitudes; production and learning to apply good attitudes; and job searching. Also has a comprehensive partial hospitalization program for adults 18 and older.

*Episcopal Community Services*, 225 South 3rd St., 351–1400. Provides social services for medically needy children who are either in foster homes or their own homes.

*Family Service of Philadelphia*, 311 South Juniper St., 875–3300. Provides evaluation services to individuals and families and recommends treatment.

*The Family Institute of Philadelphia*, 1527 Brandywine St., 567–1396. Has a special Hispanic Mental Health Training Program to help families cope with a wide range of problems.

*Health Professional Services, Inc.*, 6182 Ridge Ave., 482-9672. Provides outpatient psychological counseling, group therapy and services for patients with addiction problems.

*Help, Inc.*, 638 South St., 546-7766. An outpatient mental health facility with a drug and alcohol unit.

*Horizon House, Inc.*, 120 South 30th St., 386–1600. Provides psychosocial rehabilitation programs for individuals 18 and older who are experiencing mental health problems. Therapy involves social skills training, educational services, and vocational and pre–vocational activities. See Chapter 34 for more information.

*Jewish Family and Children's Service*, 1610 Spruce St., 545–3290. Individual, family, marriage and premarital counseling.

*Joseph J. Peters Institute*, 260 S. Broad St., 893–0600. Treats sex offenders as well as male and female adult survivors of childhood rape.

*Philadelphia Center for Human Development*, 10360 Drummond Rd., 632–6400. Has three area locations: Germantown (438–5696), University City (387–2848), and Chestnut Hill (247–6077).

*Philadelphia Mental Health Clinic*, 1235 Pine St., 735–9379. Has special programs for individuals with eating disorders, hearing disorders, mental illness/substance abuse problems, and attention deficit disorders.

**Montgomery County:**

*Creative Health Systems*, 361 High St., Pottstown, 326–9250. Has two satellites: Spring City Community Counseling Services (948–6490), and Collegeville Community Counseling Services (489–1000). Offers partial hospitalization and drug rehabilitation programs.

*Cope Centers, Inc.*, 400 North Broad St., Lansdale, 643–5522, 855–0780. Has an outpatient center (643–4340) and an adult partial hospitalization program.

*Central Montgomery Mental Health/Mental Retardation Center*, 11 Powell St., Norristown, 277–4600. Provides case management and partial hospitalization programs as well as PIP (Preschool Intervention

Program, for children's special needs).
*Lower Merion Counseling Services,* 32–40 Rittenhouse Place, Ardmore, 649–6512. Outpatient counseling. Individual and group therapy.
*Penn Foundation for Mental Health, Inc.,* 807 Lawn Ave., Sellersville, 257–6551. Inpatient and outpatient programs for drug and alcohol treatment as well as a broad range of psychiatric clinics.

### Chester County:
*Community Services for Human Growth, Inc.,* 30 South Valley Rd., Suite 301, Paoli, 644–4455. Satellite offices: outpatient services (935–0853); partial hospitalization (935–0850); senior partial hospitalization (935–0810). Provides mental health/mental retardation case management and Aftercare.
*Human Services, Inc.,* 520 East Lancaster Ave., Downingtown, 873–1010. Provides therapy for the mentally ill and mentally retarded. Also has programs for sex offenders. One satellite: Oxford Neighborhood Center (932–8557).

### Delaware County:
*Community Care Program,* 891–8043. Offers intensive case management for chronically mentally ill patients. Family and consumer program, (891–2027); Advocacy and support, (891–2027).
*Life Guidance Services, Inc.,* 370 Reed Rd., Broomall, 328–3200. A mental health and drug and alcohol treatment agency. Has a partial hospitalization program. Outpatient only. Satellites: 800 Chester Pike, Sharon Hill (534–3636); 342 Middletown Rd., Lima (565–3636); Saint Mark's Church, Sproul and Lewis rds. (353–2507); 101 West Chester Pike (853–2210).
*Media Child Guidance,* 600 North Olive St., Media, 656–6000. Three satellites: 1124 Chester Pike, Crum Lynne (833–2020); Community School, Lorraine Ave. (896–5650); Aston Vo–Tech, Birney Highway and Crozierville Rd. (459–3030). Provides partial hospitalization, Community School and a vocational school.
*Elwyn Institute/Upper Darby Rehabilitation,* 7700 West Chester Pike, Upper Darby, 446–1485. Provides work activities, a job coach, and transitional and job retention programs.
*State Bureau of Vocational Rehabilitation,* 1062 Lancaster Ave., Rosemont, 525–1810. Provides job training and counseling for emotionally ill patients.
*Project Share of Delaware County,* 880 Main St., Darby, 583–9190. A drop–in center for mental health patients. Offers peer counseling groups and preparation for employment programs.
*Delaware County PIN,* 103 Brentwood Ave., Havertown, 521–4353. Run by parents, for the parents of emotionally disturbed children. Provides case advocacy and referral.
*Delaware County AMI,* 352 Windemere Ave., Lansdowne, 626–7530. Offers counseling and support for individuals or families.
*Main Line MH Group,* P.O. Box 243, Radnor, 688–4434. Individual

and family counseling. Provides case management services.

**Hands of AMI,** P.O. Box 485, Broomall, 446–8199. Individual and family counseling as well as outpatient programs for emotionally needy patients.

### Bucks County:

**Lenape Valley Foundation,** 530 West Butler Pike, M.R. 1, Chalfont, 345–5300. Provides marriage and sex therapy, stress management, psychological assessment and pastoral counseling.

**Penndel Mental Health Program,** 1517 Durham Rd., Penndel, 752–1544. Provides outpatient services and a partial hospitalization program along with individual counseling.

**Bristol–Bensalem Human Service Center,** 4401 Sunset Ave., Newportville, 788–5800. Offers partial hospitalization and outpatient programs as well as family–based services. Also has services for children with developmental disabilities.

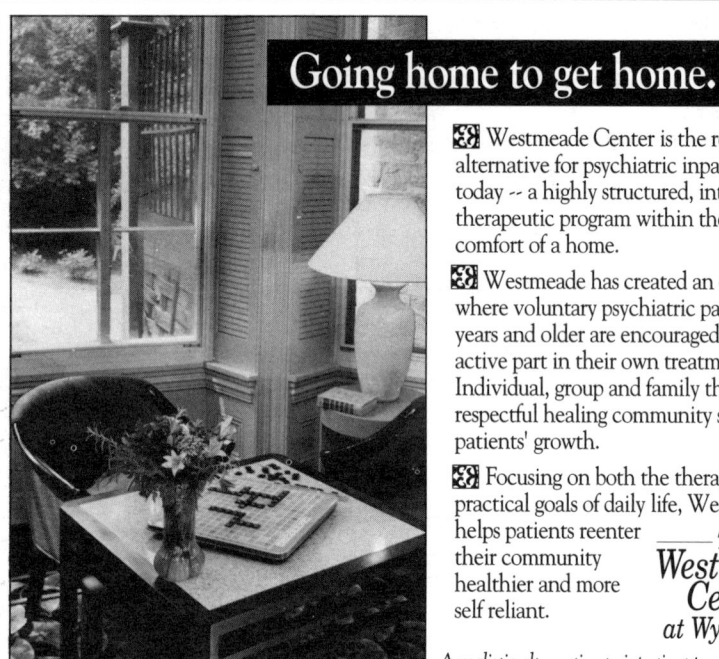

---

## Going home to get home.

Westmeade Center is the realistic alternative for psychiatric inpatient care today -- a highly structured, intensive therapeutic program within the safety and comfort of a home.

Westmeade has created an environment where voluntary psychiatric patients 18 years and older are encouraged to take an active part in their own treatment. Individual, group and family therapies and a respectful healing community support patients' growth.

Focusing on both the therapeutic and practical goals of daily life, Westmeade helps patients reenter their community healthier and more self reliant.

### The Westmeade Center at Wyndmoor

A realistic alternative to inpatient psychiatric care.

8765 Stenton Ave. · Wyndmoor, PA 19118 · 215-836-9090

# Recovery From Substance Abuse Is More Than A Quick Fix...

Stopping drug and alcohol abuse is easy, continuing abstinence is the difficult part. Riverside Clinics provides a comprehensive, professional approach to effect and support the changes necessary for continued sobriety. Our nationally recognized model programs for adults and adolescents treat the whole person where recovery needs to take place - in the community.

# RIVERSIDE CLINICS

The Leader In Community Based Recovery Treatment Programs

Bucks County • Chester County • Delaware County

**(215) 945-7100**

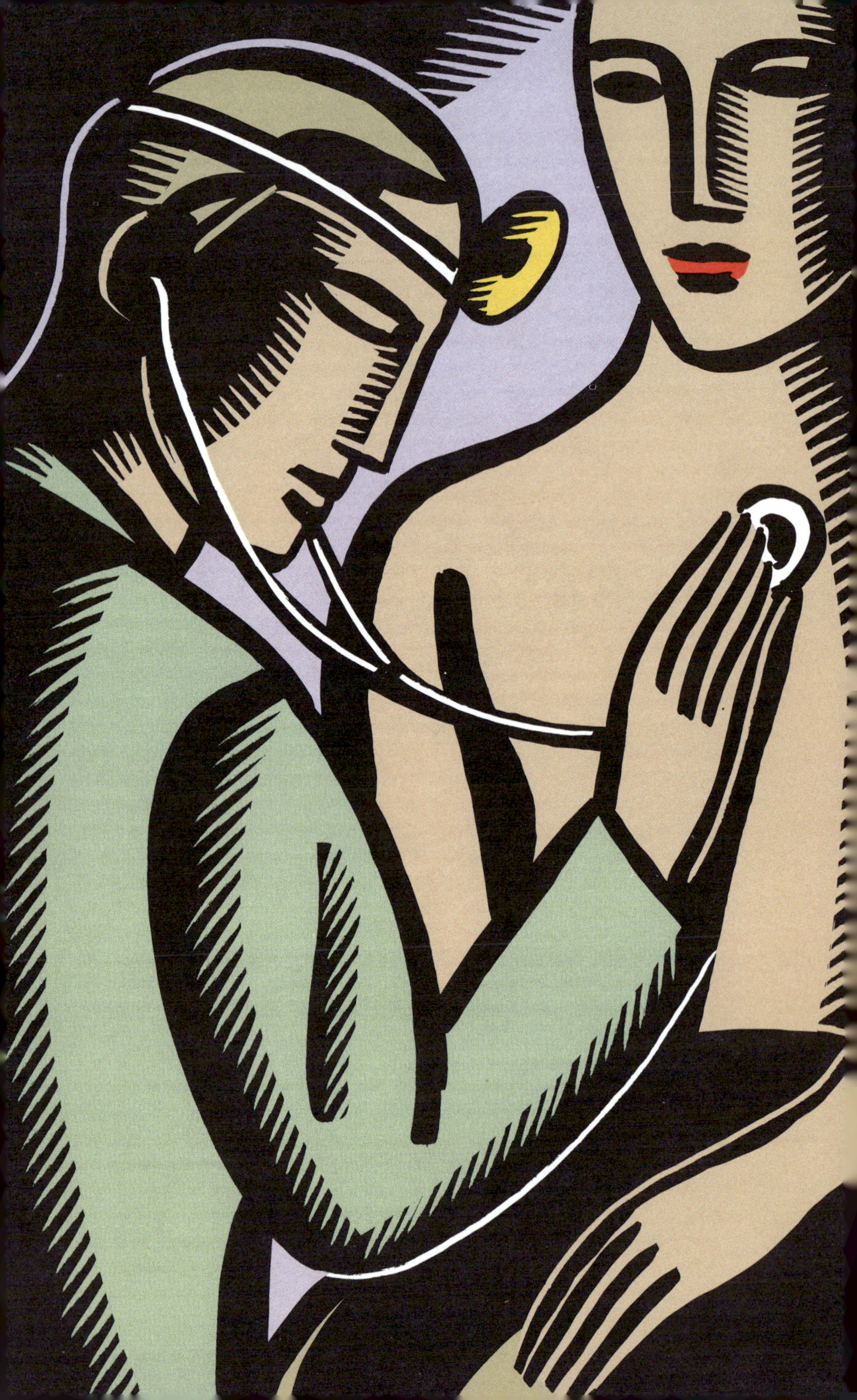

## SECTION FOUR

# A PRESCRIPTION FOR WELLNESS

# 11

# Testing, Testing

*and more testing. Billions of dollars worth of medical tests may be unnecessary. And that includes the all–purpose annual physical.*

♥ Just try to remember the last time you visited a doctor and didn't wind up having some kind of medical test. Feeling tired? Let's do a blood workup for $50. Complaining of headaches? Go get an MRI for $922. Just a routine checkup? At the least, you'll have a urinalysis and a chest X–ray—$72 for the basic front view, $157 for a four–sided picture. And heaven forbid you've got some tightness in your chest, because you'll probably need an EKG for $56, a stress test for $309, and maybe even a heart catheterization for as much as $2,160.

Okay, I'm exaggerating—but only slightly. The point is, patients have come to expect, even request, excessive testing, in part because their insurance foots the bill. And doctors will admit privately that medicine has come to rely on broad diagnostic testing far more than is necessary. Granted that the doctor's arsenal of 1,500 available medical tests has removed a lot of the guesswork from health care. But it seems the over-reliance on testing has burgeoned into too much of a good thing, in part because tests are sometimes used to produce income or avoid lawsuits rather than to obtain information.

"No one would suggest that there is anything wrong with a diagnostic test when symptoms indicate a need, but otherwise these tests are just money–makers," says Dr. Edward Pinckney, a California internist and author of *A Patient's Guide to Medical Tests*. Pinckney believes too many tests are fishing expeditions, used by doctors in lieu of careful examinations of patients. That's akin to the view of Dr. John Eisenberg, chairman of the department of medicine at Georgetown Medical Center, who says, "More important than an EKG in your pocket is developing a relationship with a doctor who knows you, your lifestyle and your family history, and counsels you according to your risks."

As Dr. Catalin Roth, medical director of the J.E. Wood Clinic at Pennsylvania Hospital, points out, "Third–party payers [insurance companies] do not reimburse doctors for ten minutes of health counseling. But you get paid $100 for doing an EKG, and as much as $250 for a flexible sigmoidoscopy. The way health care is financed, there's little incentive for doctors to spend time talking about important areas like prevention." And as for whether Americans need all the tests they get, according to Secretary of Health and Human Services Louis Sullivan, "Increasingly we're finding that a substantial portion of the care that's being . . . billed for is of unproven medical necessity and effectiveness."

We asked Dr. Arnold Relman, former editor of the *New England Journal of Medicine*, why American doctors do so much testing. One of his explanations was exactly what we'd expected: the profit motive. But he believes the whole answer goes much deeper. An enormous amount of unnecessary testing is motivated by a fear of malpractice litigation. Just in case something goes wrong with a patient, doctors can't afford to be held liable for insufficient diagnostic studies. They engage in exhaustive testing to avoid being accused of negligence. The doctor who does 20 tests on somebody and misses a diagnosis is less likely to lose a lawsuit than the doctor who did only a handful. This self–protection often gets carried to extremes. A local physician told us he overheard a conversation in which a nervous gynecologist mused that maybe he should introduce ultrasound screenings as part of a woman's annual checkup. It seems a colleague of his had been sued for missing an ovarian cancer at a stage when it was too early to be detected by manual probing.

In addition, the inclination to over–test is fueled by our obsession with expert opinions. "Americans with health insurance love to see specialists," Dr. Relman says. "In this country, 75 percent of physicians are specialists, who, by their very nature, are trained to do special tests. An awful lot of headaches and chest pains could be handled for far less money by general practitioners."

Then there is the problem of what Dr. Relman calls "technology assessment." He says, "We've got all this high–tech screening available, yet we don't know exactly what works and what doesn't. That creates a lot of uncertainty, and as a result we spend an enormous amount on services which haven't been fully evaluated." This is especially true, he explains, when a doctor is in doubt. Doctors have a do–something mentality. Because they want to know all they can, they have a tendency to engage in diagnostic overkill, opting for actions that will yield every possible shred of information. For example: While MRIs are superb vehicles for imaging neurological conditions, the machines tend to be used for a raft of other problems that less–expensive CAT scans would reveal just as well.

Tests that are increasingly being viewed as a waste of money for healthy people are:

- Chest X-rays—should only be done in the presence of symptoms.
- Electrocardiograms—many people have irregular heartbeats, so without other symptoms or family risks, the results can be misleading. In addition, a normal EKG does not rule out disease in a high-risk patient.
- Stress tests—too unpredictable to forecast heart problems.

Indeed, many medical tests are highly inaccurate. Some of the most common screenings are riddled with false-positive or false-negative results. "What does it mean psychologically to be called hypercholestemic [suffering from abnormally high cholesterol] when you're perfectly healthy, or to suffer through the false positive of a mammography?" asks Harvard Medical School's Dr. Robert S. Lawrence, who chaired the government's Preventive Services Task Force, which questioned the validity of a plethora of routine tests. "This kind of thing does real damage to people. We in modern medicine find great comfort in doing lab tests and concluding things that may not be valid. The measurable tends to drive out the important, and the behavioral issues threatening health [things like smoking, drinking and diet] get ignored because they aren't quantifiable."

A short list of common tests with significant levels of unreliablity would include the one for chlamydia, the most common sexually transmitted disease of the '80s. Its false-positive rate is 10 to 20 percent, the false-negative rate as high as 30 percent. Cholesterol tests from a good laboratory have just a 5 percent inaccuracy rate, but the popular rapid screenings done at health fairs with a finger stick are often inaccurate. If the results are abnormal, have them corroborated before getting nervous. Blood tests for mononucleosis tend to run up to 15 percent false-negative in adults and as high as 50 percent in young children. Today, Pap smears are less likely than previously to be false-negative. However, false positives are fairly common, and should always be confirmed by retesting.

Probably the biggest offender when it comes to inaccuracy is the routine blood test. Because of the way the machinery for assessing blood is designed, it takes as much time and money for a technician to do one test as to do dozens. So instead of a simple red cell/white cell count, doctors go for the package. This detailed multiphasic blood profile typically contains an alarming false positive in some category—and that opens a Pandora's box. Dr. Marie Savard, a Presbyterian Hospital internist, tells us, "It's common, for instance, for a blood test to show an elevated liver enzyme, which usually pans out to be nothing, but which forces the doctor to check on it with lots of expensive tests. Calcium often comes back borderline-high, also requiring expensive testing to rule out problems that never existed in the first place."

Frequently, improper readings are the fault of the laboratory, although that has improved since new government regulations now mandate inspections at some 300,000 laboratories. Just as problematic is how to interpret what's normal. It's quite common for someone to fall outside the so-called normal range and yet be perfectly healthy. "We do so much blood testing," explains Dr. Savard, "because it's an inexpensive screening that occasionally picks up kidney disease or diabetes, or liver problems that indicate alcoholism. What's being asked in this era of cost-containment is whether those few that are helped by an unexpected finding offset the expense and worry for the far greater numbers who are wrongly diagnosed."

What can you do to break the test pattern? The People's Medical Society advises asking your doctor why a test has been requested. Is it because you're a high-risk patient? If you're not, why bother? What is the test supposed to reveal? How reliable is the lab where the test will be processed, and what's the margin of error for the results? Are there risks? If so, are there safer alternatives that will yield comparable information?

Finally, if something wrong *is* discovered, can it be treated? A friend of ours learned through a routine blood test that she had a very low white cell count. In an effort to find the cause, she underwent an exhaustive battery of tests; every one came back normal. Though the doctor was convinced she had a nonthreatening abnormality, as a last resort he suggested a bone- marrow tap—a fairly radical and painful procedure. "What will it tell me?" she asked. The answer: nothing that would lead to medical treatment. "Then what's the purpose of going through it?" she pressed. "There really isn't any," the doctor admitted. Together, they decided to stop testing. The next time your doctor recommends some kind of medical test, be a partner in the decision.

If there is one trend in testing you want to seriously reconsider, it's the idea of an unnecessary annual physical. Many, many people see a doctor every year even though they're perfectly healthy. They're like the 60-year-old friend of mine who was telling me he'd just gotten the results of his annual checkup; happily, he was in A-okay shape for another year. I asked him if he'd gone to the doctor because something was wrong. "Nope," he replied. "I feel great, and getting checked every year gives me the peace of mind that I'm as healthy as I think I am."

That kind of reassurance may be the *only* reason for healthy people to have an annual checkup. Major studies and reams of research indicate that this staple of American health care may have outlived its usefulness as a general rule. The head-to-toe yearly physical, first introduced in 1914 by the Metropolitan Life Insurance Company for all its employees and policyholders, may well have become an anachronism.

That doesn't mean people shouldn't see a doctor unless they're sick. But the all-inclusive, expensive ($400 to $500) routine exam may no longer make either medical or economic sense. "`Routine' checkup implies nonthinking," says Georgetown Medical Center's Dr. Eisenberg. "It's a tragedy that people so often get the tests they don't need, but don't get the tests they do need. The traditional knee-jerk evaluation without regard to risk factors is bad medicine."

Instead, what doctors and their patients ought to be practicing is an individualized approach to health care, based on something called risk assessment.

Using a variety of criteria, doctors today can place patients in high– or low–risk categories; those labels in turn will dictate who needs to be examined for what problems. For instance, a woman whose mother or sister has had breast cancer would fall into a high–risk category, requiring annual mammograms as early as age 35. Yet a woman with no family history of breast cancer would fall in a low–risk group, and could postpone her first mammography until she's well over 40. As Dr. Savard explains, "Today we evaluate patients by looking at their family history, their lifestyle—do they smoke or drink?—various genetic and environmental factors, even their emotional makeup. Then we decide how often to see them and what tests they need. For somebody who has no risks and no symptoms, there are just a few basic areas that need occasional checking. Beyond that, risk factors should be used to determine precisely what needs periodic monitoring."

The value of seeing a family doctor once a year for a preset battery of tests first came into question over a decade ago with a landmark report issued for the Canadian National Health Service. Another study in London compared 3,292 patients who'd had regular health checkups with 3,132 who didn't; the results showed no appreciable differences in the health of one group as compared to the other. But the strongest argument against routine physicals arose from an exhaustive research project undertaken from 1984 to 1989 by the U.S. Preventive Services Task Force. After collating and reviewing some 2,400 worldwide studies of the screening and monitoring tests commonly used by doctors— things like X–rays, blood work, EKGs—it concluded that a vast majority are a waste of time and money. As simply stated in the *Annals of Internal Medicine*: For the nonpregnant adult without any symptoms of illness, no evidence supports the need for a complete physical examination as it's usually defined.

The task force found a surprising number of medical staples to be ineffective—or even useless. Into the don't–bother basket went such customary procedures as taking the temperature and pulse and breathing rates, chest X–rays, and resting EKGs for patients without any signs of heart disease. The 300–page report contained a long list of diseases and conditions that could be eliminated from routine screening unless indicated. By contrast, there was a rather short list of mandatory age– and gender–related evaluations suggested for healthy adults in the average– or low–risk categories. Here are the specific recommendations. Upon reaching the ripe age of 20, all men and women should:

- Visit the dentist annually;
- Have their blood pressure taken every two years, because that's the only way to discover the presence of hypertension;
- Have their weight checked every four years, because obesity is so clearly linked to a number of diseases.

Those guidelines remain constant throughout life. In addition, it's a wise idea to get a onetime full–body examination for moles that might develop into melanoma, the deadliest of skin cancers. Anyone found at risk should thereafter be checked annually.

Beyond this general list, there is a target list. When men hit age 60, they should follow the above guidelines and add an annual vision and hearing exam. Also, men this age ought to be probed for the possibility of an aneurism. The rupturing of aortic aneurisms—the ballooning of a weak blood vessel, similar to a bubble in a tire—accounts for 1.3 percent of all deaths among men over 65 in England. Early detection and surgery greatly reduce the risk.

At around 50, men should ask their doctors about having a new blood test for diagnosing prostate cancer. PSA (prostate specific antigen) appears to be a valuable, highly sensitive screening tool, but it does have a high rate of false positives, and is still too new to be universally recommended.

The list for women contains certain additions based on reproductive cancer screenings. From ages 20 to 39, females need exactly the same tests as males, but they also require Pap smears every one to three years. The death rate from cervical cancer has dropped 70 percent since this test was introduced in 1943. The Pap smear also picks up viral infections, so many doctors advise women with multiple sex partners to consider having one done annually. Women with a family history of ovarian cancer should discuss with their doctors a screening called Ca 125. This is the test Gilda Radner did not have; it might have saved her life.

For the decades between 40 and 60, women should stick to the teeth, weight, blood pressure and Pap test regimen, while adding, after age 50, a breast examination by a doctor that includes a mammography. From age 60 on, women require the same screenings as their male counterparts, and should continue to have mammograms annually and Pap tests every three years.

That's it. As far as the task force is concerned, if you're healthy, these few screenings are the only ones you need until something goes awry and the doctor orders further tests to make a diagnosis. The task force findings received tremendous attention in the medical community, most of it positive. Professionals bought 30,000 copies of the report, and a number of medical schools adopted it as a textbook in preventive medicine. As might be expected with such a revolutionary report, there was also a critical faction, and it was loud and angry. "We were attacked for taking a minimalist approach, for relying too much on data and not enough on human needs," says task force chairman Dr. Lawrence. "A number of sacred cows fell by the wayside, and those that worship the cows were most upset."

Both the American Cancer Society and the Heart Association protested when the task force dropped several procedures they'd heartily endorsed. Take, for example, breast self–examination and mammograpy for women under 50. The report did not support breast self-examination. While it is perfectly useful as an adjunct to a physician's visit, studies show that alone, it can't replace a clinical examination. And regarding the controversial question of whether to begin annual mammographies before age 50 for low-risk women, Dr. Lawrence says, "The data just don't support it earlier. The incidence of breast cancer in women is 20 per 100,000 at age 30, but it rises to 180 per 100,000 at age 50, and the curve keeps climbing."

Most of the physicians we interviewed questioned the wisdom of the task force's elimination of biennial fecal occult blood tests as a preventive colon cancer screening. You might want to do this test at home with a kit purchased from the drugstore, but be advised: Certain foods or vitamins will give a false-positive or false-negative result. Men and women whose close relatives have had colon cancer might want to schedule a colonoscopy between the ages of 40 and 50. If abnormalities are found, periodic screenings should follow. Finally, the doctors I talked to favored at least one cholesterol test by age 20, as a baseline. If the total falls around the normal level of 180, it need not be checked again until age 40, and only every five years or so thereafter.

Dr. Catalin Roth includes certain inoculations as part of her recommendations for routine health care: a tetanus booster every ten years after age 20, a flu and pneumonia vaccine after 65, and a revaccination for rubeola (measles) for anyone born after 1956. (The vaccine that was first introduced in 1957 and administered until 1965 doesn't give complete protection.) Dr. Roth, an advocate of preventive medicine, sums up the attitude among enlightened doctors toward the old-fashioned routine checkup: "I think if an individual has had a blood pressure reading, a cholesterol check, and a good family history to assess risks, and everything is normal, that person does not need a complete physical with lab tests every year. Those executive physicals are unnecessary. It is useful for everybody to check in occasionally with a doctor who knows them, and a woman should see a gynecologist annually, who can manage the rest of her general health care."

While you're bidding goodbye to your yearly going-over, you might as well give up another cherished medical myth. A Denver physician, Dr. Sylvia Oboler, did a study concluding that hardly any significant information is uncovered by a doctor's probing touch. Of all the hands-on maneuvers doctors perform, the only one of any real value in healthy people under 60 is feeling for breast lumps in women. "Poking and prodding make people feel good, because it's what they expect from a doctor," says Charles Inlander, president of the People's Medical Society. "But today we can get far more accurate results from sophisticated technology than from a doctor's hands. That's why the concept of the old-fashioned physical is like using a prop-driven plane in the era of the jet."

Indeed, patients would benefit if doctors cut down on poking and prodding and increased their talking and listening. The task force strongly urged family doctors to spend less of their average 12-minute visits with patients on tests and pulse-taking and more on counseling, particularly in those areas where behavioral changes can really modify risks. These include discussions about diet, aerobic exercise, tobacco and drugs, using seat belts, practicing safe sex and buying smoke detectors. Rather than taking chest X–rays, doctors should be advising patients to stop smoking.

Critics of the task force's strong pro–counseling position complained that the government wasted its money in studying preventive health measures, only to conclude that doctors ought to spend more time advising patients about diet and wearing seat belts. Dr. Lawrence's retort: "If we did more of that, we'd have a healthier nation and wouldn't need to do all this screening in the first place." Dr. Lawrence has a fantasy that one day everybody will have access to guidelines on who really needs to be examined, and for what. Then patients can say to their doctors, "Wait a minute. According to the task force, I don't need to have this test. Why are you doing it?" In the meantime, you can use this article to check up on yourself.

*If you need help:* The People's Medical Society, in Allentown, publishes a newsletter which frequently reports on medical testing. To request copies, call 770–1670. For clear, concise consumer information on what you'll experience from a wide range of common tests, check out Dr. Philip Shtasel's *Medical Tests and Diagnostic Procedures: A Patient's Guide to Just What The Doctor Ordered* (Harper & Row, 1990).

## Do You Have Special Needs for Special People?

**Newborn Nurses** *is the premier nurse-owned pediatric home care company serving the Delaware Valley. We are dedicated to providing quality family centered care through specially designed programs.* **Newborn** *can provide all your pediatric needs.*

**Pediatric Respiratory Program**
Ventilators
Apnea Monitors
Pulmonary Nurses
Respiratory Therapy Services

**Pediatric Rehabilitation Program**
Physical Therapy Services
Rehabilitation Nurses
Wheelchairs and adaptive equipment

**Pediatric Feeding Program**
Formulas
Pumps
Supplies
GI Nursing

**Pediatric Infusion Program**
Chemotherapy
Antibiotic Therapy
TPN
Blood Product Administration
IV Nurses

**Newborn Nurses**
1-800-253-9111—PA
1-609-235-7617—NJ
Serving the Delaware Vly
24 Hours a Day

# THE EXECUTIVE HEALTH & WELLNESS CENTER
## HAHNEMANN UNIVERSITY

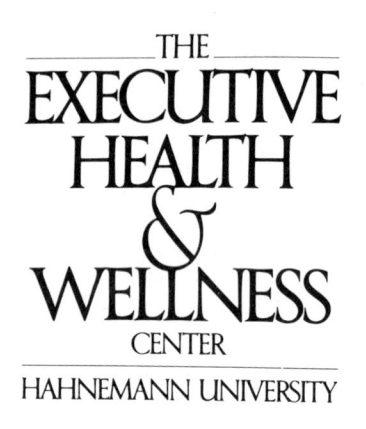

## A Healthy Concern

It's what we have for you at the Executive Health & Wellness Center of Hahnemann University Hospital. The Executive Health & Wellness Center is a multi-specialty health-care practice created to keep pace with the unique needs of busy men and women.

At one convenient Center City location you'll receive on-going care with full-service testing (including cardiac stress testing, gastrointestinal exams, allergy and asthma diagnosis and treatment, and, for women, PAP smears and mammograms) all conducted by expert Hahnemann faculty members. We offer a high level of personal service, minimal waiting times and active follow-up.

So call the Executive Health & Wellness Center today at **215-299-3800** or stop by at 2 Logan Square, that's 18th Street between Arch and Cherry Streets in Philadelphia, and let us show you our healthy concern for your good health.

### Discover **Hahnemann** Healing

# 12

# The Dark Side of the Sun

*Summer can leave you with more than a tan.*

♥ In a totally unscientific experiment, I asked 15 people what they thought was the most commonly occuring cancer. Only two answered correctly: skin cancer. In 1992, according to the American Cancer Society, an estimated 600,000 Americans will be diagnosed as having some form of skin cancer. This is more than three times the incidence of lung cancer. One of those I questioned said he hadn't even considered skin cancer as a response: "I thought you were talking about serious cancer, the kind that kills you." Wrong again. The proportion of lung cancer mortality is much, much higher—91 percent—but skin cancer claims lives, too. This year it will cause 7,800 deaths, most but not all from one serious type known as malignant melanoma. The real tragedy is that nearly all these skin cancer deaths can be prevented.

The skin is the body's largest and least protected organ, which makes it particularly vulnerable to the primary cause of most skin cancers—the ultraviolet rays of the sun. Heredity plays a lesser role, as do some environmental factors. Pennsylvania Hospital dermatologist Dr. Paul Gross recalls a patient whose job involved washing fruit baskets. The fruit had been sprayed with a potent insecticide; over the years the man developed some 150 small and totally curable job–related skin cancers.

Cases like his are in the minority, though, and for most of us, sunlight is the major culprit. Unless you spend your entire existence indoors covered with a shroud, you have some chance of getting skin cancer. It can take years of exposure to develop, and hours baking in the sun as a teenager can be responsible for a cancer 20 years later. Don't lull yourself into thinking you're no longer at risk just because in the last few years you've been heeding the warnings and using sunscreens.

Early in this century, skin cancer was a disease of the poor, outdoor laborer. Back then, pale skin was a status symbol, because it showed you had easier ways of earning a giving than digging ditches or picking fruit. Today it's just the reverse; a sun–splashed body says you can afford the leisure of lolling on the beach or tennis court. That coveted tan is actually a brownish pigment called melanin, which acts as a protective buffer against ultraviolet rays. Blacks already have a heavy coat of melanin, and consequently a low incidence of skin cancer. Among whites, the most susceptible are those who freckle easily. While freckles in themselves are innocent, they are produced as a response to sun damage, and are a warning sign of sun–sensitive skin.

For the one American in seven who'll be told this year that he or she has skin cancer, the diagnosis of basal cell carcinoma will be cause for relief. Named for the cells in the lower level of the epidermis, where it develops, basal cell is completely curable in the initial stages. That is why it has such a benign reputation. Different from most cancers because it almost never spreads to other organs, it's classified as a cancer mainly because if not treated, it will continue to grow uncontrollably and indefinitely. An untreated basal cell cancer will eventually bore deep into the body. People have been horribly disfigured by ignoring a tiny basal cell carcinoma near the nose or eye until it literally destroyed the entire adjacent organ.

"There's absolutely no reason for this to happen," says Gross, "yet fear and denial traumatize people. I saw a man with a basal cell carcinoma on his eyelid. Every time I wanted to remove it, he insisted it was getting better. Eventually he lost the eye and half his face." If you spot a small, fleshy translucent bump—especially on your head, neck or hands—and it hasn't disappeared after a month, have it checked.

The second most common skin cancer, squamous cell carcinoma, is more dangerous, because it can spread into the lymph system. It typically appears on the ears or face as a scaly, sometimes ulcerated patch that may bleed spontaneously. Together, basal and squamous cell carcinomas will cause about 2,000 deaths this year, even though they are 95 percent curable. The conventional methods for destroying these cancers are scraping them off and burning the base with an electric needle (electrodesiccation); removing them surgically by cutting out a wedge of skin; or freezing the cells by injecting or spraying them with liquid nitrogen (cryosurgery). Radiation treatments and topical chemotherapy are other alternatives. The methods are equally effective; the choice depends on the location of the cancer and the kind of scar the patient prefers. Surgery leaves a fine line; burning or scraping produces a whitish mark.

With *all* the standard techniques, the doctor must remove as much as a quarter–inch of normal surrounding tissue to ensure that the entire cancer has been eliminated. In some circumstances it isn't possible to take a little extra to cover the margin of error, and a more exacting procedure, that is performed in Philadelphia by only a handful of doctors, may be preferred. Mohs' surgery, named for the surgeon who devised it, takes away what's absolutely necessary and no more. The tumor is removed in two to four stages, and each piece of tissue is examined microscopically until it's certain the root has been reached.

University of Pennsylvania dermatologist Dr. Leonard Dzubow, who underwent special training and a two-year fellowship to learn the Mohs' technique, suggests there are four situations when Mohs' should be considered: when the lesion is near the eye or on the nose and it is important to keep the wound and scar as small as possible; when the lesion is in a crease, where it is difficult to tell how far or deep it has grown; when the cancer has been treated unsuccessfully and what remains is jumbled in scar tissue; and when it's simply too hard to tell the borders of the tumor with the naked eye. While the cosmetic results and cure rate are excellent, the cost of Mohs' surgery is about $950, at least double that of the conventional approaches.

The third category of skin cancer is the smallest, the most virulent, and the most rapidly escalating. In 1992, malignant melanoma will strike 32,000 people, and kill 6,700. By the year 2000, the incidence will jump from the present 1 in 135 to 1 in 90, making it the third most common cancer in America. Despite these grim statistics, there is reason for optimism. While the number of cases has been increasing, due to greater public awareness, Dr. Edward Bondi, an associate professor of dermatology at the University of Pennsylvania, says, "We're curing 80 percent of melanoma today, and without any new research findings we could increase that to 95 percent with more early detection." In Australia, the relentless sun beating on a fair-skinned population causes more skin cancer than anywhere in the world. Yet the death rate has dropped dramatically as a result of a vigorous ad campaign that depicts an oddly mottled leopard asking, "Have you checked your spots lately?"

In America, the classic melanoma patient is an affluent, well-educated professional who works indoors and overdoses on sun when the weather gets nice. Most are diagnosed before the age of 50 (in contrast to basal and squamous cell patients, who tend to be older), and there is evidence that a bad case of youthful blistering sunburn is a precursor. While the sun is undoubtedly one factor, there are other, unidentified causes of melanoma, which can occur on places the sun rarely reaches, such as the back, breasts, buttocks and between the toes. More than any other type of skin cancer, melanoma seems closely tied to family history, especially when the family shares in the occurrence of abnormal moles in what is referred to as dysplastic mole syndrome.

Moles are not in themselves a sign of melanoma. The average adult has at least 20, usually formed before puberty. The moles to worry about are ones that suddenly look different from before, or moles that appeared in adolescence and over the years increased in size. Moles fitting that description, as well as any dark spots that appear suddenly and don't go away, could possibly be early signs of melanoma. See your dermatologist quickly. Dr. Bondi sadly recalls patients who believed they had "black mole cancer" and couldn't be treated, which became a self-fulfilling prophecy only because they waited too long in seeking medical treatment.

Today there is hope for those melanoma patients whose disease has spread beyond treatment by operation. Dr. Wallace Clark and his colleagues at the Pigmented Lesion Group of the University of Pennsylvania have published the results of a decade of research in mathematically predicting the survival chances of individuals with advanced melanoma. By feeding into a computer certain data—things like the site and thickness of the tumor, and the patient's sex and immune response—and matching them with the characteristics of certain melanoma patients, doctors are able to tell fairly accurately who will live and who will die, and use the information as a guide to the most effective treatments for keeping alive those sufferers who are at risk.

A number of these experimental treatments are already being done in clinical trials at some area hospitals. In the realm of chemotherapy, at Thomas Jefferson University Hospital, Dr. Michael Mastrangelo, director of medical oncology, is working with a promising regimen that combines four drugs given at once rather than serially, while at Presbyterian Medical Center, Dr. Donna Glover uses high doses of platinum. Some oncologists are even more excited about advances in immunotherapy. Penn's Dr. DuPont Guerry has been trying monoclonal antibodies, the so–called "magic bullets" for cancer treatment. There is some clinical evidence that they either kill the cancer or stimulate the immune system to fight it off.

Unquestionably, it makes most sense to catch melanoma when it can be cured. Too often melanoma is ignored because it doesn't hurt and doesn't cause any symptoms. It just looks funny. But that's why it's so easy to spot. Do yourself a favor and begin a simple monthly check that could save your life. Stand naked in front of a mirror, and take three minutes to examine your body front to back and from head to toe, scanning for growths that exhibit the "ABCDs" of melanoma: asymmetry (one half doesn't match the other); border irregularity (the edges are notched, ragged or uneven); color (the pigment looks mottled, with varying shades of brown and black and even dashes of red, white or blue); and diameter (greater than the size of a pencil eraser, or bigger than it was in the previous month's self–examination). Three minutes a month—it's worth it.

In addition to self–examination, every doctor we interviewed urged the regular use of sunscreens. Dr. Frederick Urbach, of Temple Medical Practices in Fort Washington, advises applying a sunscreen with a 6 or 8 SPF every day from March to October on the face, neck, ears and hands—because just walking to work or playing tennis exposes you to damaging ultraviolet rays. At the beach, avoid the sun between 11 a.m. and 3 p.m., and smear on at least a 15 SPF sunscreen in the off–hours as well, remembering to reapply it when you sweat or swim. Dermatologist Paul Gross wishes people were as concerned with their health as with their appearance: "I have more luck getting people to stay out of the sun for fear they'll get wrinkled than I do for fear they'll get cancer. Then, 20 years later, they're sorry they didn't listen."

*If you need help:* Any questions about suspicious spots should be answered by a dermatologist who's been trained to recognize even the earliest skin cancers. However, if you have any family history of melanoma, it might be wise to visit a specialized pigmented lesion clinic. Doctors there are highly experienced in screening for the disease and pinpointing those at highest risk. They also have access to the most advanced treatments. In Philadelphia there are clinics at Thomas Jefferson University Hospital, 955–4947, and the Hospital of the University of Pennsylvania, 662–6926. Basal or squamous cell carcinomas can be removed by either a dermatologist or a plastic surgeon; the former tends to be less costly. If you are interested in Mohs' surgery, those trained to perform it locally include Dr. Leonard Dzubow, 662–6534; Dr. Anthony Benedetto, 546–3666; Dr. Steven Greenbaum, 955–4947; and Dr. Wayne Marley, 639–7546. For general information, contact the Skin Cancer Foundation, 475 Park Avenue, New York, NY 10016.

## Comprehensive Radiation Oncology

To help patients fight their cancer with the full range of technology available today, **Penn's Department of Radiation Oncology** provides a broad range of services. Our specialists are recognized internationally for their advances in cancer care, research, and education.

Radiation Oncology services include:

- **Comprehensive radiation programs** for every type of cancer.
- **New methods of radiation** and **investigative drugs**, many not available elsewhere.
- **State of the art imaging** techniques, using CAT and MRI scans.
- **Stereotactic Radiosurgery** - for targeted radiation delivery to the brain.
- **Conformal Radiation Therapy** - delivery of high doses of radiation to the tumor site, while sparing normal tissue.

For information or referral, call 215-662-2428 or 1-800-777-8176.

**UNIVERSITY OF PENNSYLVANIA MEDICAL CENTER**
University of Pennsylvania School of Medicine
Hospital of the University of Pennsylvania
Department of Radiation Oncology

University of Pennsylvania
CANCER CENTER

# A Heritage of Healing

Our heritage began 225 years ago, when we founded the nation's first school of medicine. Today, our drive to expand the frontiers of medicine continues as we pursue the highest standards in education, research and patient care.

Our more than 800 physicians are leading experts in more than 50 medical specialties and direct more than 200 specialty programs.

These specialists see patients at the Hospital of the University of Pennsylvania, which offers the most advanced technologic and diagnostic resources available today. Our faculty members are recognized as the Delaware Valley's premier physicians for many specialties.

Many of our physicians in selected specialties also see patients at Penn Medicine at King of Prussia.

For information about our services or to schedule an appointment in Philadelphia or King of Prussia, please call our referral counselors at:

## 215-662-PENN (7366)

**UNIVERSITY OF PENNSYLVANIA MEDICAL CENTER**

University of Pennsylvania School of Medicine
Hospital of the University of Pennsylvania

# 13
# Why Fat Makes You Fat

*And why there is only one real way to get thin.*

♥ If you are a devotee of diet books, you might just as well read nursery rhymes. The latest research on the diet front suggests that the secret to staying thin comes from none other than Jack Sprat—the skinny little man who ate no fat. The belief that weight control is strictly a matter of cutting calories has been declared obsolete, and it now appears that all calories are not alike. Calories derived from fatty foods are actually *more* fattening.

Conventional dietary wisdom counts calories on the assumption that 100 calories of apple are the same as 100 calories of cheese, even though fat is denser and on a per–weight basis has a higher caloric content. (One gram of fat has nine calories, while one gram of protein or carbohydrate has only four.) New findings suggest that the numbers game is only part of the whole picture. The equally important component is the way we metabolize those calories. It's been found that when we eat protein and carbohydrates, the body works mightily to burn them up, but it puts forth very little effort converting fat into energy. As a result, the amount of fat in our diet becomes as critical to weight loss as the number of calories we eat in a day.

Each of us uses a given number of calories daily just to keep our body machine running and our weight in neutral. Caloric requirements vary from individual to individual, and are based on things like height, weight, activity and genes. (The rule of thumb for determining your 24–hour base caloric need is as follows: body weight multiplied by 12 for sedentary women, by 14 for sedentary men, by 15 for moderately active women, by 17 for moderately active men, by 18 for active women, and by 20 for active men.) Weight gain used to be considered a function of taking in more calories than the body required for daily maintenance.

But now that simple equation—too many calories equals too many pounds—no longer computes.

For example, the Chinese eat 20 percent more calories per unit of body weight than Americans, but they have practically no obesity. That's because they live on a plant–based diet, heavy in vegetables and grains but light on fat—only 15 percent. Compare that to the average American diet—40 percent fat, and loaded with dairy and oils. To determine the role of fatty foods in diet control, the Lipid Nutrition Laboratory in Washington, D.C., did a study in which 28 women of average weight cut the fat intake of their diets from 40 percent to 20 percent, without lowering the number of calories they took in daily. After nine months, they lost an average of 1 percent of their body fat. Another study at Stanford examining the daily dietary patterns of obese men found the heftiest of the lot ate the fattiest foods, but didn't necessarily down the most calories. Even laboratory rats put on low–fat diets gain less weight than rats on an equal–calorie high–fat diet.

The human body is amazingly efficient at changing the fat from food directly into body fat. When you slather 100 calories of butter on a baked potato, the body expends a mere three calories of energy to metabolize the butter, leaving 97 calories of fat for that storage bin in your thighs. On the other hand, it takes 23 calories to metabolize 100 calories of a carbohydrate. What's worse, once the body is into a low–work fat mode, it tends to stay there. Fat–laden diets make the body more sluggish, while the extra effort required to convert carbohydrates raises the overall metabolic rate. In a 24–hour period of gorging on pasta and veggies, your metabolism will be more active than if you overload on cheese snacks and fried chicken.

There's even more good news about carbohydrates. The energy they supply almost never turns into body fat. First of all, carbohydrates don't go from the lips to the hips. Small quantities settle in the muscles and the liver in the form of glycogen, a sugar the body uses as a primary energy source. Secondly, while the body can sock away huge amounts of fat, its capacity for storing glycogen is quite limited.

The scientific term for the energy expended converting food into energy is *thermogenesis*, and as you might have expected, this scientific principle has already been translated into a new diet fad. The truth is that trimming the amount of fat in your diet can make a difference, but that difference depends entirely on how much fat you're consuming these days. Don't expect miracles unless you're up there in the 30–to–40–percent bracket.

There are several simple tricks to reducing dietary fat. Start reading labels to become familiar with the fat content in packaged foods. Ingredients are listed in descending order of their quantity, so be wary. For example, frozen diet dinners are highly varied in fat content. A Weight Watchers Chicken à la King meal contains 29 percent fat, while an Armour Dinner Classics Lite Chicken Breast Marsala has only 18 percent fat. Grains are tricky, too, because some breakfast cereals are made with coconut and palm oil: Shredded Wheat is 10 percent fat, but

Grape Nuts has no fat at all. The traditional diet snack cracker can also be fat–saturated. If you rub a cracker with a napkin and there's a grease ring, it's got too much fat. The same goes for packaged mircrowave popcorn. Made in an air popper, corn is a great low–fat snack. Popped in the packet, it may be as much as 50 percent fat. And don't be taken in by milk that's 1 or 2 percent fat. Milk has just 4 percent fat to begin with, so only skim milk is truly fat–free.

If all this is too bothersome, you can thank modern science for partially solving the fat problem with "fake fats." Several large food companies market substitutes for cooking oils and spreads (products like Simplesse and Olestra) that have the flavor of fat but don't get converted *into* fat.

What attracts us to fat is not just the taste—fat is also filling. Dr. Steven Peikin, head of the division of gastroenterology and liver diseases at Cooper Hospital University Medical Center in Camden, explains in his book, *The Feel Full Diet*, that fat releases a hormone initiating a chain reaction that ends with the brain getting the message that you've eaten enough. Studies show fat craving is highest when people are most hungry and lowest after they've eaten. It's no accident that sweets (the sugary carbohydrates) come at the end of the meal, rather than the beginning. If you want to lower your appetite and the amount you eat at mealtime, Peikin recommends a high–satiety snack of a bowl of hot soup or a tablespoon of peanut butter on a celery stick 20 minutes before sitting down at the table. Your brain will think you're full, and you'll put less on your plate.

The study of fat has produced some bad news for chronic dieters: Dieting itself may be fattening. The yo–yo syndrome gaining/losing/gaining/losing may ultimately *add* to your fat content. Weight loss is a combination loss of both fat and muscle. Say you lose 20 pounds on a diet; 15 of them will be fat, and five muscle. But when you regain those 20 pounds, 17 will be fat, and only three muscle. You will weigh the same as before, but your body composition will have more fat. Not only is fat harder to take off than muscle, but as mentioned earlier, the higher the ratio of fat to muscle, the lower your metabolic rate, and the less you can eat just to keep your weight the same. In addition, the new fat may settle in a different place and cause another set of problems. Studies done by the Obesity Research Group at Penn indicate that upper–body fat puts people at a higher risk for heart attack and diabetes than lower–body fat. A potbelly is a greater health hazard than thunder thighs.

The best way to dissolve body fat is through exercise. But just as all calories are not alike, neither are all exercises. Stop–and–start exercises that require spurts of energy, like racket sports, calisthenics and weight–lifting, burn more of the fuel stored in muscles than in fat cells. Continuous aerobic activities, like walking and jogging, use more of the energy deposited in the fat bank. Exercise also has a positive effect on boosting the body's metabolic rate—the dieter's greatest ally. Stanford University conducted a study in which 32 sedentary middle–aged men embarked on a yearlong running program without going on a low–cal diet. The more they ran, the more fat they lost—even when they increased their calorie intake.

Of course, there are some people who lose weight and exercise regularly, but are still stuck with flabby tummies, saddlebags and saggy bottoms. For them, the answer to eliminating these pockets of genetically or hormonally derived fat may be liposuction. Except in cases of massive weight gains of 80 pounds or more, it appears that our total number of fat cells is fixed by adolescence. A fat cell has the expandability of a balloon; gaining or losing weight merely increases or decreases the size. Only liposuction can permanently reduce the number. Dr. Leonard Dzubow, associate professor of dermatology at HUP, says, "Liposuction works best on people who are already slender but can't get rid of bulges. It's a fallacy that liposuction is an alternative to diet. It should not be used for weight reduction. It's a procedure to change and reshape the contour of the body by removing the fat that lies right under the skin."

When first popularized in the late '70s, liposuction developed a reputation for being a dangerous procedure. Removing large of amounts of fat from several different body parts under general anesthesia sometimes resulted in serious complications, from shock to infection, when too much body fluid was sucked out along with the fat. Today, many

---

It's your choice to get help to break through the cycle that's destroying your life. And it's your choice to select the program that is best for you.

The Renfrew Center is here to help you focus on your day-to-day symptoms and the underlying reasons you have your eating disorder. Our staff has years of experience working exclusively with women who have anorexia, bulimia or who compulsively overeat.

At our residential centers we have helped thousands of women who have not had success elsewhere. You deserve to get help – and you deserve the best help. Choose both. Call today and ask for our free brochure.

Most Insurance Accepted

THE RENFREW CENTER

*The country's first residential facilities for the treatment of women with eating disorders.*

Philadelphia, PA • Coconut Creek, FL
**1-800-RENFREW**

pm

*If you have an* **EATING DISORDER** *you have a choice.*

Anorexia. Bulimia. Compulsive Overeating.
**Call Renfrew.**

doctors, like Dzubow, use a much more conservative approach, working under local anesthesia with a narrow instrument that draws out small amounts of fat from only one area at a time. "Done this way, liposuction is really a very safe procedure," he says, "even less risky than dermabrasion, which is far more common."

By the next century—hey, it's only a few years away, gang—we may no longer have to worry about fat at all. Some drug laboratories are conducting experiments with pills that instigate thermogenesis and actually trigger the body to burn fat faster. Unlike the diet pills of yore, which speeded up just about every body process to a dangerous level, these new thermogenic agents seem to increase metabolism with minimal side effects. If the trial studies pan out, we can look forward to a time when it will be possible to have an ice-cream sundae every night—and go to sleep happy, instead of guilt–ridden.

*For further reading*: *The T–Factor Diet*, by Martin Katahn, Ph.D. (Norton), clearly spells out the principles of thermogenesis and has a listing of the fat content of hundreds of foods. An excellent guide to eating healthy amd keeping slim is *The California Nutrition Book*, by Paul Saltman, Joel Gurin and Ira Mothner (Little, Brown). *The Feel-Full Diet* by Dr. Steven Peikin (Atheneum) is available by special order.

# We help heart patients beat the odds.

The Episcopal Heart Institute is waging war. We're battling cardiovascular disease with state-of-the-art techniques involving Eximer lasers, angioplasty, cardiothoracic surgery and more. And we're doing our absolute best to win.

Learn more about the amazing advances in cardiac care now taking place at The Episcopal Heart Institute. Call us at (215) 427-7247 to find out how we can help you beat the odds of heart disease.

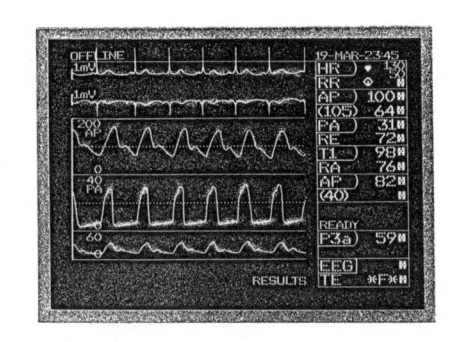

**EPISCOPAL HOSPITAL**
100 East Lehigh Avenue • Philadelphia, PA

# Only one hospital can offer this combination of experience, technology and facilities for women's health...
## The Graduate Hospital.

- An internationally renowned staff of gynecologists with one of the most advanced gynecologic cancer treatment and research programs in the region.

- A team of cervical disease specialists headed by the immediate past president of the American Society of Colposcopy and Cervical Pathology and the only cervical cancer screening program in Philadelphia utilizing both cervicography and the Pap smear.

- The gynecologist who performed the first laparoscopic hysterectomy in the United States in 1988.

- The only board-certified female urologist in the tri-state area and one of only 50 in the United States.

- One of the most comprehensive bladder disorder programs in the Delaware Valley with expert, progressive treatment for urinary incontinence and interstitial cystitis.

- A nationally-known eating disorders program offering residential, day treatment, outpatient and inpatient components.

- A dedicated mammography program certified by the American College of Radiology and staffed by board-certified mammographers with over 40 years of combined experience.

- The only Fischer Mammotest™ System in the Delaware Valley for diagnosing breast disease, providing patients with a chance to avoid open biopsy surgery.

- Board-certified surgeons dedicated to the detection and management of breast disease using state-of-the-art procedures for breast preservation and reconstruction.

*The Graduate Hospital offers a wide range of services and expertise in women's health care that is unsurpassed in the Delaware Valley. And we make sure that sensitivity and understanding are a high priority. So when you're looking for a hospital that meets the special needs of women, **we're confident you'll choose Graduate.***

**Physician Referral Service**
**1-800-654-GRAD**

**THE GRADUATE HOSPITAL**
One Graduate Plaza  1800 Lombard Street  Philadelphia, PA 19146
Graduate Health System

# 14
# A Change of Thought on Change of Life

*For years, menopausal women worried about the risks of hormone therapy. Now they're talking about the benefits.*

♥ "Is it warm in here, or is it me?" asked one of the three women at the table, fanning herself furiously with the menu. Her companions, both successful career women closing in on their 50th birthdays, nodded sympathetically at the classic symptom of a hot flash.

"Aren't you taking hormones?" asked a second woman at the table.

"No. I've read too much about the risks of breast cancer, and I'm afraid," she replied. "I'm trying to tough it out, but I don't think I can last. I haven't had a full night's sleep in months. I wake up two or three times; my nightgown's soaked. And talk about moody! I'm up and down like a yo-yo."

"Well, I think you're nuts," her friend said. "I've been on estrogen for four years. It took a while to get the dosage adjusted, and I'm not thrilled with getting my period every month, but I must say, I feel terrific. It's kind of like slowing down the aging process." She grinned. "And that includes getting my sex drive back."

The third woman had been listening intently. "I need to be be convinced that hormones are safe," she said. "My sister gained weight when she started. She complains to me about feeling bloated half the month, and she gets headaches she never had before. Her doctor swears by hormones, but my doctor has some reservations. How do you know who to believe?"

To take hormones—or not to take them. That is the question plaguing millions of middle-aged women caught in the hormone conundrum. Having reached that transitional stage once quaintly labeled "change of life," women want assurance that it's safe to take manufactured replacement hormones to augment their bodies' declining production of estrogen and progesterone. What they're getting, however, is a very mixed message. One day the media hypes the risks of hormones; the next they tout the benefits. Studies seem to conflict with one another in their findings. Medical professionals are either enthusiastic or cautious. One group of hormone users raves about the results; another rails against the side effects. Instead of helping women make a decision, the abundance of information is just making them more confused.

When the available data are examined, the benefits of HRT (hormone replacement theory) far outnumber what most people call "the risks"—but what Dr. Marie Savard prefers more appropriately to call "the uncertainties." Two of these are significant. One is the issue of breast cancer, which has jumped from striking one in 22 women in 1977 to one in nine women in 1990. Estrogen has been established as a growth factor in breast tumors, *but not as a cause*. More about that later. The other cloudy area is the role of progesterone in HRT. Nearly all the data collected thus far come from women taking only estrogren. Except in cases of endometrial cancer, where progesterone clearly eliminates the problems caused by estrogen, any positive or negative effects of combined hormone therapy are yet to be firmly established. There are some studies coming from the University of Georgia which suggest that the addition of progesterone reduces the chance of cancer. If that finding is supported by other studies, it might shift the balance in present attitudes.

The term "menopause" technically refers to a woman's last menstrual period. The several years during which she cycles from erratic periods to none at all are called perimenopause; the decades after her periods cease are called postmenopause. Approximately one–third of all premenopausal women in America are surgically thrust into instant menopause—most by hysterectomies. The rest gradually begin the hormone descent somewhere in their mid–40s, when the ovaries start putting out less and less estrogen and progesterone. The uneven spiking of hormone levels causes the symptoms of perimenopause—the hot flashes, mood swings, irregular bleeding, night sweats and vaginal dryness that send women to their gynecologists shrieking for relief. At this point many doctors will commence HRT, based strictly on the woman's symptoms or on the results of a simple blood test that measures an increase in her follicle–stimulating hormone (FSH) level. The rise of that pituitary hormone signals the beginning of the end.

Today some 43 million American women are candidates for hormone replacement, an option that was not available to most of their mothers. In the narrow view of some HRT opponents, the mere fact that women now live far beyond menopause is no reason to mess with Mother Nature. Nora W. Coffey, director of HERS (Hysterectomy Educational Resources and Services), says," You can't improve on what nature gave you. The idea that women need hormone substitutes suggests we are somehow deficient and should have been born with an estrogen pump."

In-depth research into hormones dates back only to the 1940s. By the mid '60s, doctors were actively writing estrogen prescriptions at five times the dosages used today. The first sign of trouble came with the release of a major study in 1975 reporting a fourfold increase in endometrial cancer among women taking estrogen by itself. (Estrogen causes changes in the lining of the uterus, which can lead to cancer.) It has since been proven that adding progesterone to the hormone package causes a monthly sloughing of this lining and completely eliminates this danger. Nevertheless, the widely reported study planted a fear of hormones in women, and gave rise to persistent misunderstandings of the links between hormones and cancer.

"Endometrial cancer is the only cancer ever unequivocally validated—at a cellular level—to be related to *unopposed* estrogen," says Winnfred Cutler, Ph.D., president of the Athena Institute for Women's Wellness and author of *Love Cycles: The Science of Intimacy*. An advocate of combination hormone therapy, Dr. Cutler has analyzed 3,500 studies on women's health and hormones. She says, "Those who suggest hormones cause any other cancers are not in labs studying cells, where to date there has been no cause-and-effect established."

The whole area of hormone therapy research does a disservice to women. At present there is an appalling absence of solid, double-blind scientific studies comparing hormone takers with matched control groups. Which is why the National Women's Health Network remains cautiously critical of HRT. Yet it does support short-term use of hormones—up to three years for severe menopausal complaints.

What's not well understood by the general public is that the bulk of research data about hormones comes from epidemiological studies. These are statistical compilations—not standard clinical tests. The results measure only the rate at which a disease occurs in a particular group.

Within a data base of 36 epidemiological studies performed over the last decade examining the link between between HRT and breast cancer, 32 showed no effect, and four found a minimal increase in the risk. Recently the Centers for Disease Control lumped together a slew of major studies in a trendy new procedure called meta-analysis, and arrived at an overall 1.3 percent increase in breast cancer among women taking estrogen for 15 years or longer—but no increase in risk among five-year users.

What do these figures amount to? Not much more than a minor warning in the jargon of epidemiologists, and even less in the eyes of Dr. Lila E. Nachtigall, a well-respected New York gynecologist and researcher who has been working in the field of hormone replacement for 22 years. She says, "So long as the figures for estrogen and breast cancer hover at 0.8 to 1.3 percent, that's too low for the likelihood it's a carcinogen. For an obvious cancer link, the incidence would be three, four or five times greater, like it was with endometrial cancer."

While nobody has proof that hormones trigger cancer, it has been found that estrogen does speed up the growth of some breast tumors.

This is the reason hormones are generally not prescribed for women with family histories of breast cancer. Among the important questions yet to be answered: Does estrogen precipitate the tumors, or does it only accelerate the growth of certain already present lesions? What is the effect of progesterone? And if hormones make small cancers grow to the point where they can be detected and treated, is that all bad?

For a cancer specialist like Presbyterian Hospital's Dr. Donna Glover, the "growth factor" alone is enough to give pause. "I wouldn't tell all women not to take hormones," she says. "I'd tell them to weigh the risks, since estrogen is known to be a growth accelerator with ovarian, endometrial and breast cancer." She advises women on HRT to be extremely conscientious about monthly breast self–examination, and to have yearly mammograms. She says, "If you discover a breast lump and it doesn't disappear after your period, get a mammogram. Then get an excisional biopsy that cuts out a piece of the lump for the pathologist to examine. Conversely, if the mammogram suggests the lump is benign, don't go home and forget about it. Verify the diagnosis with either an ultrasound or a needle aspiration, to see if the lump is a cyst, or a solid mass that should be removed."

At this point, the worry about hormones and breast cancer stems more from what we don't know than from what we do. For now, bear in mind that the cancer risks, on paper, are relatively small. That certainly doesn't mean hormone replacement is for everybody. In addition to a personal or family history of breast cancer, there are other contraindications. Dr. Bernard Eskin, professor of obstetrics and gynecology in reproductive endocrinology at the Medical College of Pennsylvania, would not give hormones to anyone with liver disease, a history of phlebitis or thrombosis, cardiac disease of unknown origin, or uterine bleeding problems. A sliding scale of personal risk factors, including fibrocystic disease or cancer in a sibling or parent, should be discussed with your doctor.

In the view of many doctors, the compelling case for the important health benefits of HRT far outweighs the hue and cry against it. Dr. Mona Shangold, director of the Sports Gynecology and Women's Life Cycle Center at Hahnemann University Hospital, is often asked by her patients if it's safe to take hormones. "I tell them it's safer to take them than not to take them," she says. At least 25 studies, including a recent look at 48,000 nurses over a ten–year period, have shown that women who take estrogen can expect a 50 percent reduction in heart disease, which kills more than twice as many women as all forms of cancer combined. Another massive problem for older women is osteoporosis, which 40 percent of them develop; many of them never recover from falls or fractures. Although calcium and exercise can reduce the peak bone loss that accompanies menopause, neither is as effective as estrogen. (You can get a bone density test that will determine if you're at risk for fractures.) If you decide against taking hormones for heart disease or osteoporosis, be sure to discuss other options with your doctor.

In addition to its protection against heart disease and osteoporosis,

HRT combats the psychological and intellectual problems of menopause. The mid–life woman can be a walking complaint department. Where has her sex drive gone? Why is she so irritable and moody? What the hell is wrong with her memory? All these changes are related to estrogen, which regulates sexual desire, enhances mood, and even affects brain chemistry. For many women, HRT restores lost balance and provides a sense of well–being associated with youth and vigor.

But for others, taking hormones can create its own set of problems: breast tenderness, nausea, bloating, fluid retention, headaches. Often these can be eradicated by changing pills, dosage or regimens. Most doctors recommend taking a combination of estrogen and progestin, because that mimics the natural production of the menstrual cycle. Don't be alarmed if your doctor has to juggle the formula for several months before finding what works for you. Because our bodies produce highly individual levels of hormone, there is no single right way to take the replacements. Some women never adjust to the pills, and quit. Others put up with several months of mild weight gain and then stay on hormones without trouble for years.

Of the myriad estrogen preparations on the market, the three most popular oral pills in the United States are Premarin (.625 mg. dose), Ogen and Estrace. Some women prefer the estrogen patch, which provides continuous–release estrogen through the skin. As yet, it has no proven benefits over the oral dose, and some women get an allergic rash from it. Provera is the most commonly used progestin. There is no proper time to start hormones—let your symptoms be your guide—and no fixed time to stop. Dr. Shangold says, "There is no evidence at present that taking them forever is harmful." Those in the more cautious school would set a five–year limit.

The hormone debate is likely to rage for years to come. Although the NIH is about to embark on a much–needed controlled study, the results are years away. Obviously, no drug is risk–free. Even aspirin can be dangerous. But until the gray areas of HRT are cleared up, women may have to rely on something besides research data to decide whether HRT is right for them. "Women know how they feel with hormones and without them," declares Dr. Marie Savard. "It's a quality–of–life issue, and nobody talks enough about that."

*If you need help:* For a fine layman's approach to this problem, we suggest the revised and expanded new edition of *Menopause: A Guide for Women and the Men Who Love Them*, by Dr. Celso Ramon–Garcia and Winnifred Berg Cutler, Ph.D. (Norton). The concerns about HRT are well explored in the paperback *Women's Health Alert*, by Dr. Sidney Wolfe and the watchdog group Public Citizen Health Research Council (Addison–Wesley).

The Athena Institute for Women's Wellness holds periodic workshops on women's health issues; for information, call 642–3073. The Sports Gynecology and Women's Life Cycle Center at Hahnemann University Hospital can be reached at 246–5190.

## THE LANKENAU HOSPITAL

Cardiology
Cardio-Thoracic Surgery
Gynecologic Oncology
Gynecologic Surgery
High-Risk Pregnancy
Infectious Diseases
Internal Medicine
Neonatology

Nephrology
Obstetrics & Gynecology
Ophthalmology
Pathology
Pediatric Ophthalmology
Pulmonology
Sports Medicine

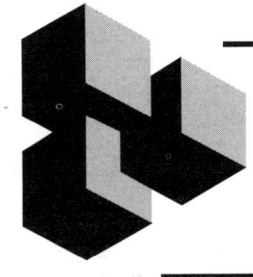

Recently, Philadelphia Magazine recognized doctors who practice at The Lankenau Hospital as among the area's best healthcare providers in the medical specialties listed above. We're pleased, but they could have mentioned doctors in the following areas, as well:

Allergy, Immunology & Rheumatology
Anesthesiology
Emergency Medicine
General Surgery
Neurology
Orthopaedics

Otolaryngology
Physical Medicine & Rehabilitation
Psychiatry
Radiology
Sleep Disorders
Urology

If you would like more information about the outstanding physicians who practice at Lankenau, call The Lankenau Hospital Physician Referral Service at 215-645-2001.

100 Lancaster Avenue, west of City Line
Wynnewood, PA 19096

As a member of the Main Line Health System, Lankenau® is affiliated with The Bryn Mawr Hospital, Paoli Memorial Hospital, and Bryn Mawr Rehab.

# 15 How Can You Sleep at Night?

*If you chronically take sleeping pills, the answer probably is: You can't.*

♥ If reading this makes you drowsy, don't blame it on my writing style. You may be among the four in ten Americans who aren't getting enough sleep. Insomnia has become one of the most common complaints in the doctor's office, spawning nearly 200 sleep disorder centers around the country and a spate of scientific research on what keeps people from falling and staying asleep.

Nobody ever *died* from lack of sleep. In fact, a disc jockey in Los Angeles (probably looking for a citation in the *Guinness Book of World Records*) stayed awake on the air for ten days straight until, no longer able to fight it off, he conked out at the microphone. There is no medical evidence that one night without sleep will affect the next day's performance, or that a few restless nights damage the immune system. On the other hand, chronic tossing and turning does rob the body and mind of the critical downtime we all need to operate at our best.

For most of us, the magic number for a restorative night is eight hours, but that is by no means universal. A woman came to the Abington Memorial Hospital Sleep Disorders Center complaining that she fell asleep each night at midnight and awoke at 4 a.m. Although she rarely felt tired, she was certain she had a sleeping problem, because she'd always been told that people need eight hours. After carefully questioning her, Dr. B. Franklin Diamond, the center director, told her to go home and stop worrying. "You should judge your sleep needs by the day, not by the night," he says. "How much sleep you require is determined purely by how you feel and function when you're awake. If you're not tired on four or six hours, that's enough for you. And if you're still tired after eight, you need to sleep longer."

Experts say that sleep needs are set in the genes, so it's useless to try to train yourself to get by on less sleep. Also in our genes is a program to get sleepy twice every 24 hours. The peak time for exhaustion is in the dead of night, between 2 a.m. and 7 a.m., at which time the dawn's early light triggers a rise in the hormones that switch on the body's wake–up signal. There is another distinct drop in alertness in mid–afternoon, between 2 p.m. and 5 p.m. Siestas, it turns out, are a biological response, not the result of oversize sombreros or of eating too much at lunch.

While people often characterize themselves as "good" or "poor" sleepers, those terms rattle Dr. Karl Doghramji, a sleep specialist and psychiatrist who heads the Sleep Disorders Center at Thomas Jefferson University. When people have persistent sleep difficulties, he believes there is usually an underlying cause—and chronic insomnia has many of them. In the physiological category are the identified sleep disorders, like restless leg syndrome, a neurological problem characterized by involuntary kicking or twitching of the leg muscles, and sleep apnea, characterized by god–awful snoring that's an attempt to restore a temporary cessation in breathing. In the psychiatric category are common problems like anxiety, usually linked to trouble falling asleep, or depression, typically marked by awakening before dawn. Dr. Doghramji estimates that 30 percent of the insomniacs who come to his clinic fall into this mentally troubled group. Most of their sleep complaints can be alleviated through nondrug strategies, or, in some cases, by medications outside the sleeping pill category. Sometimes drugs prescribed for prevailing medical conditions wind up creating their own sleeping problems. Diet pills, decongestants, some stimulant drugs for asthma, and certain drugs like Lomotil and Regalan, prescribed for digestive upsets, can all interfere with sleep.

By far the largest group of insomniacs suffers from some kind of stress or tension. Frequently there is a major precipitating cause that upsets the normal pattern of life—a new job, a loss, an illness, a divorce. Other folks, the worrywarts, are simply predisposed to sleeping problems by nature, because they can't shut off their thoughts when their heads hit the pillows. Regardless of the origin, what begins as a few bad nights all too often escalates into a serious sleep problem sometimes referred to as "conditioned wakefulness." As Abington's Dr. Diamond describes it, "The bed becomes a battlefield. In addition to being worried about whatever they're worried about, they're also afraid they won't be able to sleep. That fear keeps them awake."

The all–too–simple cure for this kind of insomnia is a sleeping pill. Most doctors agree that pills on an occasional basis, especially to get through a crisis, can be quite helpful. "Occasional use of sleeping pills under the direction of a physician to prevent progression of transient insomnia into chronic insomnia is a valid treatment," says Jefferson's Dr. Doghramji. A low–dose pill every other night for a few weeks, or even every night for up to one month, is relatively harmless. But we are not a society geared to moderation, and most people keep on popping the pills without recognizing that after about six weeks, sleep medications do more to *disrupt* sleep than enhance it.

Consistent use of pills alters the basic architecture of sleep, diminishing by as much as 50 percent the amount of deep sleep so critical to feeling rested. Added to the disturbance of sleep cycles are the problems of dependency and withdrawal. A rebound effect is likely to occur after a month or so of daily pill usage. The body becomes so dependent on the drug that if it's stopped abruptly, the insomnia will return, more severe than it was originally, leading the sufferer right back to the sleeping pill. The way to avoid this vicious cycle is to gradually wean yourself off the pills. Cut the dosage in half every three nights, until there is nothing left to take.

The popularity of sleeping medications exploded in the late '60s with the introduction of the benzodiazepines, a new class of sleeping pills in a branch of the same family as Valium. Previously, most doctors had prescribed barbiturates like Seconal, Nembutal and Luminal as sedatives. These knockout drops had a lethal potential for overdose: a few too many and the sleep became permanent. The benzodiazepines were heralded as far less dangerous, because instead of depressing the central nervous system, as barbiturates did, they seemed to block the stimuli that interfere with sleep. The first to hit the market was Dalmane, followed by Halcion, Restoril and Doral.

Despite the comparative safety of this class of drugs—fatal overdoses are rare—they are not without side effects. Dalmane (flurazepam) can linger for more than 100 hours in the body before being completely eliminated. Moreover, interaction with other drugs—Tagamet, for one—can exacerbate the pill's hangover effect. This buildup explains why people habitually taking Dalmane may feel tired during the day.

Halcion (triazolam) is a short-acting medication, less likely to accumulate in the blood. For many years it enjoyed a reputation as the perfect sleeping pill, particularly among trans-Atlantic travelers. Halcion was recommended to me about four years ago by a physician as a great way to sleep on a plane and get through the first few nights of waking at odd hours after arriving in a far-off time zone. Although I never take sleeping pills at home, I've used Halcion on long plane trips and have never had the slightest problem.

Others have not been so fortunate. In early 1989, the TV show *20/20* aired a segment of horror stories about Halcion. Among other things, it told of a stockbroker who after a year on Halcion became severely psychotic, and of a woman who murdered her mother while taking the drug and had no recollection of the crime. Reports of amnesia caused by Halcion crop up often in the press. Dr. Diamond had a patient who gained a great deal of weight using Halcion because he got up every night for an eating binge, but forgot about it the following morning.

Despite the negative publicity, Dr. Daniel Hussar, Remington Professor of Pharmacy at the Philadelphia College of Pharmacy, believes the flap over Halcion is exaggerated, and that adverse reactions are usually the result of excessive dosage, inappropriately extended usage, or interaction with other medication. (This may explain actor Burt Reynolds' claim that Halcion nearly killed him. He was taking up to 50 pills a day, and lapsed into an eight-hour coma when he tried to quit cold turkey. His recovery took more than a year.) Dr. Hussar explains, "It's not surprising that occasionally people will suffer temporary memory loss from benzodiazepines, since amnesia is a well-known characteristic of this family of drugs. In fact, they are often used just for that advantage. Their cousins, Valium and Versad, are frequently given prior to surgery or in conjunction with other procedures to calm patients and make them forget their discomfort."

Although warnings about Halcion still circulate, fear should be allayed by the findings of the FDA, which, after examining the literature, decided only to list *potential for temporary amnesia* on the drug label. A committee set up by the American College of Neuropsychopharmacology to review all the published data on the pill was chaired by University of Pennsylvania psychiatrist Dr. Charles O'Brien. He reported that the worst problems are rare. Morever, a recent article in *DICP, The Annals of Pharmocotherapy* examined a large number of studies on benzodiazepines and concluded, "It's not clear that triazolam [Halcion] predisposes patients to amnesiac episodes to any greater extent than the other benzodiazepines." Its authors do suggest, however, that elderly people and patients with prior psychiatric histories should not take these drugs. The safest course for Halcion is short-term use at the lowest dosage of .125 mg.

Common but not very effective alternatives to prescription sleeping pills are over-the-counter preparations, like Nytol, Sominex, Sleep-eze and Compoz. They usually contain the same component that causes drowsiness in antihistamines. Within a week or so the body develops a tolerance, and sedation begins to diminish.

All the sleep specialists I interviewed approve of sleeping pills for temporary, short-term use only. Chronic sleeping problems should be addressed with treatments *not* found in the medicine chest. Most popular is the Bootzin technique, named for the behavioral therapist who's had great success with the following advice: Go to bed only when sleepy; if you can't sleep after 20 minutes, go into another room, and read a boring book or watch a dull TV show until you're very tired. Repeat this step as many times as necessary, and don't nap during the day at all. (If you must take a quick daytime snooze, do it at a regular time, for not more than 20 minutes.) Finally, set your alarm for the same hour every day regardless of how little you have slept or when you turned out the light. Apparently, a consistent rising time is critical to establishing the circadian rhythm of sleep.

Sometimes simple lifestyle changes can improve sleep. There are no data to support either side in the hard vs. soft mattress argument; it's merely a matter of personal preference. Not so for the hot vs. cold room debate. It's been documented that 60° to 65° is the best temperature; above 75° definitely disturbs sleep. Nothing, however, supports those who believe that people sleep better in an arctic chill. If you live on a street with lots of traffic, or even if you have a loud air conditioner, the noise may be affecting your sleep more than you realize. Try blocking it with earplugs, or a sleep machine that produces white noise. And if you find that light wakes you in the morning, get a sleep mask.

Just because you don't experience the coffee jitters, it's a mistake to assume you aren't sensitive to caffeine. A Coke or cup of cocoa in the late afternoon can be enough to delay sleep that night. When you can't fall asleep, don't try a glass of wine to relax. While alcohol may help you close your eyes, it will fragment the sleep that follows. So will nicotine. Even exercise and food influence sleep. Numerous studies have found that a steady exercise program deepens sleep, but it should be performed in the morning or late afternoon. And though diet centers might disagree, try a light snack before bed. Too many people go to bed hungry, and are awakened in the middle of the night by nothing more serious than growling stomachs. Finally—and this is no joke—use sex as a sleeping pill. Research shows it's safe, it works, and it has only positive side effects.

*If you need help:* All too frequently, sleeping problems are a symptom of something else. If you are a chronic insomniac, you should check out your problem with a sleep specialist, whose treatments include training in biofeedback and other relaxation techniques. Some local sleep disorder centers are: Abington Memorial Hospital, 576–2226; Medical College of Pennsylvania, 842–4250; Thomas Jefferson University, 955–6175; and the Hospital of the University of Pennsylvania, 662–7300.

---

Fairmount Institute offers innovative treatment for adults, senior citizens and adolescents struggling with drug abuse, alcoholism and emotional problems.

**Rebuilding shattered lives...**

Treatment is tailored to each patient's unique needs. Hospital and out-patient services are provided in an attractive setting adjacent to Fairmount Park. Our professional staff is led by dedicated physicians, psychologists, social workers and registered nurses.

For over 65 years we have been a leader in innovative, effective treatment. Fairmount Institute accepts most major insurance plans.

**Fairmount Institute**
561 Fairthorne Ave., Philadelphia PA 19128

A Tradition of commitment to quality care. 1-800-235-0200

# One of the Delaware Valley's great hospitals is on your side.

    At Cooper Hospital/University Medical Center, we take pride in being able to put the finest medical facilities at your doorstep. And because we are a teaching hospital, our physicians, nurses and other professionals are among the finest in the country.

    Yet, while we're respected for medical excellence, we're remembered for the kind of warm and caring treatment too many major hospitals tend to forget.

    And you don't have to cross any bridges to get that special treatment. Because we're right here, on your side, South Jersey.

## Cooper Hospital/University Medical Center

The Clinical Campus of the University of Medicine and Dentistry of New Jersey/Robert Wood Johnson Medical School at Camden
One Cooper Plaza, Camden, New Jersey

# 16 Pain Is Their Speciality

*Physiatrists seem to be able to do what other doctors can't.*

♥ Jill heard about it from Ted, who was referred by a friend who had an aunt with an enlightened physician. Ted recommended that Jill see a physiatrist. At first she thought he was suggesting her problem was psychosomatic; then he explained that physiatrists aren't shrinks. They're physicians who treat, among other things, back and neck pain, and who believe that surgery is the course of last resort.

So Jill, who had already been diagnosed by two orthopedists and one neurosurgeon as having a slipped lumbar disk that they'd be delighted to operate on, took herself to a physiatrist (pronounced fizz–ee–AT–trist). After a thorough examination, she was given a 15–minute daily exercise program so mild that she thought it was a waste of time. But she tried it anyway. Within a week, the pain had subsided. The physiatrist cautioned that she should expect relapses, but if she did the exercises twice a day for one year and once a day for the rest of her life, they would not be severe.

That was nine years ago. She can't remember the last time she had an episode with her back. She even made a believer out of her skeptical 65–year–old father, who was suffering from such acute pain in his knee that it awakened him out of a sound sleep. The physiatrist put him on a different exercise program, and within a few months he was able to comfortably walk through a large art exhibit at a museum with marble floors.

It would be misleading to suggest that you'll find these extreme success stories sitting in every physiatrist's office. This medical specialty doesn't have the franchise on magic wands. But it can provide valuable nonsurgical, non–pharmacological help for people with a variety of back, neck, and sports–related injuries. It's estimated that 31 million Americans suffer from back pain; in desperation, many of them choose surgery on the recommendation of an orthopedist or neurosurgeon. A more conservative alternative would be to seek a second opinion from a physiatrist.

Physiatrists are board–certified physicians who practice in the field of physical medicine and rehabilitation (PM&R). The physical medicine component dates to the 1930s, when physical agents like heat, cold, water, electricity and therapeutic exercises were first injected into mainstream medicine. Its importance increased after World War II, when physical medicine joined hands with rehabilitation in an expanded effort to help disabled soldiers return to society.

In 1949 the two disciplines merged into a single speciality that, in its early years, was hidden away in the basement of the hospital. Today PM&R is the third most popular residency program among medical students. It seems to attract young doctors who have particularly strong people skills and an optimism about achievement in the face of adversity. They'll need it: Much of their work involves rehabilitation of patients with spinal cord injuries, strokes, multiple sclerosis and muscular dystrophy. Only lately are physiatrists being consulted by a wide spectrum of able–bodied people suffering from some kind of chronic or acute musculoskeletal pain.

One cardiologist we interviewed had been operated on twice for a herniated disk; he finally turned in desperation to a physiatrist to rescue him from an agonizing back attack. He was so impressed with the results that he's moved physiatry to the top of his list of primary consultants for patients with back pain. He says, "Why wait for bed rest and everything else to fail?"

Another believer is Dr. Edith Levitt, who limped into the Physical Medicine and Rehab Clinic at Graduate Hospital, her body contorted by an agonizing back spasm that had already lasted five weeks. (A muscle spasm is the body's way of immobilizing the area around an injury, but the spasm itself becomes an additional source of pain.) The first task of Dr. Francis Bonner Jr., the department chairman, was to assess the source of Dr. Levitt's pain. There are some 256 causes of back pain, ranging from lumbar strain to a ruptured blood vessel to a tumor. An appropriate diagnosis was crucial to determining whether he could help her or would simply refer her to another specialist. In addition to the normal imaging techniques—CAT scans and MRIs—physiatrists will use tests like electromyography to assess muscle capacity. If Dr. Bonner found evidence of cancer, for instance, he'd immediately refer a patient to a surgeon. On the other hand, if he found evidence of a herniated disk or a pinched nerve, he'd advise trying his conservative approach, and saving surgery as a last, rather than only, option.

Regardless of the root of the problem, the physiatrist will concentrate on treating the result rather than the cause. That approach sets him apart from most other doctors. In the traditional medical model, illness is approached as a disease or dysfunction to be medicated with drugs or removed by surgery. The physiatrist is more concerned with how the ailment interferes with a patient's ability to cope at home, on the job or at play. He analyzes anatomy and physiology as they relates to activity. "Our work," says Dr. Bonner, who is also president of the Pennsylvania Academy of Physical Medicine and Rehabilitation, "is designed to improve function, regardless of the pathology of the disorder."

It turned out that Edith Levitt had a nonoperable condition of degenerative arthritis of her lower back, which included some damaged disks and the joints on either side. She was immediately given heat and electro–stimulation to ease her muscle spasm. Next Dr. Bonner injected the area of her pain with a local anesthetic laced with a bit of cortisone. That was followed by an application of ice, and an abdominal binder to support her back. Within a few days, she was standing straight and ready to begin a mild exercise program that she'll gradually build to 15 minutes a day. "None of this will cure her arthritis," says Dr. Bonner, "but it will make her able to manage it."

Adapting to and coping with pain is a primary goal of the physiatrist. "We focus on practical, everyday survival skills," explains Dr. Keith Robinson, of the Hospital of the University of Pennsylvania department of PM&R. "We help people master their environment in the most mundane terms. We want the patient to control the pain, rather than having the pain control the patient." That might mean teaching a 30–year–old rower with muscular pain in his forearm another way to handle the oars, or giving pegboard exercises to an arthritic patient to strengthen his fingers so he can button his shirt.

"We recognize that the psychosocial piece of pain may be as important as the organic piece," says Dr. Robinson. "Let's face it—we all need attention. There are socially acceptable ways of getting it, and nonacceptable ways, of which pain is a primary response. We do a lot of psychological intervention." It's not unusual for patients to report that physiatrists were the only doctors who spent time talking to them and took their pain seriously. That was the case with a woman who worked for a food manufacturer in Northeast Philadelphia. Her job involved sealing hundreds and hundreds of cookie boxes every day, and as a result of this repetitive action ("accumulative trauma," as it's officially called) she'd developed acute pain in her shoulder and a numbness and tingling in her arm. The conventional muscle and nerve studies appeared normal, and her boss was beginning to look at her as a malingerer.

Luckily, she found her way to the office of Dr. Ernest Baran, a physiatrist and bioengineer who views the body as an electrical system. He applies techniques similar to those used in circuit testing and signal analysis to studying nerve conduction problems. As a result, he can pinpoint where along a nerve route an injury occurs, and whether the injury is on the coating of the nerve or the inner wire. The former will heal with rest, some drug treatment and physical therapy; the latter may require surgery to relieve the pressure. Dr. Baran found that the cookie lady had a blockage of the nerve at her shoulder. She was temporarily assigned to another job, to give the injury time to heal, and then given "work–hardening" exercises that rebuild weakened muscles. And almost as important, her reputation was salvaged.

Work-related injuries are becoming a major part of the physiatrist's practice. A common problem with which they have great success is carpal tunnel syndrome, an injury caused principally by the way one uses his or her wrists and arms. It's treated in the early stages by simply splinting the wrist, perhaps accompanied by a cortisone injection and when necessary a lesson in a new way to do the activity. The syndrome gets its name from the tunnel that carries nerves, which can be irritated by a repeated motion—like hand sewing or drilling—that overworks the surrounding tendons. The symptoms, most frequently experienced at night, are numbness and burning in the hand, especially the thumb and index finger. "It's important to catch this early," says Dr. Francis Naso, a physiatrist in the department of Physical Medicine and Rehabilitation at Thomas Jefferson University Hospital. "The longer it goes, the more the muscle degenerates, weakening the hand. I've seen people who've ignored the symptoms for six months and can't use their thumbs."

In general, it makes sense at least to consult a physiatrist for any problem involving a sprained or strained muscle, a pinched nerve, or a disk. There are a number of palliative modalities in his bag of tricks. During the acute phase of a pain attack, the physiastrist may use injections of local anesthesia laced with steroids, electronic equipment that provides deep heat or muscle stimulation, braces, anti-inflammatory drugs, and sometimes rest. One patient was aided immensely by a simple foam lumbar cushion, to support his back when he sat.

Physiatrists are great believers in exercise, on the theory that if the muscles are strong, there is less trauma to an injury. The exercises they prescribe won't even work up a sweat, and are multipurpose: They strengthen, improve flexibility, and build endurance. "For disk problems especially," says Jefferson's Dr. Naso, "we prescribe exercises to strengthen important muscles in the abdomen and back that support the spine. In over half the cases we see, chronic, recurrent back pain can be managed over a lifetime with a therapeutic exercise program. On the other hand, we may not be able to do much for unremitting back pain that radiates down through the extremities. That person should see a surgeon."

Physiatrists would seem to be the physicians for the holistic '90s. While they are not miracle workers, they are willing to step beyond their scientific training to examine a wide range of alternatives that many traditional physicians ignore. As Penn's Dr. Robinson says, "This is very creative work. You're always scratching your head to help patients find a less painful way to do things. There's no cookbook medicine here."

*If you need help:* Some area hospitals where you'll find board-certified physiatrists in the department of physical medicine and rehabilitation are: Graduate, 893-2341; Thomas Jefferson University, 955-7445; the Hospital of the University of Pennsylvania, 349-5574; Abington, 576-2160; Bryn Mawr, 251-5400; Chestnut Hill, 233-6200, Our Lady of Lourdes, 609-757-3879. Dr. Ernest Baran can be reached at Rehabilitation/Electrodiagnostic Medicine Associates in Lafayette Hill, 834-6000.

# 17

# That Certain Smile

*What's new at the dentist's office.*

♥ Peter Quinn looked hard at the man seated in his dentist's chair, and went back into the office to consult his notes again. There it was in black and white: Mr. X, age 50. Hard to believe. The poor fellow looked about 75, and had the mouth of a 90–year–old. Many years earlier, he'd lost his lower teeth. Because he'd worn dentures for two decades, his jawbone had eroded to a mere half–inch sliver, and the lower part of his face had collapsed like a leaking balloon. He could no longer even keep the dentures in his mouth, because there was no bone to anchor them. And forget fine dining. This guy ate the same baby food as his granddaughter. Was there anything, he asked, that Dr. Quinn could do?

A year or two ago, the answer would have been, not much. Today dentistry is advancing so rapidly that Quinn was able to build a new jaw. The dentist used a combination of a cadaver mandible purchased from a tissue bank and a piece of the patient's own hipbone, attaching both to what little remained of the original jaw. When they'd all knitted into a strong three–inch base, Quinn surgically inserted titanium screws fitted with magnets into the new jawbone to keep the dentures in place. Now the young grandfather looks like he's had a face-lift, and he's eating apples instead of applesauce.

Today's dentist has options that his predecessors never even dreamed about. For instance, Quinn, who is chairman of oral and maxillofacial surgery at the University of Pennsylvania Dental School, is involved in research to develop a new artificial jaw joint, similar to the ball-and-socket joint used by orthopedic surgeons to create artificial hips. These new metal prosthetic joints allow patients whose jaw joints have been destroyed by trauma, arthritis or cancer to chow down a meal within a few days of surgery. In another technique, Quinn works with a synthetic material that's chemically related to normal bone to build a base for dentures or dental implants on top of existing weakened jawbone. His colleagues in periodontics are experimenting with this same synthetic compound to replace bone eaten away by gum disease.

Hardly anybody goes to the dentist these days just to have a tooth filled. The commercial with the grinning kid saying, "Look, Ma, no cavities" is about as dated as an ad for a five–cent cigar. Dentists now know that the decay caused by sugar is related to the length of time the sweet stuff sticks on your teeth. The rapidly swallowed sugar in a Coke may be less troublesome than the gooey sugar found in raisins. That means it could be worse for your teeth to suck on Life Savers all day than to chomp an occasional candy bar. And someday, when the vaccine to prevent decay gets perfected, kids will be able to nibble chocolates all day long without Mom complaining that they're bad for your teeth.

Meanwhile, thanks to fluoridated water, 50 percent of youngsters between five and 17 no longer have any cavities at all. Those who can't drink their protection from the tap can get it at the dentist's office, from special sealants that form a barricade against the bacterial army that eats into enamel. Much as a manicurist applies a thin coat of nail polish, the dentist now has the material to paint an invisible shield on children's permanent teeth, closing off the pits and cracks where decay loves to lurk.

While the decline of tooth decay is good news for parents, it's been bad news for legions of dentists who made their livings plugging cavities. Dental schools are compensating for the changing demand in dental services by reducing enrollment and radically changing their curricula. Enrollment nationally has dropped from a peak of 6,300 in 1978 to 3,800 in 1991. "This is now a scientifically based profession, not a technical school for filling holes," says Penn's Dr. Quinn, who typifies the medically oriented new breed; he holds degrees in both dentistry and medicine. "Today we need fewer and better–trained dentists, who are able to do a scope of things that traditional dentists never imagined."

Or that traditional patients never expected. Our parents took it for granted that if they lived long enough, they'd probably wind up losing their teeth. For future generations, the prospect of false teeth will be the exception, rather than the rule. Right now, dentists are working with man–made choppers that Dr. Louis Rose, chief of dental medicine at the Medical College of Pennsylvania, refers to as the "third set of teeth. Once there were only baby teeth and adult teeth. Now there are dental implants. We've entered the space age of dentistry."

What makes the newest implants so different is a process called osseo–integration. Earlier implants were fastened to the gums by plates resting on top of the bone, and tended to slip and loosen with time. Today's titanium implants actually form a biological bond with living tissue. In a two–part procedure, the dentist inserts tiny posts directly into the jawbone. In roughly three to six months, when the bone and anchors have knitted together like tightly woven cloth, permanently fixed false teeth are screwed in.

Dental implants aren't for everybody—or for everybody's pocketbook. They cost anywhere from $500 to $1,500 for the surgical portion of the process, and the caps are additional. Most insurance does not cover the cost. But for patients with no medical problems that might impede healing and enough jawbone to work with, the implants are the closest thing to nature's own. They can be used to replace a single lost tooth, to anchor a bridge of several teeth, or as substitutes for an entire denture.

Just as dentists have found a way to permanently replace teeth, they've also discovered what causes most adults to lose them in the first place. No longer will it be inevitable to outgrow the pimples and cavities of youth only to find yourself saddled with gum disease in middle age, and the prospect of painful scraping and surgery to cure it. The cutting edge in periodontics no longer rests solely in the dental surgeon's hands. It now includes the medicine cabinet as well.

Research has shown that gum disease is actually an infection, possibly even contagious, that strikes three out of four adults. The culprit is plaque, a bacteria–rich by–product of the human food processor. Plaque sticks to our teeth, irritates and infects our gums, and, if untreated, eventually attacks the bones that hold our teeth. For the simple control of plaque, the American Dental Association has approved Listerine used twice daily, as well as tartar–control toothpastes like those made by Crest and Colgate. Recently, scientists have actually identified the particular bacteria that cause gum disease and pinpointed the antibiotics that can fight them. Much as dermatologists administer drugs to clear up acne, dentists are now prescribing tetracycline and penicillin to cure infected gums. It's already possible to isolate which bacteria are infecting a patient, by sending a smear to the lab for culture. "We're talking about chemotherapy that may in the long run assist in eliminating the need for surgery," explains Dr. Mark Snyder, a Center City periodontist.

Another big gun in the gum–disease wars is antibacterial mouthwash, available by prescription (Peridex is one brand), that destroys the little buggers before they can form plaque. While they are effective, consider the caveats before you throw your Scope away. Dr. Snyder advises, "The mouthwashes are a tool, not a panacea. They tend to stain the teeth, and they can lull a dentist who isn't an expert in periodontics into thinking the disease is cured, because the surface of the gums is improved, while the real problem below the gum line is ignored."

While the professionals worry about healthy gums, the rest of us fret about a pretty smile. It's been about ten years since dentistry extended the word "bonding" to mean something more than the relationship between mothers and babies. The revolution in cosmetic dentistry is still going strong, because the materials keep getting better. Eight years ago, Haddonfield general dentist James Soffer would not have considered remodeling his wife's smile with bonding materials. Now that he's able to polish the material to the luster of natural teeth, he recently brought her into the office and in two hours sculpted her crooked grin into a set of perfect pearly whites.

The versatility of today's bonding agents makes them usable anywhere in the mouth. These soft, puttylike composite resins, which are hardened by light, can be applied to fill cavities or spaces, repair chips, cracks and discoloration, reshape crooked teeth, make small teeth larger, and in some cases even straighten a smile without orthodontia. And the cost is hundreds, not thousands, of dollars.

If you're thinking that you've seen some of those bonding jobs and they looked like Chiclets, that too has changed. There are new porcelain custom–contoured veneers that resemble false fingernails. Originally, these "fronts" were attached to the teeth with an epoxy that hardened rather quickly, leaving the dentist very little time to play Michelangelo. Today the laminates are fixed with light–cured composites. The dentist can take as long as necessary to shape and mold them; then he or she zaps them with light, and they're good for seven to ten years.

Bonding is not a dental specialty, but it is an art. While every dentist is qualified to do it, you might want to ask to see some before–and–after pictures before you put yourself in anybody's hands.

No matter what wonders the men in white coats develop to lure us into their dreaded chairs, they still haven't come up with the one thing patients want most: painless dentistry. But they're getting close. There's a new anesthesia technique for needle–phobics that blocks pain through electrical impulses. Two little spongelike receivers are placed on the gum near the problem tooth, and connected by a wire to a gadget that the patient holds and controls. It works on a principle of intercepting pain messages to the brain, and has the added advantage of keeping the patient occupied while the dentist drills and asks questions.

For genuine dental–phobics, as well as rich executives too busy to take the time to care for their teeth, the Medical College of Pennsylvania has a one–stop dental clinic that puts patients under general anesthesia and condenses as much as a year's worth of dental procedures—root canal, caps, bonding, gum surgery—into a single day. Don't make dinner plans that evening.

*If you need help:* Most of the procedures described above are available at your neighborhood general or specialty dentist. If you are considering implants, it might be a good idea to check out the hospitals that have implant centers. That way you're guaranteed the dentist has taken the necessary training course and probably does enough of the procedures to be considered reasonably experienced. The hospitals with established implant centers are: MCP, 842–6670; Thomas Jefferson University Hospital, 928–6215; Hospital of the University of Pennsylvania, 662–3585; Albert Einstein, Northern Division, 456–7890. For other references, call the Delaware Valley Implant Center Club, 947–6633.

For information on the single–day outpatient dental surgery clinic at MCP, call 985–1181.

# 18

# Season of the Itch

*Beating the bugs of the summer.*

♥ Insects are not particularly aggressive creatures. True, they do attack us, but usually only for food or in self-defense. The males of many species are completely herbivorous; only female mosquitoes, ticks and fleas, for instance, feed on humans and animals, because their reproductive systems require a blood meal to produce eggs. The bug bite itself doesn't make us itchy and blotchy; that's due to the saliva the bugs release into our bloodstream as part of their digestive process. And you can't really fault an insect for the fact that this fluid contains toxins that can activate allergic reactions as well as infectious germs from the blood of the last victim.

So don't blame fleas for spreading bubonic plague, or mosquitoes for transmitting malaria and yellow fever. Just be grateful that bugs don't spread AIDS. Tests have indicated that mosquitoes are not hospitable hosts for the AIDS virus. *The British Medical Journal* pointed out that in Africa, where AIDS is rampant, there are almost no cases among children, who suffer by far the greatest number of bug bites.

In our part of the world, flies, mosquitoes and mites are more bothersome than dangerous. Houseflies infect food, but they don't bite. (Stable flies, horn flies and greenheads do, however, bite viciously, thanks to the stylet they use to stab through the skin.) Among mites, the most troublesome are the microscopic chiggers found in orchards, parks and golf courses. They don't burrow under the skin, as is popularly believed. Rather, they crawl onto your shoes and bite their way up your leg, injecting an irritating fluid that results in little red bumps and sometimes fever. If they climb as high as your groin, they can cause intense pain. The itching gets pretty fierce, but within a week it disappears. In the meantime, preparations like Chiggerex give some relief.

What you want to avoid is scratching the itch, and thereby breaking the skin barrier. That's how bites become infected, and those infections can get ugly. Dr. Hans Liu, Chief of Infectious Diseases at Presbyterian Medical Center of Philadelphia, cautions, "If after a day or two the bite becomes red, painful and swollen, and seems to be getting worse instead of better, you might want to see a doctor."

Far more serious than infected bites are the diseases carried in our locale by ticks. They lurk in and around wooded areas, tall grass and weeds until they latch onto a human or animal; if undetected, they can feed there for days, or weeks. Wood ticks and dog ticks harbor Rocky Mountain spotted fever, which, contrary to its name, is more common in the East than in the West. Within three to five days of a tick bite, a pink rash breaks out on the hands, wrists, feet and ankles, followed by flulike symptoms of headache, fever and chills. If caught early, the illness can be successfully treated with doxycycline.

The tick you're likely to hear more about these days is the deer tick—something of a misnomer, since it feeds on mice and people as well. No bigger than a poppy seed, the deer tick carries what develops into a debilitating illness known as Lyme disease, named for the Connecticut town where it was first identified, in 1975. In 1989 the Centers for Disease Control documented 7,400 cases of Lyme disease, and the numbers have been climbing by the thousands since. Still, the problem is considered to be grossly underreported, partly due to the difficulty in diagnosing the symptoms—fever, headache, extreme fatigue and a stiff neck—which are confusingly similar to those of many other diseases, particularly multiple sclerosis. If untreated, Lyme disease can escalate into chronic arthritis, heart arrhythmias, and a host of neurologic problems, including Bell's palsy. One woman visited 29 different specialists over the course of six years before discovering she had the disease. Today several diagnostic blood tests and a newer urine test are available. Unfortunately, it takes four to six weeks after exposure for enough antibodies to accumulate in the bloodstream to get a positive reading. Moreover, the immune system often reacts so weakly that the disease may not register at all.

It's extremely important to catch Lyme disease in the early stages, when it can be effectively treated orally with tetracycline or penicillin. Most people don't even know they've been bitten until two days to five weeks later, when a rash that looks like a bull's-eye—a red circle with a welt in the center—appears. Unfortunately, about one-third of the adult victims and half the children never even get the rash, just the flulike illness often dismissed as nothing to worry about—which is not the case. Once the disease progresses, patients require intravenous or intramuscular antibiotics. The organism is tough to kill; some resistant cases have responded to a costly new drug, Rocephin.

To protect yourself from ticks when you're out in the woods or tall grasses, wear long pants tucked into your socks and a long-sleeved shirt. Put tick collars on your dogs and cats, and don't let pets sleep on furniture, where ticks can fall off them and hop on you. It's wise to check your skin for ticks after you've been in the great outdoors. If you do find something that looks like a moving freckle, forget the tick removal methods of old (drowning or smothering or burning them with petroleum jelly, nail polish, alcohol or a hot match).

The recommended method for removing ticks is to use either a pair of tweezers or your fingers, protected with a tissue or rubber gloves. (It's as easy to get infected from handling a tick as from being bitten by one.) Grasp the insect as close as possible to the skin surface, and remove it with an even, steady pulling motion. Avoid any twisting or jerking that could puncture the body and allow the infected fluid to leak out or cause the mouthparts to break off in the skin, creating a chronic irritation that could linger for weeks. Clean the wound and apply an antiseptic such as iodine, then flush the tick down the toilet.

Why some people act like magnets for insect bites while others seem quite immune to them is not completely understood. All that's known for sure is that odors attract bugs, and to scent-sensitive insects, even freshly bathed human beings don't all smell alike. Researchers have proven that mosquitoes in warm air are drawn to the odor of carbon dioxide, which is present in the breath we exhale, and to lactic acid, one of the components of perspiration. "The other odors that appeal to mosquitoes haven't yet been identified," explains Dr. Edward Davis, director of the insect neurobiology group at SRI International, a California research institute. "My suspicion is, it's these unknown odors that make one person more attractive than another."

It would seem a logical extension that if some odors attract bugs, others will drive them away—but that's not how bug repellents work. All they do is mask the appealing human odors that bring insects in the first place. The best repellent on the market is the chemical synthetic diethyl metatoluamide, discovered by the Army during World War II in a massive testing of some 15,000 compounds to find a substance that would protect soldiers in the tropics. The product with the highest level of "jungle juice" (95 percent) is marketed as deet. Cutters lotion contains 50 percent; the stick version has 35 percent, and Off spray has a 14 percent concentration. When using a lesser concentration, apply it more often. The product 6–12, made from another compound, can be used as an alternative by people who can't tolerate "deet."

If bug repellents irritate your skin, try spraying your clothes instead. For some reason known only to the manufacturer, Avon's Skin So Soft contains an ingredient that repels mosquitoes. You can also experiment with various herbs mixed into oils sold at health food stores, especially citronella and pennyroyal. The odor produced by cedar is chemically close to that of diethyl metatoluamide. Other popular herbs include lavender, wormwood, rosemary, orrisroot and cloves. Some people swear that swallowing two to three tablets of vitamin B–1 at mealtime or eating garlic repels mosquitoes—not to mention friends. Dr. Ara Der Marderosian, a professor at the Philadelphia College of Pharmacy and Science, doesn't put much stock in any natural remedies. He says, "People who claim `I used this or that herb and didn't get bitten' probably don't secrete the smells that attract insects."

Once you've been bitten, the best and cheapest remedy to relieve normal itching is ice. Ten–minute applications of an ice pack at half–hour intervals should minimize inflammation, as will topical hydrocortisone creams like Cortaid. The itch in bug bites—but not in poison ivy—is caused by histamine, released when tissue is damaged, so an over–the–counter antihistamine like Benadryl will keep you from scratching. So will a sprinkle of meat tenderizer, possibly because the papain, an enzyme used in tenderizer, neutralizes the acid produced by the bite.

Drugstore shelves are filled with creams and lotions to soothe bug bites, although some dermatologists don't like to recommend them because they may produce allergic reactions. Penn dermatologist Dr. Jim Leyden reports that a study examining products to control itching found that local anesthetics like benzocaine or xylocaine were most effective at providing relief. In a pinch, mix ammonia with water and alcohol to clean the bite and stop the itch. People with a history of asthma, hay fever or childhood eczema may itch for days instead of hours, and might want to get their doctor to write a prescription for a topical steroid or antihistamine. The worst allergic reaction to a biting insect is likely to be hives or a rash.

On the other hand, stinging insects kill 40 to 50 people annually by throwing them into anaphylactic shock, which must be treated immediately with adrenaline. The venom from wasps and bees can be more dangerous than that from a snakebite. Pennysylvania Hospital allergist Dr. Sheryl Talbot notes that the major stinging insects—bees, wasps, hornets and yellow jackets—all have different venoms, and you could be allergic to one, some, or all of them. An allergic history is no prognosticator, but anyone with one bad reaction is at high risk for the future, and should keep a bee–sting kit on hand for emergencies.

Fortunately, says Jefferson Hospital allergist Dr. John Cohn, allergy shots give effective immunity against stinging insects. "They've provided an excellent model for showing that shots do work," he says, "because tests prove there's a definite correlation between the dose of the vaccine and the level of protection."

Stinging insects, unlike the biting ones, don't come around to feed, so repellents won't keep them off. Stingers perceive motion as a threat, and attack out of self–defense. That's why you've always been told that if you remain very still, they'll ignore you. When they do sting, they inject a toxic venom intended to kill. Bees even leave their stingers behind. Rather than removing a stinger with tweezers, which may break the bulb and release more venom, try to ease it out with a dull knife. Then console yourself with the thought that bug–free winter is only a few months away.

*If you need help:* For information or referral to a local specialist for Lyme disease, contact the Lyme Borreliosis Foundation at 203–871–2900. Questions on how to get rid of bugs can be answered by Dr. Stanley Green, Penn State Extension Service, 560–4150.

# 19
# A Few Good Words About Chiropractors

*If your physician can't fix the pain, let a chiropractor*

♥ Not long ago, a friend of mine threw his back out playing racquetball and asked me for advice. I suggested that he use ice to relieve the pain, take an anti–inflammatory painkiller like Advil—and call a chiropractor. He willingly went along with the ice pack and medicine, but he wouldn't even consider seeing a chiropractor. "They're all quacks," he declared with absolute authority—although he'd never been to one.

There are a lot of people who insist there's something weird, even dangerous, about the doctors who crack backs. (Chiropractors hate that expression, by the way. The noise that sometimes occurs during manipulation is the sound made when the doctor adjusts the vertabrae back into normal alignment.) But for every one of the detractors who adamantly swear about chiropractors, more and more people just as adamantly swear by them. The loyalists frequently have bounced from one physician to another, unsucessfully seeking relief from neck or back pain. They finally tried a chiropractor as a last resort, and to their amazement, the condition began to improve.

Which brings me to another friend I'll call Claire. She works in the health–care field; she wouldn't let me use her real name, because her brother–in–law is a prominent physician, and she's sure he'd be very upset if he found out she prefers a chiropractor to the big–shot orthopedist he recommended when she first hurt her back playing golf ten years ago. She remembers that attack as if it was yesterday—a week flat on her back, and six more moving gingerly until she felt normal. For the next decade, her life was ruled by intermittent back pain and the fear of an immobilizing spasm that would again confine her to her bed.

"Finally I decided what the hell, I'll give a chiropractor a try," she says. "I got almost immediate relief. It was so liberating. Instead of going to bed, all I needed was manipulation, ice and some exercise."

That was three years ago; now she returns whenever she feels a spasm coming on. "I do still get these little doubts," she admits. "How can the chiropractor be so sure what's wrong when the M.D. doesn't know? But whatever they're doing, it sure works."

What they're doing is correcting a disorder called vertebral subluxation—the chiropractor's broad definition for any structural or functional misalignment of the spinal column. Besides being the bony structure that connects the head and trunk to the legs, the spine also serves as a conduit for the nervous system. Nerves radiate from openings between the 24 vertebrae to every part of the body. Chiropractors believe that any stress or pressure in these nerves causes not only pain at the site of the irritation, but also a variety of maladies in the organs the nerves feed. That is why chiropractors claim they can treat problems as diverse as herniated disks and constipation by adjusting the spine to remove tension on the nerves.

Chiropractic practitioners do not perform surgery or prescribe drugs, but they often suggest vitamins and give nutritional counseling as part of their holistic approach to wellness. An office visit lasts less than half an hour, and consists of the chiropractor using his hands to apply mild pressure to a specific part of the spine. The cost averages $20 to $30; it is covered by most insurance plans, but not by many HMOS.

Today it's fairly well accepted that correcting the spine may effectively relieve musculoskeletal problems. So why the tainted reputation? Dr. Dennis Rehrig, former chairman of the board of the Pennsylvania Chiropractic Society, thinks one reason is that chiropractors don't follow the medical model. "In the Western world, where pills are the solution to problems, we look like oddballs out in left field," he says. "I prefer to see us as structural engineers. We do conservative surgery, with our hands instead of a scalpel. Is there a risk? Yes. How much? Well, consider that our malpractice premiums average $3,000 a year. Compare that to orthopedic surgeons, who pay about ten times as much."

There are two legitimate areas of concern in chiropractic. One involves the question of safety: Can something awful happen as a result of manipulation? The remote possibility exists that a stroke could occur from a condition called vertebral artery syndrome, which is caused by manipulation of the neck. The risk is two to three cases per million treatments, compared to 150,000 cases of paralysis per million in neurosurgical neck operations. The other danger is misdiagnosis of a serious medical condition. A New Jersey physician told me about a patient of his who had a spinal–cord tumor that was aggravated by a chiropractor. The tumor bled into the spinal cord, and caused paralysis that was able to be partially reversed by surgery. However, such accidents are quite rare. Dr. Steven Mandel, chief of neurology at Mount Sinai Hospital in South Philadelphia, has no qualms about referring patients with soft–tissue injuries to chiropractors. "There are isolated reports where people went to a chiropractor and got worse," he says. "But in general, that doesn't happen, and those stories are more myth than reality."

Far more common than horror stories are success stories about people who've gone to a chiropractor with a backache and found that after several sessions some other disorder, like a chronic headache or PMS, also improved. Dr. Mario Spoto, president of the Pennsylvania Chiropractic Society, says he's had half a dozen female patients with lower back pain who were having difficulty conceiving, and within a year of treatment, all got pregnant. "This is not to say that we're treating infertility," he notes, "but it does show that there is a relationship between spinal alignment and other problems."

Chiropractors have been struggling for acceptance since the turn of the century, when B.J. Palmer, son of the movement's founder, began preaching his radical theory of the spine as the source of all disease. He was denounced in the *Illinois Medical Journal* as "the most dangerous man in Iowa outside of a prison cell." Physicians have been the most vocal—and vicious—critics of chiropractors, and the chief disseminators of their negative image. For decades they waged a bloody turf battle against chiropractors, culminating in a protracted lawsuit that ended just a few years ago. A federal judge found the AMA guilty of conspiring in an illegal boycott to eliminate chiropractors as competitors in the health–care system. Since that ruling, several medical organizations have begun to cooperate with chiropractors, and the AMA has declared it ethical to refer patients to them.

Despite the court victory, chiropractors still feel besieged by widespread misunderstanding of their profession. In fact, a well–known neurologist interviewed for this article wondered openly whether chiropractors can still get their diplomas from mail–order colleges!

To set him straight: There are 17 major chiropractic colleges in the United States, accredited through an organization approved by the U.S. Office of Education. More than half of this country's 36,000 chiropractors have graduated since 1977. They undergo strenuous preparation requiring two years of undergraduate study, plus four or five years of chiropractic instruction in a curriculum, similar to that of physicians, that includes anatomy, physiology, chemistry, neurology, etc. Unlike M.D.s, chiropractors do not study surgery, pharmacology or immunology. Instead they spend hundreds of hours learning how to adjust the spine. All Pennsylvania chiropractors must pass national and state licensing exams before they can become doctors of their profession.

Doctors of chiropractic (D.C.s) are often confused with doctors of osteopathy (D.O.s), because both perform manipulation. But in training and philosophy, the two are quite different. Chiropractors eschew drugs, do nothing but manipulation, and concentrate on musculoskeletal dysfunction. By contrast, osteopaths are doctors trained in a medical setting who function like M.D.s. They use manipulation chiefly as a tool to improve circulation. Many years ago, in their zeal to have osteopaths acknowledged as equals in the medical profession, osteopathic colleges cut down on the number of hours devoted to teaching manipulative therapy. But lately it's coming back into vogue. A spokesman for the Philadelphia College of Osteopathic Medicine says, "We've learned that people like to be touched by their doctors, and those physicians who don't use a hands–on approach were losing patients."

Physical therapists are also quite different from chiropractors. They attend colleges that offer bachelor's degrees in physical therapy, denoting special training in the use of machines and other physical therapies to relieve pain and repair soft-tissue injuries. They do not use manipulation. In Pennsylvania, they can only work with patients who are referred by M.D.s, dentists or podiatrists, who might prescribe a treatment program. That may explain why doctors are more likely to send someone for physical therapy than to a chiropractor.

When should you visit a chiropractor? Probably before you consent to back surgery, since adjustment may help the problem and probably won't hurt it. Based on research, chiropractors tend to be especially effective in treating acute back pain, as well as chronic lower back and neck pain and headaches. An Australian study showed that 30 patients chosen randomly for chiropractic adjustment from a group of 85 with long–term histories of migraine headaches improved radically within seven visits. Dr. Basil Snyman, a popular Center City chiropractor, finds that pregnant women respond particularly well to manipulation. "Their ligaments get loose, the pelvis gets out of place, and they often get sciatica," he says. "We can easily relieve the pressure that causes their pain."

How many treatments will you need? Dr. Elliot Rosenberg, a South Jersey cardiologist, visited a chiropractor for a problem with hip and leg pain that the Mayo Clinic had been unable to diagnose. "I went about six times," he says. "I always felt better afterward. There was a reduction in pain and increased mobility. But the relief only lasted a day or so, and I eventually stopped, because it didn't last." His is a common complaint. If you aren't getting relief after four to six visits to a chiropractor, you should seek another therapy.

On the other hand, if you've got a longtime problem, don't expect chiropractic to be a miraculous quick fix that will undo what has taken years to develop. Dr. Snyman says: "It's not always possible to cure structural and mechanical conditions, but they can be maintained. Chiropractors have great success with patients who are other doctors' failures. That's why we often joke that D.C. stands for `doctor of chronics.'"

*If you need help:* The best way to choose a chiropractor is through the referral of a satisfied patient or a physician. The Pennsylvania Chiropractic Society (to which about half the chiropractors in the state belong) will give you the name of a member in your area if you call its hot line at 800–321–4727. For more information or with questions about chiropractors, contact the American Chiropractic Association, 1701 Clarendon Boulevard, Arlington, VA 22209; 703–276–8800.

# NOTES

# University of Pennsylvania
# CANCER CENTER

**More advances have been made in cancer in the past 10 years than in any period in history...and the future holds even more promise.**

Our 200 cancer specialists are at the forefront of these advances. They bring to each patient their knowledge and compassionate support, as they fight this disease together.

We are unique in the Delaware Valley as the only cancer center supported by the resources of one of the nation's leading academic medical centers.

And we are one of only 28 cancer centers in the United States to be designated by the National Cancer Institute as a Comprehensive Cancer Center.

If you would like to speak to our referral counselors about our cancer physicians or treatment programs, or to schedule an appointment, please call:

## 1-800-777-8176

**University of Pennsylvania Cancer Center
University of Pennsylvania Medical Center**

# 20

# A Separate Piece

*What biopsies are, and why they aren't always right.*

♥ Certain medical terms routinely tossed around by doctors are almost guaranteed to trigger fear in patients. One of them is the word "biopsy." When a doctor says, "We'll send it for a biopsy," people automatically assume the worst, and sweat the hours until the report comes back: benign or malignant. It's either/or, right? Wrong. There are some biopsies that aren't conclusive, where the doctors can't classify the cells on a slide as absolutely one thing or another. The recent experience of a friend of mine is an example.

Unable to find an explanation for my friend's recurring abdominal pains, his doctor decided to take a look inside his stomach with an endoscope. After sedating him, the doctor passed a tube with a light on one end and a camera on the other through the digestive tract and snipped off a piece of an inflamed section of the stomach, which was sent for a biopsy. The report came back mixed. It looked like it might be malignant, but the pathologists couldn't say for sure. So the doctor ordered a CAT scan. That revealed no evidence of a tumor. Still lacking a diagnosis, the doctor went inside again with a larger scope, and this time took a half–dozen tissue samples. The pathologists still couldn't agree on exactly what the tumor was, but they now decided it was not malignant. That reassured my friend, although it was hardly the definitive answer he wanted.

The gray area in reading biopsies frustrates doctors and disturbs patients, who expect more concrete information than the conclusion that something is suspicious. What does "suspicious" or "atypical" mean? When should you worry about a biopsy report? And just what are biopsies, anyway?

A biopsy is nothing more than the removal of tissue from the body for diagnostic purposes. Biopsies are not always ordered because the doctor suspects cancer. They are also used to identify the cause of an infection or inflammation, and as a screening device for a patient at high risk for developing cancer, such as one with ulcerative colitis who is in danger of having that disease progress into a malignancy.

Unlike standard laboratory tests, a biopsy is a qualitative rather than a quantitative study. A blood sample, for instance, can be precisely measured: so many red cells, so many white cells, such and such a platelet count. Biopsies, on the other hand, don't use numerical assessments. Like beauty, they depend on the trained eye of the beholder, leaving the pathologist in some instances with a diagnosis that falls between an educated guess and a tough judgment call. "People don't understand that pathology is an art, not a science," explains Dr. Virginia LiVolsi, director of surgical pathology at the Hospital of the University of Pennsylvania. "At best, pathologists are trained to extract bits and pieces of information from looking at a slide. Based on experience and study, we integrate our observations into a diagnostic finding." It's no accident that many pathologists collect art as a hobby, or that they tend to have visual rather than auditory nightmares.

When cells follow familiar patterns, the pathologist has an easy time making a clear and simple diagnosis. But the human body isn't always obligingly predictable. "Cancer cells don't read textbooks, and they don't have a mirror that tells them how they should look," says LiVolsi, "so often they don't grow the way they're supposed to." Or as Pennsylvania Hospital's chief of pathology, Dr. Michael Warhol, succinctly puts it, "Cancer cells don't wear an 'M' for malignant." The real sleuthing begins when a cell appears normal, but its association with the cells around it isn't quite right. At that point the pathologist examines the cell's relationship to its companions and checks to see if it's where it belongs; a cell from the colon shouldn't show up in a biopsy of tissue from the liver. Another marker is the cell's growth pattern. Unlike normal cells, cancer cells don't recognize their neighbors, and keep growing from one organ into another. Adding to the confusion are situations where atypical cells near an inflammation or ulcer mimic cancer, but aren't malignant.

This explains why pathologists frequently find themselves navigating the murky waters of interpretation. That's the reason your doctor may say that the pathologist wants a consultation before delivering the diagnosis. In the case of a very unusual slide, the pathologist may never have encountered anything similar, and may need input from an expert. This is particularly true in smaller hospitals, where labs are not as likely to view repeated examples of a tricky problem and will send the slide to someone who has seen it more often. Another cause for uncertainty may be the sample itself—there may simply be too few cells or tissue fragments to make a definitive statement.

Typical of slides that tend to get circulated for opinion are those of certain breast tumors, lymph nodes and melanomas. "There's a danger," says Dr. LiVolsi, "in labeling something malignant when you're not absolutely sure. That starts all kinds of things in action that could unnecessarily harm or mutilate a patient if it isn't true." Sometimes the language used by pathologists frightens lay people unnecessarily. A biopsy can be described as "atypical" or "abnormal," but what the patient hears is "malignant." The terms are not synonymous. For example, fibroid tumors, breast cysts and thyroid nodules are abnormal, yet benign. The word "tumor" doesn't imply cancer, either. It's simply a medical term that designates a swelling.

There are a number of methods of obtaining sample tissue for a biopsy. The least invasive is the fine–needle aspiration, commonly used for lumps in the breast, neck or throat. The doctor takes the lump between his fingers, inserts the needle into it, and draws out a small amount of fluid, which is then smeared onto a slide. Although cheap and relatively painless, this procedure has an error rate of about 15 percent. A woman I'll call Annette had the not–uncommon experience of visiting a doctor about a breast lump and being told the biopsy was benign. He recommended monitoring the lump for a month or so. When she returned four weeks later, it had not disappeared. The physician remained sanguine and said, "Let's keep an eye on it a while longer." Annette insisted on having the lump removed, and it was found to be malignant.

This kind of thing can happen, explains Dr. LiVolsi, because the needle might miss the malignant cells. Perhaps the lump is full of collagen and scar tissue, and there aren't many affected cells for sampling. Or perhaps only some of the cells in a tumor are malignant, and the random thrust of the needle doesn't hit them. She advises, "If a fine–needle biopsy of a breast lump comes back benign and the breast lump persists for more than three weeks, have it excised."

A second type of needle biopsy, the large–bore or true–cut needle, involves a small tube and is used for, among other things, bone marrow taps and liver samplings. It gives the pathologist a larger piece of tissue to work with than the small needle, and requires local anesthesia.

Punch biopsies are done with an instrument like a cookie cutter, to get tissue from lesions on the surface of the skin. And though not usually thought of as a biopsy, a D and C (dilatation and curettage) can be a diagnostic tool to explain the reason for abnormal bleeding or pelvic pain. Finally, there are surgical biopsies done under general anesthesia; they range from little snippets removed from a tumor through a laparoscope to larger wedges or pieces of tissue taken by entering the body through an incision.

During an operation, the surgeon frequently takes samples not only from the tumor, but also from the surrounding edges, to make certain he's removed the entire mass. When a surgeon needs immediate information to determine whether a tumor is malignant and thus how the surgery should proceed, he will send a piece of tissue for a "frozen section" while the patient remains on the operating table. The soft, squishy tissue sample gets rushed to the pathology lab, where it's submerged in liquid nitrogen. It very quickly becomes a solid block that can be sliced into slivers and put onto a slide, which is then examined; the results are reported to the operating room.

But the most typical method of processing tissue samples is by submersion in liquid wax. It takes about 24 hours for the water in tissue to be replaced with wax. The hardened chunk is then shaved onto a slide and stained to differentiate the naturally colorless parts of the cell. The prepared slide is now ready to be analyzed through a normal light microscope. (Labs handle hundreds of specimens, and among the problems they can face are not always having fixed the tissue properly, and not having set aside a piece for a test that may be required later on. That's why it's sometimes necessary to get another sample.) Should the pathologists need more information than a normal microscopic viewing provides, they might turn to electron microscopy, which magnifies the cell to a point where it's possible to actually see inside the parts.

Another technique popularized within the last ten years is immunocytochemistry—the use of antibodies to type tissue. Right now, it can tell doctors what kind of cancer cell they are looking at. They hope to use it in the future to solve a greater puzzle, the mystery of the unknown primary site. By the time many cancers are discovered, the cells have traveled far from the original site, which could be anywhere in the body. For optimal treatment, both the primary and secondary tumor sites need to be located. Pathologists are currently utilizing the techniques of molecular biology to analyze biopsies of secondary tumors for clues that will reveal where they came from.

When pathologists do identify a malignant tumor, they will usually "stage" it, a kind of coding that tells how far the tumor has spread. Stage O, or *in situ*, means the cancer is still confined to its original location and is not invasive. The next four stages indicate incremental advances, from confined but invasive to having spread throughout the body. The standard wax–process biopsy can be evaluated in about a day, at which time your doctor can call the lab for a verbal report. Written reports, depending on the complexity of the slide, can take from two to ten days. Beyond that, you should push for an explanation. "Obviously, patients are anxious about biopsies," says Pennsylvania Hospital's Warhol, "but we don't do anybody a favor if we rush a difficult diagnosis and it's wrong."

If you have unresolved questions about a diagnosis, you are not out of line to request that your slide be sent to a pathologist in another laboratory. Because of the subjective nature of this specialty, there is no substitute for experience. You could also ask whether there is another kind of test that could give more definitive information. In the end, however, you may have to settle for living with a biopsy report that says you have something irregular, but not malignant. "We are taught that everything has an answer," says Dr. Warhol. "In pathology, that just isn't true."

# 21

## Under Your Skin

*Doctors know what causes acne.
And it has nothing to do with pepperoni pizza.*

♥ It's not just kids who are moaning about pimples these days. Dermatologists are noticing a rise in adult acne, particularly among women. While the increase may be related to the stresses created by adding outside work to in–house parenting, it appears the cause of adult acne is the same as that of the teenage variety.

Research has now firmly established that pimples have nothing to do with eating too many potato chips or chocolate bars. Diet is not a factor. Neither is cleanliness. In fact, too much scrubbing actually makes acne *worse*, by aggravating the condition that causes it. And that condition begins with the presence of too much oil, which causes the linings of the sebaceous follicles in the skin to shed abnormally. As a result, clumps of cells pile up in the follicle, clogging the canal and promoting a growth of bacteria that soon break down the follicle walls. The gook inside spills out into the skin, and voilà, a pimple.

Acne appears to have a definite hereditary component, but don't blame it all on your genes. It's no accident that pimples seem to pop out around major events: Stress activates the adrenal gland, which in turn increases the production of hormones that trigger the overproduction of oil, setting the whole acne process in motion.

Nobody should suffer from disfiguring acne today, because a variety of excellent treatments have been developed. First, there are ways of stemming the production of too much oil. Despite the claims of various skin products, nothing rubbed on the surface of the skin can do anything about oil, beyond clearing off what's already accumulated. What *does* work? First, drugs like Acutane internally cut down the flow of the oil machine. Second, the abnormal sloughing of the follicle walls can be treated by the topical application of a nonprescription cream like

Stridex, made from salicylic acid, or the prescription cream Retin A, made from retinoic acid. These formulations correct the excess shedding and get rid of the clustered cells. Third, to reduce the bacteria count, there are externally used products, like the over-the-counter preparations OXY-10 and Clearasil, as well as powerful antibiotic pills like tetracycline, minocycline and erythromycin, which function at the cellular level.

The cheapest treatment is one of the most important. Dr. James Leyden, a University of Pennsylvania professor of dermatology, says, "Your mother was right. Don't rub, scrub or pick at your face. Any kind of external friction, even leaning the phone against your chin, irritates the condition. When people ask what they should wash their faces with to prevent acne, my answer is, 'Gently.' I am more concerned with how you wash than with what you use." Leyden has one other bit of advice: Treat the problem early and aggressively. Where there is a family history of severe acne, children as young as nine should see a dermatologist. "There's evidence," he says, "that we can alter the course of events by getting acne under control before it mushrooms and destroys the life of an adolescent."

Because the skin is such an accessible organ for research—it's so easy to get samples to study—the dermatology department at the Hospital of the University of Pennsylvania and its medical school are involved in a number of projects with implications far beyond skin disorders. "In terms of skin research," explains Penn's Dr. George Murphy, "we always waited for a rash to occur to find out what caused it. That's like studying a forest fire after the trees burn down. Now we're doing what we call invisible dermatology, looking at the molecular level to find out what happens before a rash occurs."

One result of this basic research has been the discovery of a positive link between stress and inflammation. It's long been known that many skin rashes are inflammatory conditions caused by an abnormal collection of white blood cells in the skin. The big question has been what makes those cells leave the blood vessels and travel to the skin in the first place. The answer found at Penn is: stress. Microscopic observations show that stressful situations fire up the nerve cells in the skin. They in turn trigger the inflammatory process by causing the release of substances called cytokines. These granules make the walls of the blood vessels sticky, attracting white cells. The cells then migrate through the wall and lodge in the skin, creating inflammation.

While this important finding doesn't mean that tranquilizers will be used to treat hives, it does point to new possibilities for inflammatory problems like psoriasis. "Instead of using a topical cream after the rash and scaling occur, we can begin to look at drugs that will interrupt this cascade of events before they happen," says Dr. Murphy. "Moreover, this work gives Western medicine a purely scientific basis to explain the mind/body connection between stress and disease."

Inflammation has also turned up as a factor in what doctors call male-pattern alopecia—or what everybody else calls balding. It's already known that men lose their locks when their hair follicles die. Murphy's group was interested in the nature of the initial hit that makes the follicle sick. By examining pieces of scalp adjacent to the balding area, they discovered souped–up inflammatory cells—cells related to a scarring that damages the hair follicle and leads to baldness. One reason the popular drug Minoxidil works to retard hair loss may very well be its anti–inflammatory properties. Murphy doesn't advise rubbing corticosteroid creams on your head yet, but he does expect that this information will lead to clinical research with topical anti–inflammatory solutions.

Another major investigation coming from the Penn lab is a joint project with a materials science engineer from MIT. He's invented a promising artificial skin that could revolutionize the care of burn victims. Right now the only options for covering large, raw burned areas are the temporary substitute of pigskin (which eventually must be removed) or the slow process of culturing the patient's own skin in a lab dish to create a graft. Neither of these procedures addresses the problem of scarring, the ugly reminder of a bad burn that victims carry for the rest of their lives. Burn scars are caused not by the burn itself, but by the way skin contracts as it re–forms. The new artificial skin actually prevents crenulation. It's a thin membrane, created from natural animal substances, that closely resembles human skin in both chemical composition and in physical characteristics, like pore size. When laid over a burn site, the membrane provides a permanent matrix—a kind of scaffolding—around and into which smooth new skin grows without contracting.

While some of the nation's dermatology departments look for the skin cures of the future, others are already engaged in cutting–edge procedures, using dramatic advances in biotechnology. One example deals with a new way to heal chronic wounds and ulcers. When skin is broken, either by accident or surgery, the body manufactures repair proteins, which are carried to the damaged area through the bloodstream. But if the site doesn't have an adequate blood supply, it won't get enough of the "food" that's essential to healing. As a result, the wound never mends. For diabetics and older people with reduced blood flow, this is an ongoing problem.

Penn's Cutaneous Ulcer Center addresses the shortage of crucial nutrients with a three–pronged approach. First, patients with skin ulcers are placed inside a special hyperbaric oxygen chamber and given pure oxygen. Because of the attenuated atmospheric pressure in the chamber, a lot of oxygen gets absorbed into the bloodstream, and the enriched blood promotes healing. Second, patients are dosed with a protein called acidic fibroblast growth factor. This substance enhances the growth of new blood vessels in the wound (to bring more nourishment), and juices up the surrounding cells, so they can produce connective tissue to help the wound close. Finally, patients are given a topical ointment containing a drug that prevents unwanted clotting and causes blood vessels to dilate. Dr. Gerald Lazarus, chairman of Penn's dermatology department, reports that this combination of therapies produces a much higher success rate than is usually achieved.

Another novel technique currently practiced at Penn on a rare skin–related cancer was adapted from an existing treatment for psoriasis. For some years now, the itchy, red flakiness of psoriasis has been controlled with drugs called psoralens. Patients take the drugs and are then exposed to a special ultraviolet light. The synergy of the medicine and the rays relieves the symptoms and normalizes the skin. In a variation of this process called extracorporeal photopharesis, psoralen is being administered to patients with cutaneous T–cell lymphoma, an uncommon and lethal cancer that starts in the skin and spreads to the blood.

Two hours after taking the pill, patients are hooked to an intravenous device that draws their blood into a special machine. The drug–infused white blood cells are separated by centrifuge and doused with ultraviolet light, which alters the cell membrane in such a way that when the cells are returned to the body, they're recognized as abnormal. The immune system, which had been ignoring them and letting the disease proliferate, now sees them as foreign and begins to fight back. Some patients respond immediately; others fare better when the drug interferon is added to the package.

Dr. Alain Rook, who heads this novel program, cautions that photopharesis is not a panacea. But it is able to alter white blood cells so that the body's immune system can be stimulated to react to their hyperactivity or overabundance. As such, this technique has potential for alleviating certain autoimmune diseases. He's been conducting successful clinical trials using photopharesis on patients with scleroderma, multiple sclerosis and rheumatoid arthritis.

Not all that long ago, dermatologists spent much of their time simply prescribing lotions and potions to keep skin smooth and clear. Today, skin problems—from acne to wrinkles to melanoma—are recognized as genuine medical issues. The skin is, after all, the body's largest and most visible organ, and its care is no longer considered a frivolous pursuit; rather, it's become an important source for far–ranging medical research.

*If you need help:* The general number for the dermatology clinic at Penn is 662–2737. For information concerning photopharesis, call 662–6751. The Cutaneous Ulcer Center, which treats chronic wounds and ulcers, can be contacted at 898–3265.

# 22 Everybody Must Get Stones

*For the millions who get gallstones or kidney stones, two new forms of surgery provide faster relief.*

♥ Let's say you need your gallbladder removed. And let's say the surgeon gives you a choice between traditional surgery requiring a four-inch incision, five days of hospitalization and at least two weeks at home to recover, or a technique that uses four tiny cuts and requires at the most an overnight hospital stay and a few days off from work. Unless you're a masochist, you'll opt for the latter, which is exactly why a new procedure for an old problem has become what the *Wall Street Journal* terms "the hottest operation in medicine."

Called laparoscopic cholecystectomy, this high-tech method for excising gallbladders has created an operating-room stir comparable to the introduction of laser surgery. Dr. Thomas Dent, Abington Memorial Hospital's chief of surgery, describes it as "a gas to do. A real joy. It's the most exciting development for general surgery in 20 years."

So what's the catch? Simply that some surgeons think the chances of creating problems with this technique may be higher than with traditional open surgery. It has reintroduced risks from complications, like damage to the bile duct, that had all but disappeared. When all goes well, there tends to be a lower chance for infection, and less bleeding. But in the course of gaining experience with new equipment, doctors have accidents. Dr. Dent reports that when the procedure was first used, he heard a horror story at almost every meeting he attended. He says, "I know of at least ten deaths and 30 severe complications using the laparoscope, and I'm sure there are more." On balance, however, there is a reassuring data study suggesting that these fears may be unfounded. An analysis of 1,500 laparascopic cholecystectomies published in the *New England Journal of Medicine* in April 1991 found the complication rate among surgeons surveyed was 5.1 percent, lower than percentages of 6 to 21 percent using conventional techniques.

The gallbladder is a small organ alongside the liver, similar in size and shape to a plum tomato. Its sole function is to store bile that aids in digestion. Like the appendix, it serves no critical purpose except to cause misery in the estimated 20 million Americans who develop gallstones. For unknown reasons, the majority of sufferers tend to be women, particularly those who are fair–skinned, overweight and over 40. Gallstones in the gallbladder are created by calcified crystals of cholesterol and salts that develop from the chemical content of bile. When one of these gallstones lodges in the duct connecting the gallbladder to the small intestine, inflammation occurs, and the pain can be quite awful. Other chronic symptoms of gallbladder disease include nausea, chills, fever and exhaustion.

Since we can get along quite happily without a gallbladder, the standard treatment for the last hundred years has been to cut open the abdomen and remove it. Who can forget President Lyndon Johnson lifting his pajama top to treat America to the glorious sight of the scar from his gallbladder surgery? But the three-to-five-inch scar is only one of the unpleasant aftermaths of the operation; there are also significant postoperative pain and a slow recovery, both common to any kind of abdominal surgery. Because laparoscopic cholecystectomy eliminates that large cut in the abdomen, it vastly reduces the amount of pain as well as the time needed to recover. It costs about the same ($1,000 to $2,000), but there is a significant drop in added hospital expenses.

The procedure involves an array of instruments most general surgeons have never used before and need time and experience to master. Dr. David Paskin, chief of surgery at Pennsylvania Hospital, warns, "Laparoscopic cholecystectomy sounds simple, like it isn't a real operation. But it is, and the risks are the same as with any surgery."

In contrast to open surgery, this operation (also done under general anesthesia) relies on an instrument called the video laparoscope, a kind of periscope hooked to a TV screen. The surgeon makes a small incision just above the navel and inserts the laparoscope, with its camera attached, into the abdominal cavity, which appears 20 times magnified on a television monitor. He then makes three other half-inch incisions and inserts through them three thin, rigid tubes—the conduits for the scissors, graspers and dissectors he uses to detach the gallbladder from its moorings. Once it's free—and this is the nifty part—the fluid is suctioned out, leaving the equivalent of a limp balloon that's pulled from the body via a tube placed in the bellybutton.

The recovery is nearly as dramatic as the operation itself—and the main reason for its huge popularity. Some patients feel well enough to go home the very same day. Others are not only back to work a few days later, but hard at play. One woman beat a man at racquetball five days after the new procedure. That's about the time someone with standard gallbladder surgery would be limping home from the hospital.

As patients increasingly request the "other" way to operate on gallbladders and surgeons scramble to sign on for weekend courses that teach the fundamentals of laparoscopic cholecystectomy, the old hands in the field are spouting words of caution. There is a definite learning curve that must be rounded before even the best of surgeons achieves a dependable level of competency. Dr. Anthony Coletta, who along with Dr. David Rose did the first laparoscopic cholecystectomy in the area at Bryn Mawr Hospital and now has several hundred cases under his belt, notes, "Everything is so different through the perspective of the scope. There is no question in my mind that surgeons getting started must be properly proctored."

Dr. Matthew Kirkland, a general surgeon at Pennsylvania Hospital, readily acknowledges this operation is not at all like what he learned in his surgical residency. "It's actually combining two different things, the use of a laparoscope along with the removal of a gallbladder," he says. "We're not trained to work with long instruments, watching a television screen that reduces everything from three to two dimensions. Instead of touching and probing the body with our fingers, we have to learn to sense with an 18–inch instrument. It's a whole different tactile sensation." Hahnemann University Hospital surgeon Dr. Teruo Matsumoto admits: "I was so scared the first few times. I had to work with others and get familiar with the equipment. The first ten cases I did, I had problems and had to open up the patient to finish. Since then I've had none."

We point out these dangers not to steer you away from this quite remarkable advancement, but to warn you to press your surgeon before you proceed. Why should you be his guinea pig? You want to know where he trained, and whether the course included hands–on experience. How many procedures has he or she done? (Personally, I'd want at least two dozen.) Have there been any complications? How many were attempted but not completed without opening up the patient? Is a specially trained team assisting? How many such procedures has the hospital done, and what criteria must a surgeon meet before being granted the privilege?

The rapid success of the laparoscope in gallbladder surgery is a sure indicator its application will expand quickly into other arenas. Bryn Mawr's Dr. Coletta says, "It will revolutionize abdominal surgery." He's already done exploratory surgeries for stomach cancer with the scope; doctors in other cities are experimenting with it to remove kidneys.

Losing a kidney robs the body of a vital organ, and is far more serious than losing a gallbladder. That's why gallstones can be treated by removing the gallbladder, but kidney stones must be dissolved without damaging the kidney. Varying in size from bread crumb to golfball, kidney stones form when salts in the urine crystallize into a mass. They cause a problem when they get stuck in the ureter and block urine from passing. Urine backs up into the kidney, and the pressure causes excruciating pain. In 90 percent of the cases, stones are dislodged spontaneously; the conditions that cause them can be fairly well controlled by diet and/or medication. If you've had one stone, there's a 50 percent chance you'll have another within ten years.

While women are more prone to gallstones, men are three times more likely to develop kidney stones, particularly as they age. I remember as a youngster watching my pale, sweaty father writhe in agony for two days and drink glass after glass of water to pass a kidney stone. It was the only time outside the movies I ever saw him cry.

Fortunately for my father, the stone must have been less than a quarter-inch in diameter, because he got rid of it. Stones up to that size have a 50–50 chance of passing; with anything larger, the possibility approaches zero. A decade ago, the only option to eliminate the 10 percent of stones requiring intervention was open surgery, followed by a long, painful recovery. However, the current crop of surgical residents has probably never even seen a kidney stone removed by cutting into the abdomen, thanks to an eight-year-old noninvasive technological marvel called extracorporeal shock-wave lithotripsy.

The lithotriptor is a very expensive piece of machinery that uses sound waves to shatter kidney stones. Patients are relaxed with light anesthesia and placed either in a water bath or on a special stretcher atop a water cushion, depending on the hospital. Once the exact placement of the stone is identified, the sound wave is focused directly on it. Because the body is mostly water, the pulsations pass harmlessly through the tissue and hit the stone, pulverizing it into fragments small enough to be eliminated through the urinary system.

Dr. Kenneth Brownstein, assistant clinical professor of urology at Thomas Jefferson University, warns that lithotripsy is not for everybody. It works best if the stone is located in the kidney or high in the ureter. By far the most common motivation for the procedure is unrelenting pain. "Because tolerance to pain varies greatly, this can be a hard judgment call," he says, "and when to jump in after an attack is also very subjective. Most decisions are not so clear-cut as is the case of a pilot who could be totally debilitated by a recurrent kidney stone attack in midair." Dr. Brownstein also notes that lithotripsy is not without risks or as benign as it sounds. "Even in an outpatient facility," he says, "there is an anesthesiologist present, and a preoperative workup is required. Afterward, patients should expect bruising and some pain."

In the last few years the technology for removing stones has grown by leaps and bounds because of new instrumentation, like the flexible fiber-optic ureterscope. It enables urologists to break up stones high in the ureter, near the kidney, that used to be unreachable. Other new tools can now directly enter the kidney through the back and pulverize stones too large or difficult for other, less traumatic methods. While still invasive, this is a great improvement over the old ten-inch scar and ten-day hospitalization. Patients can go home in half the time, almost completely recovered.

The marriage of technology and medicine will surely continue to create procedures that make surgery less painful, less costly, less risky and less debilitating. In the future, you can expect hospitals to leave no stone unturned, as it were, in marketing the latest techniques. The wise consumer should purchase them with prudence.

# 23 A Little Traveling Medicine, Please

*How to wage germ warfare—and win.*

♥ The year was 1986. I remember it well, because I had the dubious distinction of having traveler's diarrhea on three continents. Like me, many Americans no longer confine their vacations to civilized spots like Paris and London. We've become more adventurous in exploring the less developed nations of the world; as a result we're picking up microbial souvenirs that aren't sold in tourist shops. Of the more than 10 million travelers who leave the country annually, 20 percent get sick. One million are exposed to malaria, and several million develop acute diarrhea from something they ate or drank. Diarrhea ruins more vacations than lost luggage, yet most travelers remain better informed about hotels and restaurants than about how to be healthy tourists.

The culprit responsible for most traveler's diarrhea is an unfamiliar strain of standard intestinal bacteria that comes from contaminated food or water. Beyond Australia, Canada, Northern Europe, New Zealand and some Caribbean islands, the risks of diarrhea vary from moderate to severe, and are best avoided by following simple rules. *You* know: don't drink the water—and that includes ice cubes—and don't brush your teeth with it. Don't eat any raw vegetables or raw fruit you can't peel, or salads made from greens that may have been washed in water. Stick to carbonated drinks from the bottle unless glasses have been carefully dried—and carry straws with you, since the rims of bottles are often contaminated. Take your coffee black (dairy products are always iffy) and your alcohol neat.

I am one of those travelers who despite being terribly careful always get sick anyway, so I was delighted to discover that there are preventive drugs—trimethoprim–sulfa and doxycycline are two—to head off the diarrhea problem. On separate trips to India, Thailand and Mexico, I dosed myself daily with doxycycline and never had a bad day. However, by killing some strains of bacteria, these drugs may predispose you to others. And the drugs can have side effects that include severe skin rashes—something I personally did not experience. Recently a number of new drugs—Noroxin, CiproFloxacin and Omniflox—have come on the market. They are useful for both prevention and treatment, have fewer side effects, and are more likely to be effective. However, the prevailing wisdom at the moment appears to be that this kind of antimicrobial drug should not be taken until the problem occurs.

The choice of whether or not to take precautionary antibiotics is worth discussing with a physician. If you choose not to ward off diarrhea with an antibiotic, there's always Pepto–Bismol. Some studies show two tablets taken four times daily to be 60 percent effective as a preventative. The pills should not be used by people with a sensitivity to aspirin, because they contain salicylate.

Common, watery traveler's diarrhea usually lasts from one to four days. It's a package deal: Cramps, nausea and malaise are all included. Once you're stricken, you can knock it out quickly with one of the above-mentioned antibiotics—which should always be packed in your travel medical kit, along with Band–Aids, aspirin, sunscreens, antibacterial ointments, antacids and mosquito repellent. Over–the–counter medicines like Lomotil and Immodium will relieve cramping and control the runs, so you can sit on the tour bus, but they won't kill the bug that caused the problem, and they certainly won't prevent it.

It's extremely important to replace fluid and electrolytes lost with diarrhea. Dr. Michael Braffman, part of a team at Pennsylvania Hospital's infectious diseases department, recommends drinking alternately from a solution of 8 ounces of fruit juice, half a teaspoon of honey and a pinch of salt, and a solution of 8 ounces of carbonated water and a quarter–teaspoon of salt. These can be supplemented with tea, broth, salted crackers, rice and toast. If the diarrhea is marked by blood and/or a high fever, call a doctor immediately.

Another travel malady that hits randomly and cannot be predicted is altitude sickness. The awful weak, dizzy, nauseous sensations are due to a swelling in the brain created by a rapid change in air pressure. A drug called Diamox, a type of diuretic, won't prevent altitude sickness, but may be taken 24 to 48 hours in advance to hasten the process of acclimatization.

The most unavoidable aspect of long–distance travel seems to be jet lag. Nearly every function in our bodies is timed on a day–night cycle that, if it were regulated by external cues from the sun and moon, would make adjusting to different time zones quite simple. Unfortunately, our body rhythms respond to an internal clock, and there is no drug to reach in and reset the hands. However, there are some tips to minimize the discomfort while the body puts itself on local time.

Begin when you board the plane by drinking lots of water or fruit juice during the flight. The cabin air is exceedingly dry, and your system dehydrates after hours of simply sitting there breathing it. Try to avoid coffee and alcohol, because they are diuretics, and bring along high–fiber snacks to handle the constipation that accompanies dehydration. You may want to pass on the liquor cart entirely and consider taking a mild sleeping pill instead. Dr. Braffman sees nothing wrong with a low-dose sleeping pill if you know you can get six hours of uninterrupted sleep. You might want to pop another pill the night you arrive at your destination, so you don't wake up at 3 a.m because your body thinks it's time for breakfast.

When it comes to travel–related medical questions, it's wise to bypass your family doctor and consult a specialist in infectious diseases. There are local experts in travel medicine at Pennsylvania Hospital and the Medical College of Pennsylvania who can tailor standard travel health advisories to the background and needs of individual travelers. Dr. Donald Kaye helped organize the travel health program at MCP. He cautions tourists that it's not enough to be informed on what's safe to eat and what shots are on official lists. It's also important to check out the potential dangers related to pre–existing medical conditions.

"For instance," Kaye says, "I might tell a pregnant woman calling for information on immunizations for East Africa to stay home until the baby is born. There are all kinds of things people don't think about." He points out that St. Petersburg, which isn't typically considered a third–world city, happens to be a major source of giardia, a parasite that commonly causes severe stomach upsets. Another little-known travel warning concerns contaminated freshwater lakes or streams in certain parts of Asia, Africa and South America where swimmers can easily pick up a parasitic worm. And a stop in Mexico City or Cuzco, Peru, could be a serious health hazard for anyone with a heart or lung problem, because of the altitude.

Since travelers' medical histories and itineraries vary greatly, it's usually not a good idea to rely on the advice of a travel agent when it comes to required inoculations. Which shots are a must and which are a maybe depends on what parts of a country you visit, what season you go, and how long you stay. Until a decade or so ago, anybody leaving the United States for developing countries had to carry proof of a smallpox vaccination in his passport. With the elimination of that disease, no shots are necessary. However, most vaccines fall into the category of recommended rather than required, and the recommendations may vary depending on the source.

A good jumping–off point for guidelines are the Centers for Disease Control, which maintain up–to–date info on disease outbreaks. For example, while the yellow fever vaccine is required by law for entry into certain countries, the virus happens to be active in many places that don't demand inoculation. You may not need a shot to get past immigration, but you may want it for your own protection. The same goes for cholera, which is being reported in parts of Africa, India, Southeast Asia and Central and South America. The vaccine is rather weak and only 50 percent effective, and is not required for travel from the United States. However, you'd need it if you were planning to stop in India and then go on to Pakistan.

There are several other vaccinations that adventurous travelers should consider. Typhoid fever, while rare in Europe, is not uncommon in parts of Asia. Shots (or the newer oral vaccine) should be taken for any prolonged stay in the third world, particularly if you'll be wandering off the beaten path. Rabies is a significant risk in some parts of the world, and shots are suggested for stays exceeding 30 days in the rural parts of certain countries like India. Last year, six trekkers in Nepal contracted meningitis, which might have been avoided had they been informed of an outbreak in the Kathmandu Valley. Fairly current data on the status of diseases is published by the CDC in a biweekly bulletin called *Morbidity and Mortality Weekly Report.* Pennsylvania Hospital's Dr. Braffman is one travel specialist who receives the publication—and reads it. As a result, he knew when an unusual number of polio cases had been reported in Israel and was able to advise his patients headed for the Holy Land to get booster shots.

According to the CDC, polio boosters are part of what should be a standard immunization package for third-world travel. That package also should include a tetanus booster (lasts ten years), gamma globulin as protection against hepatitis A (lasts a few months), and an MMR II (measles/mumps/rubella) booster for people born after 1957. Even if you're not planning a trip, you should have this immunization.

Unfortunately, there is no inoculation to protect travelers from malaria, a disease that's a major cause of death outside the United States. The standard program for malaria protection is a drug called choloroquine or mefloquine that must be taken before, during and after exposure. Unfortunately, some strains of malaria have become resistant to these regimens, which makes it critical that you discuss malaria prevention with a knowledgeable physician. In parts of Thailand, for example, doxycycline may be preferred.

In addition to drugs, common sense must prevail. Malaria–carrying mosquitoes are night creatures that prey from dusk to dawn. When the sun goes down, rub your body with deet repellent, wear long–sleeved clothes, and sleep under netting. It can be terribly romantic.

*If you need help:* For a complete and personal approach to travel health, call the infectious disease specialists at either the Travel Health Advisory, Immunization and Treatment Service of the Medical College of Pennsylvania, 842–6465, or the Travel Medical Consultation Service at Pennsylvania Hospital, 925–8010. General information on required and recommended immunizations is available weekdays from 8:30–4:30 from the Philadelphia Department of Public Health, 875–5640, or the Centers for Disease Control, 404–639–2572. To order *Health Information for International Travel,* call the government printing office, 202–783–3238. It costs $5 and can be charged to a credit card. The order number is 017–023–00184–1.

# 24

# Cold Comfort

*How to fight the winter blahs.*

♥ Birds do it; bears do it. In fact, all the creatures in the animal kingdom exhibit a response to winter's cold and darkness, whether it's a long sleep, a thicker coat of fur and fat or an increased metabolism. Human beings, sheltered in warm homes with plenty of electric sunshine, were long thought to be immune to these severe seasonal changes. So why do our spirits sag and our bodies slow down once winter comes? Apparently we, too, have a hibernation response, and it accounts for our feeling fat, depressed and tired from first frost to first blossom.

What we experience as the winter blahs is actually a physiological slowdown precipitated by diminishing daylight and falling temperatures. The culprit is a hormone called melatonin, a kind of natural tranquilizer secreted when it gets dark. Its production is regulated by our light–sensitive pineal gland. Year-round, when the sun goes down, the pineal starts increasing melatonin. That accounts in part for our getting sleepy at night. It also explains why as the daylight hours decrease, we naturally slow down.

Animal reaction to winter is triggered as much by changes in light as by falling temperature. For example, breeders have learned to lengthen the fertility period of horses by turning on strong lights in their stalls in December; that tricks their sex hormones into believing spring has come early. Our own systems are just as vulnerable to the amount of light we receive.

In experiments conducted at the National Institute of Mental Health, Dr. Alfred Lewy found that when he awakened people in the middle of the night by shining a bright light on them—one as brilliant as the dawn of a July day—their pineal glands immediately stopped making melatonin. That's why in spring and summer we jump out of bed, wide awake, at 7 a.m. Winter is a different story. As far as the pineal is concerned, ordinary household light is no better than living in the dark. Some scientists believe that the weak light of a December morn doesn't stop the pineal from producing melatonin. Instead of shutting off, the hormone supply just slows to a trickle—until night signals the gland to step up production once again.

Dr. Lewy concluded that too much melatonin is the reason people get more depressed in the winter. The symptoms of these winter blues, which he named Seasonal Affective Disorder—SAD—are quite different from the ones typically associated with depression. Instead of feeling hopeless and despairing, SAD sufferers are jumpy and anxious, and mutter about cabin fever. Instead of the usual weight and appetite loss characteristic of most depressions, they crave sweets and starches. About 70 percent lose interest in sex. But when spring arrives, their mood lifts, and the world looks fine once more.

While the serious depression of SAD is an extreme example of winter misery, it appears that everybody who lives in a seasonal climate undergoes some degree of emotional and physical alteration. "Clearly, things happen to people when the days get short and cold," says Dr. Peter Whybrow, chairman of the department of psychiatry at the University of Pennsylvania. "Like animals preparing to hibernate, we slow down, eat more, and feel more irritable and lethargic." Fortunately, there are some specific ways to cope with the winter doldrums beyond taking a vacation in the sunny Caribbean. Dr. Whybrow has collected them in a book called *The Hibernation Response—Why You Feel Fat, Miserable and Depressed from October Through March and How You Can Cheer Up Through Those Dark Days of Winter.*

Some of winter's problems are beyond our control. Cold doesn't kill germs as effectively as the ultraviolet rays of sunshine, so we catch more flus, sniffles and coughs in winter than in summer. Moreover, heating systems have a tendency to dry out an important natural germ filter, our mucous membranes, and that leaves us more susceptible to infections. Raising the humidity in your home to around 45 percent is a good way to compensate.

On the other hand, we can do all sorts of things to fool Mother Nature, and one of the most important, according to Whybrow's book, is to let there be light. Since 1980, doctors have been successfully curing severe winter depressions with a program that uses neither drugs nor psychotherapy, but a daily regimen of exposure to a superpowered light that makes any dull January day into a bright June morn. If you identify with the symptoms of winter depression, you can create synthetic sunshine by purchasing a high-intensity light box and keeping it on from two to four hours every day. Whybrow keeps one of these boxes by his bed, and switches it on when he rises at 6 a.m. Even if you don't suffer from SAD, he thinks it's a wise idea to increase your morning light, even if only by opening your curtains and turning on all the lights when you rise.

Whybrow also advocates creating an environment that brings the look and feel of spring to at least one room of your home. Fill it with plants, and keep it relatively humid. For lighting, keep away from energy-saving sodium bulbs. Yellow light tends to be depressing, and has been related to reports of nausea. A combination of bright incandescent and fluorescent lighting is best.

Bringing light to your life will certainly improve your mental outlook, but it won't make you feel warmer on a freezing day. The hibernation response is as much physical as emotional. Nature has given us a number of automatic responses to handle cold. Shivering, for instance, is the body's way of warming up, by sending our muscles into a rippling frenzy that generates heat. The accompanying goose bumps are designed to literally make our hairs stand on end; the erect hairy coat they create traps air and makes a layer of natural insulation. Since man has evolved into a fairly hairless creature, this mechanism doesn't work nearly as effectively as it did in the Stone Age. But it's still great for furry animals.

We civilized folks get our insulation from clothing, but we could survive clad only in our birthday suits. That's not to suggest we should, but we can learn to love winter a little more by training ourselves to be more comfortable in the cold.

Begin by forgetting what your mother told you about bundling up. Too much heavy clothing prompts our bodies to cool us off with perspiration. We defeat the purpose of keeping warm when our natural cooling systems are battling our overcoats. What we want to do is raise our temperature through internal forces. This can be accomplished by a fairly simple exercise program.

Whybrow calls it "acclimatizing," and swears it works. In the fall, he says, when the weather begins to cool down, don a light jacket rather than a heavy one and go outside for a brisk 30-to-45-minute walk every day. You'll feel chilly at first, but not for long, as the exposure to cold stimulates your body to become a more efficient heat-producer. Little by little, your system learns how to warm itself by a process called visceral thermogenesis—a fancy term that means you heat yourself from the inside out. The liver and thyroid learn to respond almost instantly to cold by rapidly increasing their metabolic rate and pumping out heat-producing hormones.

If cold-training isn't your cup of tea, here are some winter dress codes to help you fight the windchill. Protect your torso; a warm body can actually prevent cold extremities. It's also important to keep your head and neck covered; that's why Mother Nature allows the hair on our heads to grow longer than anywhere else on our bodies. As a general guideline, natural fibers like cotton and wool are better insulators than synthetics; loose and layered clothing is preferable to anything too snug.

Finally, there is the matter of warmth and body weight. It's no accident that Eskimos are short, squat and solid; that's the best body type to conserve heat. Dr. Whybrow says that if you live in a cold climate, there's no sense trying to take weight off in late fall and early winter. When temperatures drop, your body doesn't know you've got a freezer full of food, and an oil burner. Like a wild animal's, it anticipates life-threatening food shortages and wants to layer in some extra fat for protection. It even starts using calories more efficiently. You'll burn 10 percent fewer calories bicycling a mile in November than you will in April, and in winter you'll eat more, too, because it takes calories to produce body heat.

Dr. Whybrow has developed a weight control anti-hibernation diet that meets the special nutritional needs of winter without adding 20 pounds of extra fuel. He recommends a daily intake that is less than 30 percent unsaturated fat (corn and olive oil rather than butter), 50 percent complex carboyhydrates (pasta rather than candy), and 20 percent protein.

To keep depression low and energy high, what you eat and when you eat it is critical to the success of this diet. Try to make breakfast your main meal of the day, and schedule as many as five more mini-meals before 9 p.m. The goal isn't to eat more, but to eat more often, giving your body a better opportunity to convert food to fuel instead of storing it as fat. Whybrow notes that researchers have found "performance and body temperature maintenance were higher when volunteers ate three meals within eight hours than when they had one meal containing the same calories."

Make the first three meals very heavy on protein, and the last three heavy on carbohydrates. During the day, you want to boost energy by concentrating on protein-rich foods, especially those high in tyrosine, a protein that tells the brain to get moving. It's found in things like eggs, green beans, whole wheat bread and skim milk. Forget about pancakes, cereal and muffins for breakfast, and have a chicken sandwich instead. Later in the day you can down high-carbohydrate goodies that are rich in tryptophan, a protein that promotes relaxation and gets us ready for sleep.

Also pay attention to what Whybrow calls "winter warrior" nutrients. A recent survey of American women showed their diets to be low in iron, calcium, magnesium and vitamin C. If you find that you're almost always cold, you may not have a circulation problem, but an easily cured nutrient deficiency. Now, wouldn't that be just the news to warm the cockles of your heart?

***If you need help****: The Hibernation Response*, by Peter Whybrow, M.D., and Robert Bahr, is published by Arbor House. If you have questions about a balanced winter diet, call Dial–A–Dietitian at 215–748–9222, a service of the Philadelphia Dietetic Association.

# NOTES

**METHODIST**
*Rapid Recovery Surgical Center*

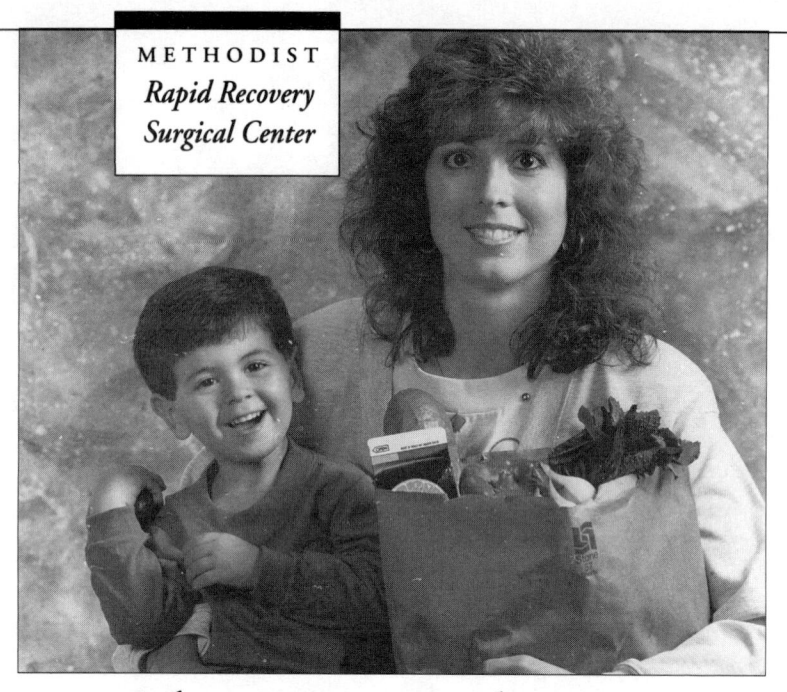

# Where You Heal Faster and Go Home Sooner

Today, new procedures mean a shorter hospital stay for many kinds of surgery. Specially trained physicians at Methodist Hospital's Rapid Recovery Surgical Center are dramatically changing the way surgery is done.

Methodist surgeons and gynecologists using lasers, scopes and other advanced equipment have helped hundreds of patients spend less time in the hospital, and less time recovering at home.

Many operations can now be done at Methodist's Rapid Recovery Surgical Center – from gallbladder surgery to sinus surgery and even removal of ovarian cysts, hernia repair and permanent treatment for stomach ulcers.

Best of all – these kinds of operations now require just a few stitches and leave almost no scars to see.

For surgery or a second opinion, discuss your options with a Methodist doctor. Methodist's Rapid Recovery Surgical Center gets you home fast, and well.

For information, and to receive fact sheets on surgical procedures suited to Methodist's Rapid Recovery Surgery, call (215) BROAD ST.

## ✣ Methodist Hospital
2301 South Broad Street, Philadelphia, PA 19148

# 25

## Light Fantastic

*Lasers are the latest bright idea in surgery. They can do some things that scalpels can't touch.*

♥ I don't recall ever seeing a episode entitled "Buck Rogers in Surgery" on the old space adventure series, but if those movies were revived today, Rogers and his miraculous ray gun would be right at home in a modern hospital. The light–shooting weapon he aimed at his defenseless enemies has developed into an innovative surgical instrument. Today lasers are removing warts, soldering detached retinas, opening clogged arteries in the heart, vaporizing hard–to–reach brain tumors, and fusing spaghetti–thin blood vessels. In addition, experimental lasers have already begun to move beyond the operating arena into the doctor's office, where they're being looked at to control pain and heal wounds. And it's expected that someday the laser will replace the dental drill in preparing cavities for fillings.

The word "laser" is an acronym for "light amplification by stimulated emission of radiation." You don't have to be an Einstein to decipher what that means, although he was the scientist who first promulgated the theory on which lasers are based. To understand lasers in the simplest of terms, you need to grasp three concepts. First: Light carries energy, and the more intensely focused the light, the greater its power. The light released by a normal bulb scatters in every direction, and contains many different wavelengths. Its diffusion dilutes its strength. By contrast, the laser compresses its light energy into one highly focused, narrow beam, with a single pure color and a single wavelength. This intensity gives the light its obliterating power.

Second: Einstein theorized that an atom of any natural substance could be stimulated to release light energy. Practically speaking, most elements need too much of a charge to produce significant energy, so the sources of laser power are limited to certain gases, crystals, metals or chemical dyes. The lasing medium, as these substances are called, determines what the laser can and cannot do. If you've heard a surgeon say he'll be using a carbon dioxide or argon laser, that gas is what receives the charge. In the future, as new lasing mediums are developed, lasers will become increasingly specific in the tasks they perform.

Third: If you took high school physics, you may recall that each wavelength of light has special properties. Different kinds of lasers have been developed to take advantage of these unique attributes.

For example, the carbon dioxide laser is an excellent cutting and fusing tool, because it penetrates only superficially but can destroy anything in its path. While it may look (and smell) to the patient as though the laser is burning tissue away, in actuality the laser doesn't burn like a traditional cauterizing tool. Instead, its energy heats the water in cells to the boiling point, causing them to explode and vaporize. This popular laser has many broad applications; Temple University vascular surgeon Dr. John White has been experimenting with it as a fast and reliable alternative to hand–sewn sutures. The laser joins blood vessels by literally melting the ends of veins and arteries together. This becomes particularly meaningful to people such as diabetics, who have trouble recovering from surgery because their wounds close slowly, if at all.

Another laser, the argon, has a wavelength enabling it to permeate some mediums without being absorbed. In demonstrating the argon laser, a doctor may place a small amount of clotted blood in a beaker of a water. The laser will penetrate the water with little effect while vaporizing the clot. This quality makes the argon laser ideal for passing through the clear liquids of the eye to repair damage to the retina.

Lasers have the capability to cut, burn, vaporize or seal cells by one or more of three basic processes. They may accomplish their goal by producing heat. They may create a chemical reaction that literally breaks apart the molecular bonds holding cells together. Or they may generate a shock wave that ruptures tissue apart. In scientific jargon, these are known as the photothermal, photochemical and photoplasmic effects.

In a surgeon's hand, a laser functions as a finely tuned scalpel, with some added advantages. There is less blood loss, because the heat from lasers coagulates as it cuts, and there is less infection, because the heat also sterilizes. Lasers are so exacting that they can kill cells on an individual basis, a technique especially helpful when a tumor grows in such a way that cutting it out poses the risk of damage to surrounding tissue.

This precision has been particularly valuable in easing the pain of some patients who have inoperable tumors blocking vital passages. The laser can bore a hole through the blockage, and create an opening that gives temporary relief to someone who might not be able to swallow because of an obstruction in the esophagus. At Pennsylvania Hospital, Dr. Michael Unger, director of pulmonary endoscopy and research and development of lasers, is using the laser quite successfully to kill lung tumors inside the airways that previously would have been considered inoperable or would have necessitated removing the entire lung. While this procedure doesn't cure the cancer, it does prolong and improve the quality of life.

Lasers make excellent tools for destroying growths without traumatizing the adjacent tissues—especially in the case of skin cancers—but there's a downside, too. Once the tumor is vaporized, nothing's left for a pathologist to examine. That can leave a small degree of uncertainty about the completeness of the surgery.

It's not surprising that these flashy by–products of space–age technology have so captivated the public imagination that their hype often exceeds their practical application. Rushing to embrace this sexy new medical toy, some surgeons are using lasers in circumstances where they have no advantages over standard surgical techniques. The things lasers do well, they do exceedingly well. But they should be considered as adjuncts to the scalpel, not as replacements.

Dr. Harvey Lerner, an oncological surgeon at Germantown Hospital who is well–versed in lasers, frequently gets phone calls from people specifically requesting laser surgery. "They think we can shine a laser light and they won't need an operation," he says. "In the case of something like hemorrhoids, it makes sense to use a laser rather than the standard method. We can do the procedure on an outpatient basis, and some patients report less postoperative pain. But usually people are better off being operated on with a knife."

When Dr. Lerner was explaining to me how lasers work, I volunteered to let him demonstrate by lasing two benign moles on my chest, about the size of saccharine tablets, that I'd had for as long as I could remember. We used to call these things beauty marks, probably as a way of avoiding how ugly they look when exposed by a bathing suit or strapless dress. In the past I'd spoken to a plastic surgeon about removing them, but I was put off by the idea of being cut into and scarred.

The laser surgery took less than five minutes, and all I had to endure was a slight hissing sound. Dr. Lerner injected the area with a mild anesthetic, so I felt nothing. He applied a sapphire–tipped YAG laser to the moles, which in effect killed them by truncating their blood supply. Within two weeks the scabs fell off, and eventually the little pink dots around them faded away. Today you can't tell the moles ever existed. I've been lased and lived to talk about it.

The earliest lasers crossed the line from space to medicine in 1964, when a laser mended a detached retina. Until then, it had not been possible to operate inside the eye itself. By the early '70s, ophthalmologists were using lasers to treat a problem called diabetic retinopathy, a form of blindness so common among diabetics that it's the third leading cause of sight–loss in this country. Dr. Myron Yanoff, professor and chairman of ophthalmology at Hahnemann University, says, "Once we were able to do nothing for diabetics but watch them lose their sight. Now, with the laser, most can be helped. It's really quite marvelous."

Today lasers are used routinely by eye surgeons for everything from spot–welding complicated cases of detached retinas to treating glaucoma. In a condition known as acute close–angle glaucoma, patients develop a kind of drainage problem that results in the buildup of pressure in the eye. A zap of a special YAG laser dissipates the blockage, the way Drano clears the drain in a clogged sink. Patients who've already had cataract surgery sometimes develop a secondary condition in which a thin, membranous scar forms. Lasers can dissolve this in an instant.

Someday a new "cool" laser (so–called because it works on very, very short pulses that generate almost no heat) may make eyeglasses obsolete for nearsighted people. Myopia is a condition caused by the eye being longer than normal. The cool laser, called the excimer, has the capability of reshaping the cornea, actually correcting the defect instead of compensating for it like glasses do. Dr. Yanoff spent six months in Germany learning how to use this laser as a cutting instrument, and he's already working with it in certain kinds of cornea transplants. In addition, he heads one of only four FDA–approved sites for testing an even newer development, the holmium laser, which can reshape the cornea to correct farsightedness.

From their beginnings in ophthalmology, lasers moved quickly into general surgery. Most surgeons will acknowledge that there's still nothing that cuts so well as a 12–cent stainless–steel scalpel, but for certain specific procedures, lasers perform with much greater efficiency. They are superb for reducing blood loss, because they seal while they cut, and they can often used with only minimal anesthesia. That doesn't mean lasers have the aim–and–shoot capability of Buck Rogers' ray gun. They can't zap through the skin and repair tissue deep within the body. However, lasers can reach interior organs when they are threaded through instruments known as endoscopes. These have long served primarily as diagnostic tools, but when enhanced by lasers they become surgical tools as well.

Most scopes enter the body through one of its openings (mouth, nose, etc.) or via tiny incisions. Say a doctor puts a scope down your windpipe and discovers a dot–size growth on the vocal cords. He certainly can't pass a scalpel down the scope and shave it off. But he can send a pencil–thin laser through the scope, and by delicately manipulating its beam destroy the tumor one cell at a time without harming the vocal cords themselves.

Today the laser has broad applications in gynecological surgery. It increases the cure rate for genital warts, and opens blocked fallopian tubes that may be causing infertility. Lasers have revolutionized the treatment of endometriosis, a condition in which tissue that should line the uterus grows somewhere else instead, causing severe menstrual cramping and often infertility as well. Before the advent of lasers, endometriosis could only be treated with medication or major abdominal surgery. Now the unwanted tissue can be destroyed relatively simply by using a laser through a laparoscope. Some gynecological surgeons favor the laser for treating early pelvic cancers, because it can be much more precise than the traditional methods of freezing or burning, and the end result is no scarring or infection in the remaining tissue.

In contrast, many others oppose the choice of a laser procedure as a substitute for hysterectomy to treat women who have severe bleeding problems. "Insurance companies like it because it's cheaper," says one surgeon I interviewed, "but unless the woman is a poor surgical patient, I think it's better to remove a problem uterus than to leave it and run the risk of it becoming diseased in the future." And another caveat comes from Dr. Lerner, who warns women not to be misled into thinking that lasers create less disfiguring mastectomies.

Some urologists find lasers helpful for patients who because of poor health or the difficult placement of their tumors would not otherwise be candidates for surgery. In certain cases where the ureter is blocked and in some kidney and bladder tumors, the laser can be used through a cystoscope to destroy a cancer that's unreachable with a scalpel. Moreover, the surgery can be done on an outpatient basis, without general anesthesia.

In orthopedics, Dr. Eric Mitchell, who operates at Graduate Hospital, routinely works with lasers when he does arthroscopic surgery on knees. He says, "The laser can trim cartilage inside the knee a lot more accurately than the conventional grabbers and biters. It lets me sculpt, rather then cut."

And in dermatology, lasers are old hat in the removal of keloids and warts. What's getting attention is a special laser that interacts with red blood cells. It's been a godsend for people disfigured by large birthmarks, called port–wine stains or hemangiomas, that come from the presence of abnormally large and unnecessary blood vessels. The tunable dye laser takes advantage of the affinity of certain wavelengths of light for certain colors. When this laser is focused on the birthmark, explains University of Pennsylvania dermatologist Dr. Leonard Dzubow, its energy gets absorbed only by the red pigment of hemoglobin. The short bursts produce heat that injures the blood vessel wall, gradually shutting it down so that blood no longer flows into it. The small surrounding vessels are unaffected. Depending on the size, it may take several applications for the stain to disappear.

This same technique can also destroy tiny spider veins, or, for that matter, tattoos. If you were one of the free spirits of the '70s who celebrated your liberation with a discreet tattoo that no longer fits your lifestyle, you could call Dr. Ronald Kirschner. The professor and chairman of facial plastic surgery at the Philadelphia College of Osteopathic Medicine and former chair of the Laser Institute of America has a successful track record in wiping out these reminders of one's colorful past.

The principle that makes it possible for particular lasers to be absorbed only by particular colors has great potential in cancer therapy, either by itself or as an adjunct to chemotherapy or radiation. Whereas most lasers in medicine use heat, these lasers operate strictly by photochemical reaction. Special substances are injected into the bloodstream and are absorbed preferentially by cancer cells, but are not retained by normal tissue. The laser beam activates these substances, triggering a chain reaction that destroys the tumor. The laser has no effect on the surrounding tissue, but the injected substances do cause a hypersensitivity to sunlight, so patients must avoid direct sun for up to 30 days following a treatment. Such "photodynamic therapy" is already widely practiced in Japan and Europe and used experimentally in the United

States. Pennsylvania Hospital's Dr. Michael Unger has been conducting investigational trials with it on lung cancer. "It's very promising," he says, "but we need more data."

Likewise promising is a procedure for treating heart disease using the excimer (cool) laser, which because of the way it pulses light can vaporize tissue without the presence of heat. That means it doesn't burn tissue. Initially these cool lasers (similar in principle to those used in ophthalmology) were used to dissipate plaque in the larger arteries of the leg. Now they are being tested to clear even the more delicate and tiny arteries inside the heart.

The primary method for cleaning plaque from arteries without submitting to bypass surgery has, until now, been the balloon angioplasty: A catheter with a balloon on the end is threaded through the artery to the blocked area. When inflated, the balloon flattens the plaque against the vessel wall and opens the passage. If the balloon acts like a bulldozer pushing plaque out of the way, the excimer behaves like a magician's wand. It breaks the plaque down into particles about the size of white blood cells, to be carried away in the blood flow.

This "excimer laser coronary angioplasty" has become an excellent alternative for patients who aren't candidates for standard balloon angioplasties because their blockages are too long, or are located in small arterial branches that the balloons can't reach. Dr. William Untereker, of the Philadelphia Heart Institute of Presbyterian Medical

---

## Neurosurgery at Penn

The specialists in the **Division of Neurosurgery** at the University of Pennsylvania Medical Center provide comprehensive treatment and care of all surgical diseases of the brain and spine. All of the latest surgical and microsurgical techniques including preoperative embolization and radiosurgery are available.

Our board-certified specialists provide highly skilled care for patients with:

- Aneurysms
- Brain tumors
- Cerebrovascular diseases
- Disorders of the spine
- Head trauma
- Neuro-ophthalmologic tumors
- Pituitary tumors
- Vascular malformations

For more information, please call our referral counselors at 215-662-PENN (7366), or Neurosurgery, 215-662-3487.

### UNIVERSITY OF PENNSYLVANIA MEDICAL CENTER

University of Pennsylvania School of Medicine
Hospital of the University of Pennsylvania

Center, has performed excimer angioplasties in 204 patients since 1990, with a 93 percent success rate. One of his patients was a 65-year-old stockbroker who played golf three days later.

If you are contemplating laser surgery, make certain you choose a surgeon who has been certified in the use of lasers, and be sure to question him pointedly about the advantage of using a laser for your particular operation. In the current climate, where lasers seem to be recommended for just about everything, Temple University surgeon John White, who teaches courses for doctors in laser technology, advises a healthy dose of skepticism. Dr. White says, "In skilled hands, the laser has about the same risks as the knife. The key word is *skilled*." By the time a surgeon finishes school, he or she has had years of practice with a scalpel. A laser is an equally dangerous weapon, and you should closely scrutinize the doctor's experience with it. Where did the doctor study lasers, and for how long? How many laser surgeries has he done? Ten would be fine for removing a wart, but you'd want five times that to remove a piece of your liver.

In the meantime, the breadth of possibilities for future laser usage keeps growing. The goal of research in laser technology is to refine these instruments to the point where a particular wavelength of light can be matched so accurately with a target tissue that it will affect only that target and nothing around it. That will take technology far beyond anything Buck Rogers ever imagined.

---

# No Pain. No Veins.
### A new laser treatment for vascular and pigmented blemishes.

If you work hard to look good, you know that nature doesn't always cooperate. Those tiny spider veins, age spots, freckles, broken blood vessels, or blotchy red areas on your skin are good examples. They may appear because of heredity, exposure to sun, even pregnancy. There is virtually no way to prevent them. But there is a very simple way to remove them.

VASCULASE™ is an advanced laser treatment for vascular and pigmented blemishes. It uses safe laser light to erase problem veins. Treatment takes only minutes, with only moderate discomfort. And best of all, you can see the results as soon as the treatment is over.

Call THE LASER CENTER for more information or to arrange a physician consultation.
**Exclusive in Philadelphia** - only available at THE LASER CENTER.

THE LASER CENTER

Northeast Medical Center - Pavilion
Roosevelt Blvd. and Welsh Road
Philadelphia, PA 19114
**1-215-969-VAIN (8246)**
**1-800-368-VAIN (8246)**

Metalaser Technologies™

Vasculase™ is the trademark of Metalaser Technologies, Inc. ©1991 Metalaser Technologies, Inc.

# "Why do I need a doctor when I'm not sick?"

The best time to choose a physician is when you are well. Your primary care physician is the one you will see for most of your health needs. He or she supervises your ongoing medical care, coordinating with other specialists if necessary, and helps you practice preventive care so you won't get sick.

For help in asking the right questions when choosing a doctor, call 248-8069 for your free copy of "A Primer on Primary Care."

Most primary physicians are trained in family practice, obstetrics and gynecology, internal medicine or pediatrics. It is important to choose the physician that's right for you and your family. When you're ready to choose, let Chestnut Hill Hospital help find the doctor who meets your needs. **The Chestnut Hill Hospital Physician Referral Service is available from 8:30-4:30 weekdays by calling 248-8069.**

Your health is our primary concern.

## Chestnut Hill Hospital
A SERVICE OF CHESTNUT HILL HOSPITAL HEALTHCARE

8835 Germantown Avenue
Philadelphia, PA 19118
(215) 248-8200

# 26 Nothing to Sneeze At

*A look at some new ways of treating allergies.*

♥ Clearly, Shakespeare did not have allergies. If he'd been battling the sneezing and wheezing of a hay fever attack, he would not have been inspired to pen a sonnet about the perfect days of June, a month that for roughly one in five people heralds the miserable arrival of allergy season. Doctors don't understand why some people experience only a runny nose while others suffer coughing and itching, but they do know you can't catch allergies. And you can't cure them, either, though you can outgrow them, and alter their natural course with allergy shots. Allergies are both inherited and activated by something in the environment. That means a child born in Los Angeles with an allergy to ragweed will never experience symptoms as long as he remains within the state border—because there's no ragweed in California. But let that child come East to visit relatives one August and return the same time the following year, and chances are he'll be sneezing soon after the plane lands in Philadelphia.

There are many kinds of allergic disease, ranging from asthma to eczema, but the most common by far is allergic rhinitis, often characterized by an onslaught of sneezing that seems to raise the normal two quarts of mucus produced by the body each day tenfold. Mistakenly called hay fever or rose fever, allergic rhinitis isn't aggravated by sniffing hay or roses. The chief problem–causers are far more ubiquitous. The major indoor offenders are dust and animal dander, and if you're allergy–sensitive to these, you'll probably suffer year–round. The outdoor inhalants—pollens and molds—usually cause seasonal problems, stretching anywhere from April to the first frost of October.

You can do a bit of self–diagnosis by matching your symptoms to the seasons. Trees pollinate in March and April, and there are about eight varieties on the Delaware Valley allergy menu. According to Dr. Paul Atkins, a University of Pennsylvania allergist and immunologist, a sufferer can be allergic to any number of trees, and a sensitivity to one doesn't always mean a sensitivity to others. That's not true of grasses, which pollinate in May and June; it's likely that a problem with one grass leads to a problem with *all*. The weeds enter in July, with ragweed predominating in August and September. If your nose runs from spring until fall, you may be allergic to all of the above as well as to mold spores, which start spreading when the weather gets warm and hit their peak when plants begin to decay in the fall.

If you've noticed that you often feel worse as the allergy season progresses, that's because exposure increases reactivity. It takes a lot more grass pollen to make a grass–allergic person sneeze in January than it does in June. And to further complicate the problem, allergic people seemed primed to react to more than one allergen. A sensitivity to dogs is likely to increase a sensitivity to dust, and so on.

Allergic disease is essentially caused by a malfunction of the immune system—the body's defense against unwanted foreign invaders. Ordinarily the immune system responds to the threats of viruses and bacteria by forming antibodies against them. But in allergic people, the system also reacts to benign substances like house dust and pollen. The first encounter with an offender triggers the production of specialized allergy chemicals known as IgE antibodies; once they're stimulated, you may be stuck with this unnecessary strike force forever after.

So now you've got a trained, armed guard lying in wait. The IgE antibodies cluster like millions of detonators around the mast cells lining the skin and the respiratory and digestive tracts. If you inhale the allergen, your nose and eyes respond. If you ingest it, the result might be hives, or a stomachache. What typically happens on that beautiful June day when you're working in the garden and the air's redolent with grass pollen is that every breath you take brings trouble. The pollen enters your airways and attaches to mast cells already loaded with the allergy antibody Marines. The troops explode into action, releasing a plethora of fighting fire, including histamines and leukotrienes, which trigger other reactions—like swelling and inflammation—that combine to produce the sneezy, wheezy, itchy symptoms of an allergy attack.

Until the '60s, it was believed that histamines were the major weapon released by the allergy arsenal. That led to the development of antihistamine drugs geared towards neutralizing their effect. (ChlorTrimeton and Benadryl are two of the most popular.) For mild symptoms like a runny nose and itchy eyes, antihistamines work fairly well, but they're accompanied by the negative side effect of putting people to sleep. One alternative for some is a decongestant like Sudafed. Decongestants not only shrink swollen nasal tissues, but may act as stimulants, which is why drug companies combine them with antihistamines to counteract drowsiness. (Some popular blends are Actifed, Dimetapp, Drixoral and Trinalin.) Unfortunately, decongestants have their own unwelcome side effects, including nervousness, palpitations, high blood pressure and even impotence.

Left with the alternatives of feeling jumpy or sleepy, many allergy sufferers turn to nasal sprays like Afrin and Neo–Synephrine II—effective for occasional discomfort but dangerously habit–forming. If used for several days in a row, these sprays create a rebound effect—that is, renewed congestion when the dose wears off. Soon the user is hooked on the spray every few hours, using it for relief of a problem caused by what began as a solution.

Fortunately, a dramatic increase in our understanding of the mechanism of an allergic reaction, coupled with better medications to treat the average summer sufferer, has brightened the picture. Doctors now know that an important component of an allergy attack is inflammation, which may occur hours after exposure to an antigen and persist for days.

The latest allergy medications for hay fever are sprayed rather than swallowed. The first, cromolyn sodium, was initially used for asthmatics, and was found to have a unique effect on allergy tissues by preventing mast cells from releasing histamine. Taken four times daily throughout allergy season, along with antihistamines on an as–needed basis, cromolyn appears to ward off problems before they occur. For casual hay fever victims, it's been highly effective. Sold as Nasalcrom, the spray costs about $15 for a 20–day supply. In the view of Dr. John Cohn, a Thomas Jefferson pulmonologist, "It's probably the safest drug I give out."

The second, corticosteroids, work best after exposure, by reducing the inflammation that aggravates an attack. Any drug with the word *steroid* ought to arouse concern, but in this case there seems to be little to worry about if you follow the doctor's orders. Studies show that very little of the newer topical nasal steroids (Vancenase, Beconase, Nasacort and Nasalide) is absorbed into the bloodstream.

Finally, prescription antihistamines are now available that *don't* usually cause drowsiness, because they don't penetrate the central nervous system. Among the most widely used non–sedating antihistamines right now are Seldane and Hisminal, but other potent drugs that won't make you sleepy are in the pipeline, so check with your doctor for availability.

These new medications, in conjunction with the standard precautions for allergy victims— pull up the carpet where dust settles, keep windows closed, change air–conditioning and heating filters often or get an electrostatic air cleaner, and buy tropical fish instead of a dog or cat— provide the primary defense in allergy treatment. Most responsible allergists will try the above program before recommending immunotherapy—those dreaded regular shots. Dr. Eliot Dunsky, clinical associate professor at Hahnemann University, reports that none of his patients get shots without first trying medication.

When a patient isn't adequately helped by medication or has significant side effects from the drugs taken to control allergic symptoms, shots can play an important role in treatment, by attacking the cause of the allergy rather than the symptom. But if you don't see significant improvement after a year, you're probably wasting your time and money. If you do get relief, after five years you should take a break. In pollen and dust allergies, shots appear to be effective about 85 percent of the time when given in strong enough doses. Lately the success rate has improved, as the serums have become more standardized and the concentrations of antigen increased. Still, there is no doubt that shots are often overused, because they are a quick and easy income–producer for doctors.

The unwarranted popularity of allergy shots in recent years is also due partly to an overindulged screening tool, the RAST assay. Traditionally, allergists diagnosed allergies by pricking a patient's skin and injecting small amounts of the suspected allergen, then examining the reddened, swollen reaction. The RAST assay was supposed to do the same thing more accurately in the laboratory, using a vial of the patient's blood. In fact, RAST is at least three times more expensive than skin testing, and much *less* sensitive. Mild allergies may not show up at all. Its great appeal is to general practitioners, who can mail off a blood sample to a lab and get back an allergy report with the serum and program plan, all in a neat little package. Dr. Fred Cogen, past president of the Pennsylvania Allergy Association, found in a survey of members that only 4 percent were using RAST routinely. "It seems," he says, "to be the favored test of non–board–certified allergists."

The question of who's a qualified allergist is a hot issue among doctors

---

### WHEEZING? COUGHING? SHORTNESS OF BREATH?

## *Is It Allergy or Is It Asthma?*

#### THE ASTHMA CENTER CAN HELP YOU FIND THE ANSWER

*Coughing? Shortness of Breath? Chest tightness? Wheezing?* If you have any of these symptoms, the specialists at **The Asthma Center** can determine if you are suffering from bronchial asthma or allergies causing asthma.

Our local centers — Northeast Philadelphia, Center City Philadelphia, Bala Cynwyd, Mt. Laurel, NJ — make on-going treatment even more convenient.

Our team of physicians is on call 24 hours a day, 7 days a week through **The Asthma Center Hotline (215) 569-1111 or (609) 235-8282** to help our patients quickly when they can't breathe. When you need us we are only a phone call away.

Is it asthma or is it allergy? To help you find the answer, send in this coupon for your FREE **Asthma Center** Brochure or call our office at (215) 569-1111 or (609) 235-8282 for an appointment.

---

Return to:

**The Asthma Center**

The Professional Arts Bldg.
Suite 340
205 N. Broad St.
Philadelphia, Pa 19107

*Free Asthma Center Brochure*

Name _____
Address _____
City _____ State _____ Zip _____
Phone _____

*Convenient local offices in:*
*Northeast Philadelphia • Center City • Bala Cynwyd • Mt. Laurel, NJ*

these days, as RAST tests make it simple for any physician to treat allergic symptoms. Those who've done fellowships and gained approval from the American Board of Allergy and Immunology are particularly resentful of the incursion of ear, nose and throat specialists, who've been accused of using allergy shots to fill the void left by declining tonsillectomies. The otolaryngologists argue that they have their own elite Academy of Allergists, founded back in 1941. One of them, Temple University's Dr. Melvin Masloff, insists, "We're trained to treat disease of the nose and throat, and quite frankly, the allergists are invading *our* turf."

*Getting Help:* Many of the newest allergy medications mentioned above are available only by prescription, which means you must see a doctor first. For anything beyond an uncomplicated seasonal rhinitis, Dr. Michael Kaliner, of the National Institute of Allergy and Infectious Diseases, recommends that you visit a board–certified allergist, preferably one with a university–based practice. Expect to spend as much as $150 for an evaluation (history and medical checkup) excluding skin testing, which is not mandatory; the cost will be covered by most health insurance. You can get the name of a board–certified allergist from the American Board of Allergy and Immunology here in Philadelphia at 349–9466. For additional information, including free printed material, call the Asthma and Allergy Foundation of America, in Washington, D.C., (202)–466–7643.

# OUTSTANDING
# SHOULDN'T YOU CHOOSE

Some of the Delaware Valley's most outstanding doctors choose to practice at Temple. Why? Because at Temple, they get to work with the most modern technology, state-of-the-art equipment and superb clinical facilities. Along with other extraordinary practitioners, teachers and researchers.

And a Temple doctor is not as far away as you might think. You can find Temple physicians at satellite office locations throughout the Delaware Valley, Temple University Hospital and St. Christopher's Hospital for Children.

Give us a call. The sooner you do, the sooner you'll understand why more and more doctors and patients are choosing Temple.

## CLINICAL SPECIALTIES AT TEMPLE UNIVERSITY SCHOOL OF MEDICINE AND TEMPLE UNIVERSITY HOSPITAL:

Anesthesiology
Diagnostic Imaging
Family Practice
Internal Medicine
   Cardiology
   Dermatology
   Gastroenterology
   General Internal Medicine
   Hematology
   Infectious Diseases
   Metabolism/Endocrinology
   Nephrology
   Oncology
   Pulmonary Diseases
   Rheumatology
Neurology
Neurosurgery
Obstetrics, Gynecology
   and Reproductive Sciences
Ophthalmology
Orthopedic Surgery
   Sports Medicine
Otorhinolaryngology
Pediatrics/Neonatology
Physical Medicine
   and Rehabilitation
Psychiatry
Radiation Oncology
Surgery
   Cardiac/Thoracic
   General
   Head/Neck
   Plastic
   Vascular
Urology

# DOCTORS CHOOSE TEMPLE. A TEMPLE DOCTOR?

## PEDIATRIC CLINICAL SPECIALTIES OF TEMPLE UNIVERSITY SCHOOL OF MEDICINE AT ST. CHRISTOPHER'S HOSPITAL FOR CHILDREN:

Pediatric Anesthesiology
Pediatrics
    Allergy/Rheumatology
    Adolescent Medicine
    Cardiology
    Developmental/Behavioral
    Endocrinology
    Gastroenterology/Nutrition
    General Pediatrics
    Hematology/Oncology
    Immunology
    Infectious Diseases
    Medical Genetics
    Neonatology
    Nephrology
    Neurology
    Pulmonary Diseases

Pediatric Neurosurgery
Pediatric Ophthalmology
Pediatric Orthopedic Surgery
Pediatric Otolaryngology
Pediatric Pathology
Pediatric Plastic Surgery
Pediatric Radiology
Pediatric Surgery
    Cardiac/Thoracic
    General
Pediatric Urology

## SATELLITE OFFICES:

Northeast Philadelphia
Ft. Washington

King of Prussia
Marlton, NJ

## TEMPLE MEDICAL PRACTICES
### Call 1-800-TEMPLE MD.

# What Many Hospitals Don't Know Could Break Your Heart.

When you have a heart problem, you need the best care available. But many hospitals can't provide the range of care you might need.

So, how do you make sure you're getting the right treatment for your heart?

Choose Temple.

Temple offers the most complete range of heart treatment options in the Delaware Valley. After careful evaluation, we are able to recommend the right course of action. One that is safer and yet more effective than the more limited option another hospital might offer.

At Temple University Hospital, we've been developing and introducing the newest heart care techniques for years.

For example, Temple performed the first heart transplant in the Delaware Valley and is recognized as one of the top five programs in the United States.

We can use human heart valve replacements while most other hospitals continue to use animal and mechanical heart valves.

And for many heart patients for whom standard therapy has proven ineffective, our ability to use the newest drugs has reduced the likelihood of surgery.

If you, or someone you care about, have a heart problem, be certain that there is a complete choice of treatment options.

In matters of the heart — choose Temple.

## T TEMPLE UNIVERSITY HOSPITAL

For information about all your heart care options, call **1-800-TEMPLE MD.**

# 27

## Heart of Gold

*The moment his life ended, four other lives began anew.*

*Accident: 1. an undesirable or unfortunate happening, unintentionally caused and usually resulting in harm or loss 2. fortune; luck*

♥ Pete Campbell* walked out of the operating room, slowly pulled off his surgical gloves, and pushed his magnifying glasses away from his eyes and up onto his receding gray hairline. You could tell by the way the nurses chatted with him that Dr. Campbell was one of their favorites, always generous with his praise for their work and modest about his own. That day the busy neurosurgeon had operated on three people—saved three lives—and he felt spent. Good thing tomorrow was his day off. He couldn't wait to get to the vacation home that he and his wife Arlene had rented near Bayhead for the winter season. He'd be able to unwind in the heated Jacuzzi; maybe they'd make love, and in the morning he'd awake to the roar of the Atlantic and take a long walk on the beach in the crisp fall air. Not a bad way to spend his 56th birthday.

For umpteen years the Campbells had owned a place on Long Island, where they'd spent summers pursuing their passion for sailing. They'd sold it recently; it was just too long a ride from Pete's Hackensack office. Because they were unfamiliar with the North Jersey shore, they'd planned to explore the area over the next few months, with an eye toward buying in the future. Pete Campbell had reached that stage in his life where he was looking forward to working less and playing

---

*\*In accordance with the policy of the Delaware Valley Transplant Program to keep the identity of organ donors anonymous, the names of the Campbell family have been changed.*

more. His three kids had left home for college; his wife had a good job as a family therapist; and he'd made peace with his choice to abandon academic medicine for a clinical practice. When he first decided to leave his associate professorship at the University of Pennsylvania Medical School, back in the mid '70s, he was uncertain whether it was the right decision. But since moving to Hackensack he'd built a thriving practice, and become chief of neurosurgery at two hospitals where he was highly respected by his peers and universally well-liked. Dr. Campbell had a life most people would envy, and he treasured his good fortune. Now he wanted to relax and devote more time to improving his fox-trot.

If someone had told the Campbells five years before that they'd one day be whirling on the ballroom dancing circuit, they would have laughed and said they were more likely to be elevated to the English throne. At that point the couple hadn't danced together since their wedding in 1966—not too long after they'd met by chance at a hospital in the Bronx, where Arlene, just six weeks out of nursing school, was managing a 36-bed ward. Pete, a resident in neurosurgery, was doing research. Their romance ignited like a Bunsen burner, and nine months later they were married. He'd fallen in love with a slim, intelligent, fair-haired woman whose sense of humor clicked with his. Her Romeo was a solidly built, gentle man who had a bounce in his step and made her feel that everything she did was wonderful.

The only place the Campbells were out of step was on the dance floor, so for nearly 20 years they sat out the music. Then Arlene's father died, after a long illness that drained the family's spirit. Restless for something to "make us feel alive again," Pete and Arlene signed up for some dance lessons at a local studio and, with a little instruction, blossomed into a veritable Fred and Ginger. Soon they were competing in amateur contests and, by gosh, winning prizes. After two decades together, something totally wonderful had come along to waltz them into the future.

It was fairly late when Pete and Arlene arrived at their shore rental. By midnight they were curled around each other, asleep. When Arlene heard Pete crawl out of bed a few hours later, it never occurred to her to whisper "Be careful" just because they were in a strange house. Her husband had long been a night wanderer, frequently drifting down to the kitchen for a bowl of cereal in the wee hours. Many nights he'd be awakened by pain from the two fused discs in his neck, pain that forced him to sit a while in a chair before lying down again.

In the leaden silence of the deep night, the thud of her husband's fall sounded like thunder. Arlene jumped from bed, fumbled for a light, and found his body, bent and still, at the foot of the stairs. He must have stumbled in the dark and hit his head. What her wife's eyes refused to believe, her nurse's experience could not deny. Blood trickled from his nose, his mouth and his ears. The situation was critical. A primitive response from her years of medical training took over, smothered her rising terror, and enabled her to shift into nurse mode. She carefully rolled her husband over so he would not suffocate. "Stay with me. Just stay with me until we get a CAT scan," she whispered, though she doubted he could hear a word she said. She called the emergency squad and quickly got dressed.

The ambulance took them to a nearby hospital, and the doctors verified what Arlene had suspected—a cerebral hemorrhage from a blow to the head. Because it was a head injury, Pete Campbell was immediately evacuated to the Trauma Center at Cooper Hospital in Camden, for expert care. He arrived at 5:30 a.m.— alive, but barely. He showed only a minimal response to pain. When the doctors pinched his fingernails, he hardly moved. Within seconds he was surrounded by trauma specialists pushing oxygen tubes into his nose and mouth, lifesaving liquids into his veins, a catheter into his bladder to drain fluid. Even when a CAT scan showed massive injury to the brain, Pete Campbell was given every modern lifesaving measure available. But it was useless. By 8 a.m., his responses to stimulation had ceased entirely. He'd slipped into the state medically known as "brain death."

Until the mid-20th century, the exact moment of death was an uncomplicated matter. The heart stopped, and life ended. But the advent of sophisticated technology to artificially maintain the heart and lungs brought new definitions of death: Either the heart had to cease beating, or the brain had to cease all function. In Pete Campbell's case, machinery kept his heart and lungs going, but there was no activity in his brain. The physician brought to his bedside to establish brain death followed a rigid protocol. Since all nerves are connected to the brain, stimulating those nerves should cause a reaction. Shine a light in the patient's eyes. Pete's pupils did not move. Touch his eyeball with a wisp of cotton. Pete did not blink. Pinch his fingernail. Rub the ridge of his eyebrow. Squeeze a syringe of cold water into his ear canal. No movement whatsoever. Wiggle the breathing tube in his throat. No gag response. Try to force breathing by adjusting the oxygen and carbon dioxide flow. Nothing. Nothing. Nothing.

Had Pete Campbell responded to any of these stimuli, he would not have been declared brain–dead; instead he would have been considered in "a persistent vegetative state," which is where patients like widely publicized coma victim Karen Ann Quinlan may linger for months or years. Brain death is not common. Less than one in 100 hospital deaths—about 15,000 a year—occur this way. And only brain death carries with it the opportunity to give life, because brain–dead patients can donate their organs to other human beings. Without the heart sending blood and oxygen through the body, organs become useless within a half hour. But with life supports doing the pumping, life can be maintained until the viable organs are removed.

On that autumn day when Peter Campbell died, 1,150 people in the Delaware Valley (and more than 24,000 nationwide) were on waiting lists for organ transplants. The vast majority—80 percent—needed kidneys, but thanks to dialysis their situations tend to be less desperate. The average wait for a kidney is 14 months, although people who are difficult to match may stay on the list as long as seven years. By contrast, 15 percent of the 84 area patients awaiting hearts at the time of Pete's death and 10 percent of the 33 needing livers were in critical condition, and could die within weeks if they didn't get the phone calls that could save their lives.

Most people on the waiting lists could be rescued if doctors were just minimally aggressive in broaching the subject of organ donations to grieving families. Despite the existence since 1986 of both federal and state "Required Request" laws mandating hospital personnel to tell families they have the option to donate, the laws are neither followed nor enforced. Howard Nathans, executive director of the Delaware Valley Transplant Program, found in a study he performed that two out of three families will agree to organ donation when they're approached—but that nearly half the potential donors aren't identified by hospitals. Nor are their families told about the option. "Nobody in medical or nursing school gets trained to talk about death," he says. "Since one donor can give as many as 25 different organs and tissues, the problem isn't really a shortage of potential donors. It's a shortage of requests. Hospital staffs have got to get beyond their fear and discomfort and just ask families the simple question: 'Have you thought about organ donation?'"

Fortunately, Arlene and Pete Campbell had.

Dan Norton was spooning Cheerios into his hungry two-year-old son when his beeper squawked. A tall, lanky type with soft brown hair cut short, a sparse beard, and eyes the color of faded blue denim, Norton is one of ten transplant coordinators covering some 173 hospitals in the tristate area. He immediately recognized the phone number of Cooper Hospital, and knew that was a good sign. Cooper referred more organ donors last year than any other hospital, because the staff sees organ donation as part of its medical responsibility. If they beep, they usually mean business.

When Norton returned the call, he was told about Pete Campbell's fall and that his wife had responded positively to the hospital's offer. And in Norton's mind, that's exactly what it was: an offer, an opportunity at a time of incredible loss to perform the ultimate act of charity. "Organ recipients are on lists because they have no other choice; they want to live. They have to be there." That's what Norton, a registered nurse studying for a master's degree in health care, says to the many people who ask why he isn't embarrassed about approaching families at such a delicate time. "But donors' families have had something taken from them, and for once they have this chance to do something purely out of human goodness. I bring that to them. It's not a burden at all; it's the healing power of giving."

At 10:30 that morning, Norton entered the dreary beige hospital room where Arlene Campbell sat, pale and dry-eyed, on the edge of a blue chair. He came neither to bargain nor to persuade. His mission as he understood it was to help Arlene create something positive out of the tragedy that had just altered her existence. He introduced himself and kindly said, "Can we go down the hall and talk a bit?" She followed him to a small office nearby.

The tightness of her narrow face and slim frame told Norton how hard she was struggling to keep her composure. She was a woman who knew she had important decisions to make—but she had no doubts about this one. She told Dan that she and her husband had discussed donating their organs and agreed it was something they should do, although they'd never bothered to put that sticker on their driver's licenses. (It wasn't important. Even with the sticker, family members have to give permission.)

"It wouldn't have mattered whether we talked or not," she said in a low but steady voice. "I would do it anyway, because I know Pete would have wanted me to. There are people with burns who have nothing to hold their body fluids in. They need skin. There are people on kidney machines who have to come to dialysis every week to stay alive. I know people in situations like this who would have a different quality of life if they could get a good organ that would match and work." She looked steadily at Dan Norton. It was one of those rare times that his job was easy.

Even though Arlene Campbell was a nurse, Dan made sure she understood the brain–death protocol. Then he took her husband's medical history and gained some vital data. In his mid–50s and in excellent health, Pete Campbell was the ideal donor. He didn't smoke or drink, and he had none of the AIDS risk factors that automatically exclude potential donors. Because he had some osteoarthritis, it was decided not to take any bone. The pancreas and lungs were ruled out due to his age. What he could give: his kidneys, his liver, his corneas and his heart.

Normally hearts are taken from people under 50, but Arlene mentioned that Pete had been catheterized a few years earlier, after complaining about chest pains which turned out to be unrelated to heart disease. Norton tracked down the results of those tests, and they showed that Pete Campbell's veins and arteries were clear and that his heart was strong. Later that morning, an echocardiogram and an evaluation by a cardiologist confirmed the decision. There was no reason not to use Pete Campell's heart.

At 12:30 p.m., Dan Norton ordered in a half–dozen pizzas for the trauma unit staff. He chewed on a slice while feeding information to the data coordinator at the Delaware Valley Transplant headquarters in downtown Philadelphia. There are 68 organ procurement centers in the United States, and this is one of the busiest. Out of some 12,743 organs donated nationwide in 1990, 612 came from donors in this region. All the transplant centers in the nation are linked by computer. When an organ becomes available, the first priority is to find a local match. If none is found, the search becomes a regional one; if that fails, it goes national. As the number of regional centers has increased, the need to fly organs around the country has decreased. Five years ago, Dan Norton was on a plane two or three times a week; now it's likely to be once a month.

The facts Norton furnished for the computer search were remarkably few: Name: Peter Campbell. Height: 5'6". Weight: 146 pounds. Blood type: A positive. Age: 56. Sex: Male. Race: Caucasian. For the most part, organs are color– and sex–blind. Tissues such as skin and bone can come from anybody up to age 70 with no cancer or infectious disease. Size, and to some degree age, are factors for hearts and livers, but not for kidneys. Donor kidneys can be taken from newborns or 70–year–olds, and since they're transplanted into the groin (the diseased organs are left in place), size is irrelevant. The transplanted organ will shrink or grow to accommodate the recipient.

In less than 15 minutes the computer posted several potential recipients for Pete Campbell's heart and liver. (Because the kidneys require special tissue typing, matches can't be made until after they're removed.) Locally, no one in the Status I category—reserved for critically ill patients requiring intravenous drugs or machines to keep their hearts pumping—emerged as an ideal candidate for the heart. However, there were three likely Status II candidates on the Temple University Hospital list; because they were close by, they got priority.

Temple is one of ten hospitals in this region with a certified transplant program. When it began doing heart transplants in 1984, only 18 medical facilities nationwide were approved to transplant hearts. Today there are a total of 160 heart transplant programs around the country, six of them in the Delaware Valley. While the number of American hospitals doing all kinds of transplants has risen dramatically, to 265, the number of organ donors has remained fairly steady, at about 4,000—short of demand for several years. At the same time, the survival rates keep improving. Since the introduction in the early '80s of the rejection–fighting drug cyclosporin, 70 to 90 percent of organ recipients live at least one year. The longest-lived heart recipients are still alive after 15 years.

When Dan Norton called Temple to alert doctors there of the match, he learned that one of the Status II candidates had suddenly been elevated to critical status. If you believe in fate, then Gary Thomas was destined to receive Pete Campbell's heart.

Thomas suffered his first heart attack when he was 39 years old. Six months later, a second seizure damaged his heart muscle to such an extent that although he had a relatively nondemanding job as a florist, he was never able to work again. Over the next 17 years, as his heart disease progressed slowly from bad to worse, his breathing grew more and more labored, and his acute chest pains more frequent. Finally, in April 1991, Temple accepted him as a heart transplant candidate, gave him a beeper, and told to go home and wait. The question wasn't if his heart would give out, but when.

It happened five days before Pete Campbell died. Thomas had gone to a restaurant with his wife, and ate a bland broiled–scallop dinner. So when the pain tore through his chest, it was unlikely indigestion was the cause. Soon it felt like an elephant was sitting on his chest. By the time he reached the emergency room of Easton Hospital, near his home, the agony of taking in air was so acute that he gasped, "Help me breathe or let me die." Doctors shocked his heart out of cardiac arrest, put him on a respirator, and stabilized his condition with intravenous drugs. By Thursday he was able to be moved by ambulance to Temple Hospital, to be reevaluated by the heart transplant team. He was lying on a table in the catheterization lab when the call from Dan Norton came through: There was a heart available, and he was the match. The shock nearly gave him another heart attack.

While the computer made the emotionless decisions directing the distribution of Pete Campbell's organs, the donor was being carefully maintained on a respirator. A second round of tests to validate brain death had been performed six hours after the first, with no change noted. Doctors, nurses and lab techs bustled in and out of Pete's room, measuring flow, input, output and pressure in a routine of vigilant efficiency. Blood, oxygen and nourishment filtered through tubes into his body. Drugs and machines regulated his breathing, kept his blood pressure even, drained his wastes. Since his brain no longer provided temperature control, a heated air mattress covered him and kept him warm. A courier, summoned earlier by Dan Norton via his car phone, had already taken several vials of Campbell's blood to a Red Cross laboratory, where it was in the process of being checked for everything from hepatitis to AIDS. The hospital lab worked on other blood samples, to evaluate his liver function, electrolytes, enzymes and blood gases. Nothing was left to chance.

The long, dull hours of the afternoon lay heavily on the family. Usually after families agree to organ donation, they make their final goodbyes and leave the hospital, to grieve at home among their friends. The Campbells chose to stay until the very end. By now the children had arrived. Kate came first. A pretty blonde too devastated by her father's death to speak, she stayed close to her mother's side, clutching her hand. The boys—Mark, a freshman, and Ken, a senior—drove down separately from their colleges in New England. Sometimes they'd walk out of the room to weep privately. Then they'd go back to their mom, hug her, stroke her arm, tweak her nose. It took little imagination to visualize the five of them in a photograph on the mantel at home, snapped on one of those family vacations in the Caribbean, where they'd sometimes chartered a boat and sailed together, tan, laughing and happy.

At 6:30 p.m., Dan Norton's kidneys reminded him that he hadn't gone to the bathroom since arriving at the hospital eight hours earlier. Between monitoring the precarious state of his donor, talking to the family, gathering reports from the various laboratories, fielding all sorts of questions from the recipient's family and coordinating arrangements for the surgical recovery of the organs, there simply hadn't been time to think about his own needs. In the moment he took for himself, a crisis erupted that threatened to put everything in jeopardy. On the phone came bad news from the blood lab: Peter Campbell had tested positive for the hepatitis B antibody.

"Are you telling me I'm blown out of the water here?" Norton asked with calm intensity.

"Not necessarily," was the reply. It seemed there was a "B surface antibody test" that could determine if the infection was active, but it would be difficult to find a lab to do it at night.

Now there were all sorts of new decisions to made, including whether to tell the Campbells of the possible delay. First Martin telephoned Dr. Jeffrey Alpern, the Temple heart surgeon (he is now affiliated with Hahnemann University Hospital) whose patient had been selected by the computer, and told him what had happened. "Would you be willing to go ahead even with the positive antibody?" he asked Alpern. "It might just be the result of a hepatitis vaccination.... No, we can't wait until tomorrow. I doubt the family wants him kept on the respirator that long."

Alpern said he'd have to check with his infectious disease specialist and would get back to Norton quickly. The next call went to alert Dr. Ali Nagy from the Hospital of the University of Pennsylvania, who'd be removing the kidneys and liver. Then Martin had to locate a lab capable of doing the blood work ASAP. The Red Cross couldn't, but he found a colleague in Delaware and, with a light manner that belied the urgency, began cajoling him: "Hey, old buddy, old pal. What're the odds of getting a B surface antibody done tonight? Great. I'll have a specimen to you in an hour. At the least, we can save the liver."

Glued to the phone in the center of the trauma unit amid the noisy chatter of the changing shift, Norton made calls, took calls, made more calls. A nurse informed him that the Campbells were getting restless and were thinking about turning off the respirator. He'd just gotten up to talk to them when Dr. Alpern called back. Temple's team had decided to go ahead. They thought the risk of infection was slight, and besides, the test had a high rate of false positives.

Back to Penn's Dr. Nagy: "Temple said yes. Could you get to the Cooper operating room by 9 to start?"

He agreed.

"Try to get some rest," Norton advised. "I'll call you at 8:30 to wake you." It was settled, then. Where was the cold pizza left over from lunch? He was hungry.

Just a few minutes before 9 p.m., Arlene Campbell and her three children stood in a knot beside the tubes and wires surrounding Peter Campbell, father and husband, a man people would later eulogize with words like humble, devoted, dedicated and just plain nice. Their sobs and coughing muffled the beeping noises of the sophisticated medical machines. When they emerged from the room, they were clinging to one another in desperate consolation. Arlene had run out of tears. Her face was ashen and stiff as stone as she turned to the nurse who'd been with them since early morning, and had chosen to stay beyond her shift. "Take special care with him, okay?" Arlene murmured. The family walked slowly to the exit door, removed the hospital gowns they'd worn all day, tossed them into a bin, and went home to deal with death.

Back in the room, the nurse quickly unhooked all but a few essential tubes from Dr. Campbell's body and helped the orderlies lift it onto a gurney for the short trip to the operating room. She kept pausing to wipe her eyes with her sleeve.

The operating-room procedures for recovering organs for transplantation are exactly the same as for any other kind of surgery. Dr. Nagy and two residents from Penn arrive first. Since his patient got the liver match, he will remove that organ as well as the kidneys. A short, pleasant olive–skinned man, Nagy has been working for three nights straight but shows no signs of edginess or lack of sleep. He begins without waiting for Dr. Alpern, because his own part of the surgery takes much longer. After the nurses have shaved Pete Campbell's chest, Nagy vigorously scrubs the donor from neck to groin with sterile orange soap. Then, using a small electric saw, he bisects the breastbone and cuts a long incision down to the pubic hair, laying open the donor's torso like a bag split in half. Inch by inch, he and the residents carefully lift every organ—the stomach, the colon, the pancreas—searching for any visible trace of disease.

The liver, the body's largest organ except for the skin, lies below the breastbone like a big, shiny maroon disc. "Ah, it's beautiful," Nagy sighs. "Very smooth. Very good color. Well–profused." He's pleased.

For the next two hours, he and the residents work alongside one another, painstakingly freeing the liver and the kidneys, below and beneath it. From time to time, as Nagy's goggles steam up, a nurse removes and cleans them and then slides them back on; he cannot touch them because they haven't been sterilized. Although the radio plays quiet golden oldies in the background, there is a high degree of tension. At any moment the donor could "crash," as these doctors call it, and the organs would be lost. This surgery is particularly tedious because the liver and kidneys have a rich and complicated blood supply, so it's critical when removing them to tie off many small blood vessels and to preserve others that will be needed to reattach the organs to their new owner.

Around 11, Temple's Dr. Alpern arrives, with his assistant. Alpern is a big, balding man with slightly stooped shoulders, a thick black beard and piercing dark eyes. He greets Nagy warmly: "So here we are again." They'd been together the night before, doing the same thing at a hospital in Washington Township.

Dr. Alpern, who has performed more than 76 heart transplants since 1990, looks at the heart, declares it "a winner," and leaves the operating room to report the good news to the medical team that is preparing

Gary Thomas back at Temple. He hangs around drinking coffee in the lounge until 11:20, when he calls Temple again and tells them to go ahead and put Thomas under. From this moment on, timing becomes critical.

Three tables draped with sterile green cloths are set up to the left of the operating theater. Each holds a stainless–steel bowl, which will soon be filled with an icy preseravation fluid. The kidney table also holds two clear quart–size plastic jars marked "L" and "R"; a heavy–duty plastic bag lies on the liver table. Lined up on the floor are four red–and–white ice chests, the kind typically used for picnics.

12:10 a.m.: Dr. Nagy asks, "How long have I been at it?" A nurse replies, "Two hours, 22 minutes." He's on schedule. Pete Campbell's body cavity is filled with little black knots where all the blood vessels have been tied off.

12:20: There is a great flurry of activity. Five doctors have their hands inside the chest cavity. With Alpern standing next to him, Nagy gives the command, "Heparinize," and the organs are flushed with a solution that will wash out any remaining blood that might cause a clot.

"Clamps."
"Gauze."
"Flush."
"Stop."
"Ready when you are," Alpern says.
"Let's go," Nagy answers.

12:26: The respirator is disconnected. Quarts of a special solution that chills and preserves the organs are poured into the body and suctioned away. "Careful," Nagy warns. "Don't scratch the liver." While he packs a special ice solution around "his" organs, Alpern severs the four large vessels connecting Peter Campbell to his heart. It takes him less than five minutes to remove the organ, leaving exactly four hours to complete the transfer. That is as long as a heart can be kept viable outside a body. Thanks to improved preservation fluids, a liver is good for 24 hours, and kidneys for two days.

12:35: Alpern carries the lifeless heart, a small pinkish muscle mass dotted with yellow globs of fat, to the first draped table and lays it in the steel bowl. He trims the edges of the pulmonary veins and arteries and checks the valves for any abnormalities, which he'd repair on the spot if necessary. There are none. He slides the heart into one plastic bag, slips that bag into another, and places it on an ice bed in the cooler.

12:46: "Call Temple. Tell them we'll be there at 1:05," Alpern says to his assistant. Minutes later, having removed only their surgical masks, they are walking briskly to a waiting ambulance, carrying Gary Thomas' new heart with them. While they race through the deserted streets with the siren blaring, Dr. Nagy will finish his operation, and sew up Peter Campbell's body in preparation for the funeral director.

Gary Thomas was wheeled into surgery at Temple University Hospital at just about the same time Pete Campbell was being shaved and self. The usual lawyer's fee is $75 to $125.

A similar document, a durable power of attorney for health, empowers someone else to make medical decisions for the incapacitated person, and can also include the person's wishes about which medical procedures should be taken and which avoided. It has more flexibility than a living will.

**Resources**: *The National Academy of Elder Law Attorneys* (602–881–4005) will send you a free brochure on questions to ask when selecting an elder–law attorney. Send a large self–addressed stamped envelope to 655 North Alvernon Way, Suite 108, Tucson, AZ 85711.

## SO STAY AT HOME: HELP THAT MAKES HOUSE CALLS

Most elderly adults would prefer to live on their own as long as possible, and there are a growing number of local agencies to help them do just that.

In–home care includes a range of services. When people talk about *home health care*, they mean skilled nursing care provided by licensed professionals such as registered nurses and professional therapists. When people talk about *home care* (or "homemaker care," or "personal care"), they're referring to help with dressing, feeding, bathing and toileting—services performed by home health aides or homemakers. And sometimes the term *home services* is used for help that is not hands–on, such as errand–running, housecleaning and meal preparation.

Home health care has become increasingly important in recent years. Some elderly need it because Medicare cost–cutting has forced hospitals to discharge patients "quicker and sicker." Others rely on it to postpone or eliminate the need for a nursing home.

One elderly Main Line couple who didn't want to move to a nursing home managed at home with the help of three shifts of health aides looking after the bedridden wife and the husband, who had Alzheimer's. A private care manager monitored the arrangement for the couple's adult children, who lived miles away. (Needless to say, it was expensive, costing as much as a nursing–home stay.) But maybe your parent doesn't need skilled nursing help. Most elderly people just need help with the activities of daily living—walking, bathing, grooming, dressing, eating, getting in and out of bed.

The Area Agencies on Aging offer free services, but—this is beginning to sound familiar—waiting lists are long. The Philadelphia Corporation for the Aging's In–Home Care Program serves about 3,000 people at once, and sometimes has a waiting list half that long. The city's Community Care Option Program diverts people from nursing–home care by patching together supports at home, but it, too, is overwhelmed by demand. The program has 600 slots a year and a waiting list nearly as long. "The funds are insufficient, and don't begin to meet the need and demand out there," says Emily Amerman, the director of care management.

One pioneering concept in home care is Friends Life Care at Home.

Similar in concept to continuing-care retirement homes, but more affordable, it guarantees a continuum of long-term care at home for people who wish to continue living independently as long as possible. For an entrance fee of $5,600-$15,400 and monthly fees of $205-$220, members receive a broad range of health and homemaker services for the rest of their lives. The plan pays 70 percent of the cost of a stay at one of nine local nursing homes, if such a stay is needed. At this point the service area is limited to Northeast and Norhtwest Philadelphia and eastern Montgomery and lower Bucks counties, but some expansion is planned this year (628-8964).

**Resources**: *Bayada Nurses* is a private home–care agency founded in 1975, with 18 area offices serving Philadelphia, lower Montgomery and Delaware counties and southern New Jersey. A staff of RNs, LPNs, aides, homemakers and live–in companions provides services 24 hours a day, at fixed hourly or daily rates (546–5000).

*Share the Care Respite Program*, run by Intercommunity Action, Inc., provides health aides in East Falls, Germantown and Roxborough. Hourly rates are $7.50 to $8.50, with a two–hour minimum weekday rate or three–hour weekend requirement (482–9370).

*Episcopal Community Services* provides free RN–supervised home–care services, including Meals on Wheels, to SSI recipients and lower–income individuals in Philadelphia. Some health aide services are available on a sliding fee scale for those ineligible for the free services (351–1400).

*Jewish Family and Children Service* has worked with Philadelphia and suburban elderly since 1953. All home care is provided in coordination with a social worker, on a sliding fee scale, from two to 20 hours a week, with occasional overnight service (545–3290). In the Cherry Hill area, JFS provides homemakers through the Carl Auerbach Friends of JFS; call 609-662-8611.

*Neighborhood Home Health Service*, a private Medicare–certified agency with 15 years' experience, provides primary–care RNs who work mainly with Medicare referrals (755–6464).

*Special Care*, based in Erdenheim, has 17 offices in the tri–state area. They supply home health aides for $7.50 to $8.50 an hour (233–5323).

*Surrey Services for Seniors*, Berwyn, uses a volunteer network and small paid staff to provide home care and chore services, on a sliding fee scale, to elderly people on the Main Line between Bryn Mawr and Malvern. Formerly known as the Surrey Club, it also sponsors social programs for the elderly (647–6404).

*Senior Outreach Services*, Ardmore, is a nonprofit agency providing home care in the western suburbs. Rates are generally $8 to $10 an hour (642–2688).

*The Visiting Nurses Association of Greater Philadelphia*, one of the oldest voluntary, nonprofit home health–care agencies in the nation, dates back to 1886. The Medicare–certified agency provides health professionals and homemaker services in the City of Philadelphia and lower Bucks and eastern Montgomery counties. Also offers services to uninsured and underinsured patients (473–7600).

## NURSING HOMES:
## MAKING THE MOST OF THE LEAST FAVORITE CHOICE

Most people shrink at the idea of a nursing home. Who hasn't heard horror stories about the high cost, the institutional callousness, at times the outright patient abuse? But not all nursing homes are *60 Minutes* fodder. In many cases, a nursing home may be the best solution.

"When someone requires institutionalization, there is no alternative," says Avalie Saperstein, of the Philadelphia Geriatric Center. "Families should not be beating themselves up to put together these fragmented plans to avoid nursing homes."

Today's nursing–home population is much different from what it was even a decade ago, when such homes were a residential choice for elderly folks with no other place to live. Now the homes are much "sicker" places—the patients are older, more frail. Dementia is common, since almost half of all people 80 or older suffer from some form of memory loss or confusion. Moreover, some families use nursing homes as a temporary solution. More homes have begun to offer "respite care" of brief duration—a boon to family caregivers who want to go on vacation.

Nursing–home care is not cheap; on the average it costs $75 a day, or $27,500 a year, according to the American Health Care Association, the nursing–home industry's lobby. At Bryn Mawr Terrace Convalescent Center, one of the area's most opulent nursing homes, a suite with weekly beautician visits and limousine service for restaurant outings can cost as much as $65,000 a year.

If you have money, you'll probably have few problems getting into a nursing home, but if you're a Medicaid patient, it will be much more difficult—especially in Philadelphia proper, where 3,000 to 4,000 elderly people are on waiting lists for nursing–home beds at any given time. It's now illegal, but some participating homes may still try to get away with admitting private–pay patients ahead of Medicaid ones. In that case, getting in the door may be the hardest part. Once you're in, federal law now says the nursing home can't evict you if spend down all your savings, so as long as it accepts Medicaid—and most do.

If your relative needs a nursing home, be prepared to spend as much time looking for one as the situation allows. Several organizations publish detailed brochures on nursing–home selection. A good rule of thumb is to select four or five facilities that meet your needs, then visit each, taking time to talk to the staff and to residents and their families.

Make at least one visit—several are better—to your preferred choice. Ask questions about care for your parent's specific condition. Look at the state licensing inspector's latest report, which should be on file at the home. Learn what costs are considered "extras," not covered in the daily rate for room, board and services. Finally, don't pick a nursing home without checking with the ombudsman at your Area Agency on Aging. Every AAA maintains such an overseer to monitor local nursing homes and boardinghouses and resolve consumer complaints. These watchdogs can also help you if problems arise later.

In response to complaints about nursing homes, Congress enacted sweeping reforms in 1987 aimed at making nursing homes more responsive to residents' needs. The lesilation, which is being phased in, applies to facilities that participate in Medicare and Medicaid.

Nursing homes must now complete a comprehensive assessment of every resident, upon admission and annually thereafter. Then a "plan of care" is developed with a patient and his or her family. This individualized outline spells out daily routines, and also sets goals for resolving a resident's medical and nonmedical problems. Whenever a patient's condition changes, the plan of care is supposed to be amended.

In a separate reform, patients in nursing homes and hospitals—or their families, by proxy—are now also entitled to refuse treatment in critical medical situations. Those decisions used to be made by medical directors. Now every nursing home is required to disclose its philosophy on lifesaving measures at admission time. This issue can be particularly significant in a nursing home run by a religious organization.

Reforms have also been adopted aimed at improving the quality of the nurses' aides—the low–paid people who dress, feed, bathe and toilet nursing–home patients. Aides must now complete 75 hours of training and be certified. To address complaints of patient abuse by aides, states now maintain registries of abuse findings, so that nursing homes can check prospective employees.

Perhaps the most dramatic change involves the use of physical and chemical restraints. At one time, at least 40 percent of a typical nursing home's patients were kept in restraints—strapped into chairs or tranquilized, for example. Now the law says restraints can't be imposed for discipline or the nursing home's convenience; a doctor must cite medical reasons for using them.

Anne Kisor, ombudsman for the Coalition of Advocates for the Rights of the Infirm Elderly (CARIE), points out that chemical restraints are invisible, and advises families to be aware that some nursing homes may administer psychotropic drugs. If you're concerned, ask to see statistics on the nursing home's use of these drugs, and discuss the facility's philosophy with the medical director.

**Resources**: In the Philadelphia area, there are more than 200 nursing homes. Here is a list of agencies that can help narrow the choices and provide referral services.

*ReachCare*, 643–6701. This nonprofit counseling agency offers a free over–the–phone skilled nursing care search. Its computer—which lists 95 percent of the five–county area's nursing homes, as well as some independent apartments and life–care facilities—can supply a list that meets a client's specifications for services, cost, location, etc. Though a printout is available for $5, questions can usually be answered by a phone call. Sponsored by various grants.

*Nursing Homes in Philadelphia: A Directory and Consumer Guide* provides a description of the homes in Philadelphia and general information on a choosing a nursing home. It costs $20 (including shipping and handling), but is provided free to low–income citizens. Send a check payable to Northwest Interfaith Movement to: Long–term Care Connection, Northwest Interfaith Movement, Greene Street at Westview, Philadelphia, PA 19119; 843–5600.

A second edition of the comprehensive guide is also available for the four-county suburban Philadelphia area: *Nursing Homes in Suburban Philadelphia: A Directory and Consumer Guide.* Call 783–5067, or write to Box 574, Valley Forge, PA 19481.

*The National Citizens' Coalition for Nursing Home Reform,* 1224 M Street NW, Suite 301, Washington, DC 20005 (202–393–2018), offers clear, helpful information on reforms and patient rights.

*Health Insurance Association of America,* P.O. Box 41455, Washington D.C., 20018, helps prepare for the financial costs of nursing–home care by offering a list of long–term care policies that keep up with inflation.

Most hospitals will provide home services for patients with less than six months to live. For more information on these services, contact the following groups: *Children's Hospice International,* 901 N. Washington Street, Suite 700, Alexandria, VA 22314, 800–242–4453; *Hospice Education Institute,* 5 Essex Square, Suite 3–B, Essex, CT 06426, 800–331–1620; *National Hospice Organization,* 1901 North Moore Street, Suite 901, Alexandria, VA 22209, 800–658–8898.

## WHEN YOU CAN'T BE THERE: HIRING A MANAGER

Many of us must deal with our parents from a distance, and that's spurred development of a new industry: private geriatric care management. Think of it as hiring a consultant. Geriatric care managers, usually former social workers or nurses, will assess a person's condition, then arrange for and oversee care. Such managers are well–versed in what's available in home meal delivery, nursing and personal–care services, adult day care and long–term care.

For instance, Marsha York Solmssen and Marion Thompson, of Intervention Associates, in Wayne, helped one disoriented elderly woman continue living in her Chester County farmhouse after they set up a house–sharing arrangement and scheduled regular outings to an adult day–care center. (But first they saw that the house was cleaned up—it was a firetrap, full of papers and piles of twigs the woman had collected on nature walks.)

Geriatric care management is so new that you won't find it listed in the yellow pages. But referrals are available free from the National Association of Private Geriatric Care Managers, based in Tucson (602–881–8008), or for $2 from Children of Aging Parents, in Levittown, a nonprofit information center and support group for caregivers (945–6900).

If you feel you need guidance in selecting a care manager, Aging

Network Services, of Bethesda, Maryland, can help. They evaluate your case, then call on a network of 250 social workers nationwide, matching them with families for an initial fee of $275 (301–657–4329).

A good care manager may recommend a geriatric assessment—a comprehensive physical workup, offered by many hospitals today, that can include examinations by neurologists, psychologists or psychiatrists, and specialists in geriatric medicine. It can pinpoint, for example, whether a person has dementia or just a nutritional problem.

Private care management doesn't come cheap. Most geriatric managers charge from $50 to $150 an hour. (Family members typically pay for the services themselves.) But they may be able to give a client more personalized attention than care managers at public agencies like the AAAs. There are also care managers who work for insurers—but they might have a vested interest in keeping costs low, or in limiting your choice of services.

Be forewarned: Geriatric care management is an unregulated industry, so it's important to shop carefully. Says Betty Mullen, the director of the American Association of Retired Persons (AARP) Women's Initiative program, "I was in Florida a couple of years ago at a long–term care conference, and I was told that a bunch of MBAs, recent graduates, had hung up shingles as care managers–without knowing anything about the whole area of geriatrics and where to go for help."

The National Association of Private Geriatric Care Managers has established voluntary standards for the profession, but consumers should check a care manager's background, experience and references. A good full–time care manager should handle no more than 50 to 75 clients, the AARP says.

**Resources**: There are other private care managers in the area, but the Greater Philadelphia Association of Private Geriatric Care Managers is the only professional organization. The following belong to the association:

*Comprehensive Health & Human Services Inc./Eldercare*, 8329 High School Road, Elkins Park, PA 19117; 635–6849. Contact: Sheila R. Bergman.

*Comprehensive Health & Human Services Inc./Eldercare*, 435 East Lancaster Avenue, #211, Wayne, PA 19087; 686–5579. Contact: Barbara R. Feinstein.

*Geriatric Planning Services*, Main Line Federal Building, #201, Front and Orange streets, Media, PA 19063; 566–6686. Contact: Anneta Kraus.

*Intervention Associates*, P.O. Box 572, Wayne, PA 19087; 254–9001. Contact: Marsha Solmssen, Marion Thompson.

*Retirement & Transition, Inc.*, P.O. Box 572, Wayne, PA 19010; 527–4578. Contact: Caroline V. Holton, Helena A. Stewart.

*The Patient Advocates*, 512 Garwood Drive, Cherry Hill, NJ 08003. Contact: Ira L. Mazer.

*Supportive Care Services, Inc.*, 507 West 9th Street, Wilmington, DE 19801; 302-655-5518. Contact: Thomas J. Posatko.

*AgeWise Family Services,* 1250 Glenburnie Lane, Dresher, PA 19025; 659-2111. Contact: Susan P. Weiss, Roberta Rosenberg.

*JoAnn M. Burke,* 100 West Evergreen Avenue, Chestnut Hill, PA 19118; 836-1280.

*Star Systems Consultation & Training, Inc.,* Madison House, Suite D-122, 3900 City Avenue, Philadelphia, PA 19131; 477-2211. Contact: Janice Brown.

## PAY NOW, STAY PUT: THE LIFE–CARE OPTION

Imagine spending your retirement years being coddled like a college kid. You'll never lift a mop or a snow shovel. You'll share meals with friends every night without bickering over how to split the bill. There will be art instructors, hairdressers, bank tellers and medical staff available right where you live. And most importantly, if and when the time comes that you need nursing–home care, you don't have to worry about the cost, the move or waiting lists.

This is life in the continuing–care retirement community—also known as a life–care community. (They're sometimes called retirement communities, although that can be misleading; some retirement communities offer housing only.) It's a relatively new concept in elder care that has caught on in the past two decades, growing from 380 communities nationwide in 1973 to over 700 today; in the Philadelphia area, where such communities started, there are more than 40. A onetime entrance fee, along with monthly service fees, generally pays for your apartment, outpatient health care, and your stay in the on–site nursing home, if and when you need that level of care.

These places demand fairly deep pockets. Studios for singles, the least expensive option, generally start at $30,500 at places like Rydal Park and Rosemont Presbyterian Village; prices climb to more than $200,000 for your own villa at the most exclusive communities, such as White Horse Village in Newtown Square. Most facilities have a clause providing a prorated refund if a resident decides to move, or dies, within a specified period of time.

These communities remain solvent for one simple reason: The management takes the calculated risk that not every resident will require the expensive nursing–home care they offer. And of those who do, some may not require it for years, allowing management to invest the sizable entrance fee in the meantime.

Many of these communities have waiting lists. If you're not ready to move out of the house, it is possible to get your name in ahead of time. Planning ahead is essential, because the application procedure itself could take several months: Admission is based largely on ability to pay and on current health. A physical is usually required, as is information from your doctor. Then there are admissions committee meetings, interviews, and visits to the facility, all of which should be taken care of before the applicant's health deteriorates beyond the point of acceptance. "We turn a lot of people down—I'd say 30 to 50 percent of our applicants," says Joan Sterrett, marketing director at Martins Run, in Media. "They wait too long. They're not approved."

While life–care communities look into your finances, you should be looking into theirs. From the late '70s to the mid '80s, a flurry of news stories reported on several such places that went bankrupt or incurred financial problems due to fraud and/or mismanagement. It is of some comfort to note that no Pennsylvania life–care community has shut down for financial reasons. Three have sought protection under federal bankruptcy laws, but through reorganization plans they stayed open, and no residents were forced to go elsewhere.

About 15 percent of the nation's 700 homes are currently accredited by the Continuing Care Accreditation Commission, an organization formed in 1985. (To obtain a list of facilities in this area, see below.) The accreditation process is costly and time–consuming. And new communities must be 90 percent occupied for a year before the commission will consider their applications.

**Resources:** *The Pennsylvania Insurance Department* has free brochures and a *Directory of Licensed Continuing–Care Communities*. For the brochures, send a business–size envelope with your request to the Insurance Department Press Office, 1326 Strawberry Square, Harrisburg, PA 17120. For the directory, send a $5 check with your request to the same address.

*The Continuing Care Accreditation Commission* also has free brochures, including an accredited facilities list and an explanation of the accreditation process. Write to the CCAC, Suite 500, 901 E Street NW, Washington, DC 20004–2037; or call 202–296–5960.

*The American Association of Homes for the Aging*, the above commission's parent organization, offers *The Continuing–Care Retirement Community—A Guide Book for Consumers*, for $4. Send a check and your request to AAHA Publications at the above address. Other good sources include: *American Health Care Association*, 1201 L Street NW, Washington, DC 20005, 202–842–4444; and the *National Consumers League*, 815 15th Street NW, Suite 928, Washington, DC 20005, 202–639–8140.

## ADULT DAY–CARE CENTERS:
### RELIEF FOR YOU, RECREATION FOR THEM

It's 10:30 on a Thursday morning, and a few elderly women are sitting on sofas in a big, cheery room, tending to needlework projects. At a table, another group plays Trivial Pursuit, fielding questions like "Who was the 'It Girl'?" One woman sits hunched over all by herself, moaning and crooning to a stuffed animal.

Just a typical day at Adult Day Care of Chester County, in West Chester, one of 45 such centers in Southeastern Pennsylvania.

Adult day care is one of the bright spots in elder care. Just 20 years ago, only 12 such centers were operating in the whole country; now there are 2,200. They offer older people a structured, stimulating way to spend the day, and provide respite to caregivers who work or just want time off to see a movie or run errands.

At Adult Day Care of Chester County, the 30 to 35 clients participate in daily activities, and can also take showers and naps at the center. A hot lunch is delivered by nearby Chester County Hospital. A nurse is on hand all day. A local beautician visits three mornings a week.

Pat Shull, owner of the center and head of the Pennsylvania Adult Day Care Association, says almost half of those in adult day care have Alzheimer's or some other dementia. But even those who seem most confused benefit in noticeable ways. For instance, one client insisted on bringing in a cake for her 50th wedding anniversary, even though her husband had died a year and a half earlier. The staff announced that she was remembering a special day and wanted to share. "She didn't say anything," says Shull, "but her face was so radiant, we didn't need to turn the lights on."

Though services and hours vary from center to center, most charge about $30 a day for a noon meal and snacks, personal care, social services, supervision by a physician and/or registered nurse and aides, recreational programs, physical therapy and counseling. The centers usually operate Monday through Friday during working hours. Fees are not covered by Medicare or Medicaid in Pennsylvania, but New Jersey Medicaid pays for "medical" daycare (a registered nurse on staff).

**Resources**: *Coalition of Advocates for the Rights of the Infirm Elderly*, 1315 Walnut Street, Philadelphia, PA 19107.

*Pennsylvania Adult Day Care Association*, P.O. Box 934, Exton, PA 19341; 431–9699.

*New Jersey Adult Day Care Association*, P.O. Box 584, Bloomfield, NJ 07003; 609–234–5999.

See hospital listings for specific programs.

## HOT LINES AND HELP LINES

*Senior Helpline*, 765–9040. Funded by the Philadelphia Corporation for the Aging; provides information and referrals for Philadelphians over 60, gives help on getting services and benefits.

*CARIE–Line*, 545–4437. Offers legal, financial, social and health information; operated by the Coalition of Advocates for the Rights of the Infirm Elderly.

*Alzheimer's Disease Clearinghouse*, 800–367–5115. Sponsored by the Pennsylvania Council on Aging. For caregivers or others interested in support groups, care and information.

*Alzheimer's Association of Greater Philadelphia*, 568–6430. Provides information, emotional support and referrals. Operates Wanderers Alert Program: For $25, a person's identifying data is added to a computerized registry of Alzeimer's sufferers. The association will notify a network of police agencies, emergency rooms and hospitals when a victim is reported missing.

**Publications:** *The American Association of Retired Persons* publishes several free pamphlets on elder care (601 E Street NW, Washington, DC 20049):

*Miles Away and Still Caring* (D–12748). A guide for relatives who live far away from an elderly loved one.

*Care Management: Arranging for Longterm Care* (D–13803). A guide to services available in the home.

*A Handbook about Care in the Home* (D–955). A guide to services available in the home.

*Long–Term Care: A Dollar and Sense Guide,* 1331 H Street NW, Suite 500, Washington, DC 20005. A guide to selecting insurance. Also describes alternatives to nursing–home placement.

*Making Wise Decisions about Long–term Care* (D–12435). Brochure describing services and financing.

*Home Away from Home* (D–12446). Information on boarding homes.

*Nursing–Home Life: A Guide for Residents and Families* (D–13063). How to select a nursing home and adjust to life in it.

*Before You Buy: A Guide to Long–Term Care Insurance* (D–12893).

*The Pennsylvania Department of Aging* publishes *A Manual for Family Caregivers of Older Pennsylvanians.* Good information on services available in Pennsylvania, and tips for coping with caregiving. Available from Area Agencies on Aging or by writing to the Pennsylvania Department of Aging, 231 State Street, Harrisburg, PA 17101–1195.

*A Shoppers' Guide to Long–Term Care Insurance,* 120 West 12th Street, Suite 1100, Kansas City, MO 64105. A pamphlet that includes a checklist for comparing specific policies.  —*By Marta McCave*

# As time goes by

Offering a continuum of care to meet the needs of older adults

- Geriatric Program in Psychiatry
- Physical Medicine and Rehabilitation
- Skilled Nursing Facility

**MT. SINAI HOSPITAL**
Fourth and Reed Streets
Philadelphia, PA 19147
215/339 3456

Graduate Health System

*As time goes by Mt. Sinai Hospital is there providing the care needed to restore life's vitality.*

# Love Never Grows Old.
*But Loved Ones Do.*

When you realize that your mother or father should not live alone, let The Chestnut Hill Residence help.

Chestnut Hill is a unique alternative: an elegant and gracious residential setting combined with the very best in personal care assistance. Life at Chestnut Hill is secure, stimulating and filled with friends.

Love doesn't compromise. When it comes to personal care for someone you love, select the best.

**Select The Chestnut Hill Residence.**

## Chestnut Hill
R·E·S·I·D·E·N·C·E
THE PREMIER PERSONAL CARE COMMUNITY

**247-5307**
495 East Abington Avenue
Chestnut Hill, PA 19118

© 1992 The Chestnut Hill Residence

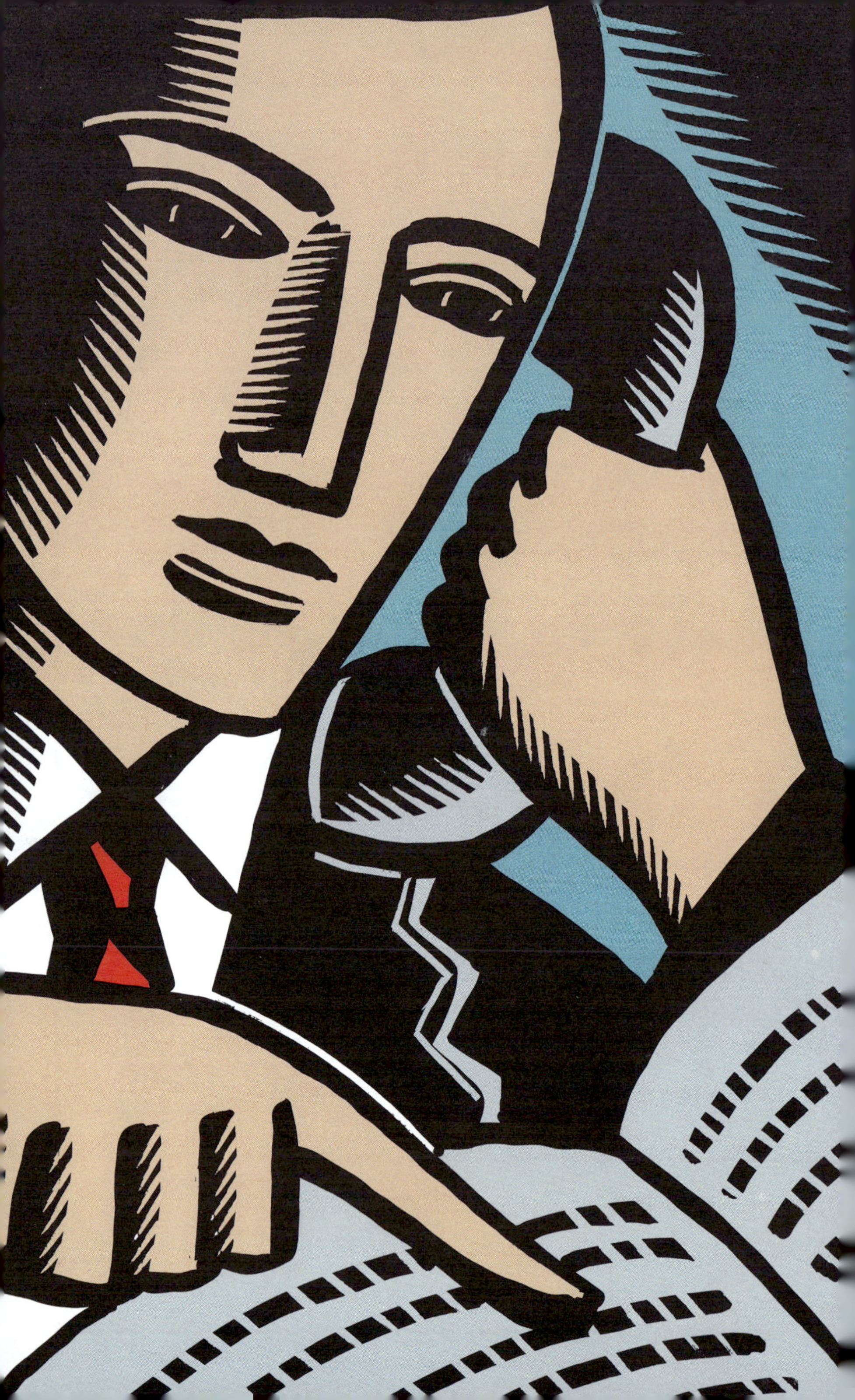

**SECTION SIX**

# FOR YOUR INFORMATION

# One of Philadelphia's health care leaders isn't in Philadelphia

*Abington Memorial Hospital offers the expertise of an urban medical center right in the neighborhood.*

From high-risk obstetrics and CHAMPS
(Childrens Hospital/Abington Memorial Pediatric Service)
to rehabilitation and geriatric assessment,
we provide expert care to people of all ages
in Montgomery, Bucks, and Philadelphia counties.
For a physician directory, guide to services,
or schedule of health education classes
and support groups, call
**(215) 576-MEDI.**

***Abington* Memorial Hospital**
1200 Old York Road (Route 611)
Abington, PA 19001

*Accredited with Commendation by the Joint Commission on Accreditation of Healthcare Organizations*

# 32

# Help!

*An A-to-Z listing of area support groups, from Alzheimer's disease to the Zipper Club.*

♥ Ten years ago, Elaine Harris began noticing that her lips were continually dry. At first she found this curious, but nothing to worry about. But her curiosity turned into panic when she started feeling pain in her muscles and joints and her eyesight became blurred. The panic ballooned into full–fledged fear when she went to brush her teeth and noticed two had fallen out. It took 13 doctors and a yearlong odyssey for Harris to find a specialist who finally diagnosed her illness as Sjorgen's syndrome, a rare and incurable disease of the autoimmune system.

Feeling distraught and isolated, Harris decided to act on the advice of a doctor friend who told her, "You must do something positive, or else you'll only get worse. You've got to get out of the victim mentality." Her solution was to seek out other victims of her disease, to comfort one another and end their loneliness. She petitioned the New York State Clearinghouse, a consumer self–help organization, to start a Sjorgen's Syndrome Support Group. Word spread to other parts of the country, and people with similar symptoms began calling Harris for more information. A second support group popped up in Seattle, then one in Washington, D.C. Now the Sjorgen's Syndrome Support Group is an international enterprise, with some 5,300 members worldwide and a monthly newsletter (called *The Moisture Seekers*) that is translated into Japanese, French and Hebrew.

Elaine Harris' success is just one example of the hottest grass–roots movement in America—support groups. Support groups now exist for practically every problem but hangnails. Those geared to medical disabilities like herpes, Alzheimer's or juvenile arthritis furnish members with the latest news in research and treatment; all of the groups offer practical information, encouragement, and down–to–earth, here's–what–worked–for–me coping skills. In response to the rapidly burgeoning numbers and varieties of groups, self–help clearinghouses have sprung up in 11 states (though not in Pennsylvania). New Jersey lists some 4,000 groups in its files; its clearinghouse can be reached from the Garden State (toll–free) at 800–367–6274, or 201–625–7101.

One unexpected bonus of self–help groups is the way they've encouraged interest and research into problems that but for their lobbying efforts would remain largely ignored. One of the reasons Elaine Harris had such a difficult time getting her disease diagnosed is that there was no single test to isolate Sjorgen's syndrome. With the focus on the disease created by her self–help group, most specialists will now perform a battery of tests when diagnosing patients complaining of dry mouth, eye problems and arthritis.

Because groups vary from small, unaffiliated gatherings in a suburban family room or church classroom to well–organized chapters of national organizations, it is impossible to determine precisely how many people are involved in the self–help movement. A recent Gallup poll claimed one in three Americans belongs to a support or self–help group, ranging from the 20 or so faithful Children of Aging Parents who come to meetings in Elkins Park to the thousands who flock daily to one of the 88,000 worldwide meetings of Alcoholics Anonymous.

The once–distrustful medical community now recognizes the advantages of support groups. There is an increasing sense of how much people can gain from others who have dipped at the same well. "Nobody wants to be alone in this isolated world," says a medical sociologist. "Often folks relate better to somebody who they believe really understands what they're dealing with. When professionals complain that there is no effectiveness to self–help groups, I tell them the numbers don't lie. They must be doing something right."

As Elaine Harris will testify, what they are doing is trading on the incredible power of the aphorism that you can't understand a person until you've walked in his shoes.

Here is a representation of the organized self–help and support groups in the Delaware Valley. The majority are on-going, but a few are still in the formation stage and may not have survived by publication. In addition, your local hospital has independently run support groups, so check there, too. Meeting times and dates change, which is why they're not included. For current information, call the phone numbers we've listed. The National Self–Help Clearinghouse number is 212–642–2944.

**Autism:** *For parents and friends of autistic children.*
Run in conjunction with the Durand Academy, 230 N. Evergreen Ave., Woodbury, NJ (609-845-0666).

**Post–Abortion Counseling:** *One–on–one counseling for women experiencing stress or grief following an abortion.*
Amnion Crisis Pregnancy Center, 895 Glenbrook Ave., Bryn Mawr (525-1557).

**Barrier Awareness Group:** *For physically disabled adults. Advocacy, support, and referral services.*
Taylor Hospital, East Chester Pike, Ridley Park (461-4459).

**AIDS:** *For those diagnosed with AIDS or testing HIV–positive.*
Abington Hospital, 1200 Old York Rd., Abington (576-2000).
Catholic Social Services Office of AIDS, 222 N. 17th Street, runs groups through its branches (families and friends invited): Montgomery County Catholic Services Office, 1339 Sandy St., Norristown (659-9195); Old St. Josephs, 321 Willings Alley (923-1723).
Hahnemann University Hospital. For women who have tested HIV–positive. Broad and Vine sts. (448-7000).
Memorial Hospital of Burlington County, 175 Madison Ave., Mount Holly, NJ (609-267-0700).
Mercy Catholic, Misericordia Division. Specifically for women with AIDS. 5301 Cedar Ave. (748-9150).
Montgomery Cancer Center. For gay or bisexual men diagnosed with AIDS or HIV. 1330 Powell St., Suite 308, Norristown (270-2703).

**AIDS Psychotherapy:** *For men and women who have HIV.*
By appointment; sliding fee. Meets in Center City. Contact Dr. Dan Estes at 567-2260.

**Al Anon:** *For the families and caregivers of alcoholics.*
175-plus meeting places in the Delaware Valley. Call for locations; 222–5244.

**Alcoholics Anonymous:** *For people who want to stop drinking.*
Over 1,500 meeting places in the Delaware Valley. Call for information; 222-5244.

**Alzheimer's:** *Run by the Alzheimer's Disease and Related Disorder Association (ADRDA), in conjunction with area hospitals. For caregivers and family members of Alzheimer's patients.*

*Bucks County*
Chandler Hall, Buck Rd. and Barclay St., Newtown (860-4000, ext. 252).
Delaware Valley Medical Center, Main Conference Room, 200 Oxford Valley Rd., Langhorne (943-3081).
Doylestown Hospital, Conference Room B, 595 State St., Doylestown (345-2577).
Medical College Hospitals, Bucks County Campus, 225 Newtown Rd., Warminster (441-6662).

*Chester County*
Coatesville Senior Center, 22 N. 5th Ave., Coatesville (383–6900).
Crozer–Chester Medical Center, 15th St. and Upland Ave., Chester (447-6006).
Kennett Area Senior Center, 427 S. Walnut St., Kennett Square

(932-8775).
Manatawny Manor, Old Schuylkill Rd., Pottstown (327-0840).
Taylor Hospital, East Chester Pike, Ridley Park (891-0222).
Trinity United Methodist Church, Eagle Rd. and Maryland Ave., Havertown (568-6430).
Wallingford Home, 115 S. Providence Rd., Wallingford (565-3232).

*Montgomery County*
Abington Public Library, 1030 Old York Rd., Abington (885-0311).
North Penn Hospital, 100 Medical Campus Dr., Administration Conference Room, Lansdale (361-4470).
Radnor United Methodist Church, 930 Conestoga Rd., Radnor (525-2127).
Lankenau Hospital, 100 Lancaster Ave., Wynnewood (645-3409).
Senior Suites, 2101 New Hope St., Norristown (455-6240).
Waverly Heights, 1400 Waverly Rd., Lower Merion (645-8600).

*Philadelphia County*
Albert Einstein Medical Center, Paley 1 Conference Room, Old York and Tabor rds. (456-8910).
Bustleton Library, Bustleton Ave. and Verree St. (885-0311).
Lankenau Hospital, Lancaster and City Line aves.(645-2000).
The Neighbors Center, 6950 Germantown Ave., Mount Airy (951-4325).
Osteopathic Medical Center, Parkview Hospital, East Conference Room, Castor and Wyoming aves., Kensington (338-5339).
Roxborough Memorial Hospital, Wolcoff Auditorium, 5800 Ridge Ave. (247-5627).

St. Agnes Medical Center, Conference Room B, 1900 S. Broad St. (584-6844).
Thomas Jefferson University Hospital, Alumni Hall, Room M23, 1020 Locust St. (955-6188).
White Rock Baptist Church, Community Services Bldg., 53rd and Chestnut sts. (879-1189).

**American Lung Association:** *Nonprofit organization offering support and information for those suffering from any lung disease.*
Abington Memorial Hospital, Widener Bldg., Classroom 1A, 1200 Old York Rd., Abington (576–2150).
Bryn Mawr Rehabilitation Hospital, 414 Paoli Pike, Malvern (526–3000).
Delaware County Memorial Hospital, 501 N. Lansdowne Ave., Drexel Hill (284–8473).
Episcopal Hospital, Front St. and Lehigh Ave. (427–7000).
Grand View Hospital, 700 Lawn Ave., Sellersville (453–4000).
Jeanes Hospital, 7600 Central Ave. (728–2000).
JFK Hospital, Langon St. and Chelten Ave. (831–7258).
Lankenau Hospital, Lancaster and City aves. (645–2000).
Medical College Hospital, Rolling Hill Division, 60 E. Township Line Rd., Elkins Park (663–6324).
Nazareth Hospital, St. Joseph's Hall, 2601 Holme Ave. (335–6556)
Northeastern Hospital, 401 Klein Professional Bldg., 5401 Old York Rd. (291–3064).
Pottstown Memorial Hospital, 1600 East High St., Pottstown (327–7097).
Springfield Hospital, 190 W.

Sproul Rd., Springfield (692–4233).
Saint Mary Hospital, Langhorne–Newton Rd., Langhorne (750–2090).
Temple University Hospital, Broad and Ontario sts. (221–3531).
Taylor Hospital, 100 Chester Pike, Ridley Park (595–6491).

**Amyotrophic Lateral Sclerosis (ALS):** *For those afflicted with Lou Gehrig's disease. Families, friends and health–care professionals invited.*

Abington Memorial Hospital, Beardwood Auditorium, Widener Bldg. Basement, 1200 Old York Rd., Abington (277–3508).
Medical College Hospitals, Bucks County Campus, 225 Newtown Rd., Warminster (441–6662).

**ALS Association:** *National organization with Philadelphia branch. Operates four support groups in the area.*

Newtown Tower Apts., Community Room A, 3400 West Chester Pike, Newtown Square (353-9617, 277-3508).
Good Shepherd Rehabilitation Hospital, 5th and St. John sts., Allentown (776-3256).
Kennedy Memorial Hospital–Cherry Hill Division, Chapel Ave. and Copper Landing Rd. (277-3508).
ALS Association, Greater Philadelphia Chapter, 1710 Romano Dr., Norristown (277-3508).

**Amputee:** *For those who have undergone an amputation. Families and friends invited.*

Abington Memorial Hospital, Widener Bldg., 4th Floor Conference Room, 1200 Old York Rd. (576-2204).
Medical College of Pennsylvania, 3300 Henry Ave., Philadelphia (842-6000).

**Anorexia/Bulimia Association of Philadelphia:** *For people with eating disorders. Separate groups for parents and friends.*

Philadelphia Child Guidance Clinic, 34th St. and Civic Center Blvd. (750-7087).

**Arthritis:** *For those suffering from any form of arthritis. Family and friends invited.*

Abington Hospital, Widener Bldg., Day Room, 1200 Old York Rd., Abington (464-6369).
Bryn Mawr Hospital, Board Room, 130 S. Bryn Mawr Ave., Bryn Mawr (526-3000).
Bryn Mawr Rehabilitation Hospital, 414 Paoli Pike, Malvern (251-5599).
Chandler Hall, Adult Day Care Room, Buck Road and Cherry St., Newtown (860-4000).
Cherry Hill Library, 1100 N. Kings Highway, Cherry Hill, NJ (609-482-0600).
Christ United Methodist Church, 1020 Valley Forge Rd., Lansdale (362-5062).
Delaware County Memorial Hospital, Meeting Room 111, 501 N. Lansdowne Ave., Drexel Hill (284-8100).
Doylestown Hospital, Conference Room F, 595 State St., Doylestown (348-8565).
Albert Einstein Medical Center, Paley Bldg., 1st Floor Conference Room, York and Tabor rds. (329-5715).
Hospital of the University of Pennsylvania, Founder's Bldg., 3rd Floor, Plaza A, 3400 Spruce

St. (662-2454).
Lankenau Hospital, Conference Room 1, MSB, 1st Floor, 100 Lancaster Ave. (645-2171).
Memorial Hospital of Burlington County, 175 Madison Ave., Mount Holly, NJ (609-267-0700).
Montgomery Hospital, Powell and Fornance sts., 5 East Conference Room, Norristown (270-2000).
Moss Rehabilitation Hospital, 1200 W. Tabor Rd. (456-9900).
Northeast YMCA, 2840 Holme Ave. (335–1222)
Pottstown Memorial Medical Center, 1600 E. High St., Pottstown (367-9863).
Reading Hospital and Medical Center, 6th and Spruce sts., Reading (375-0832).
Riddle Memorial Hospital, 1068 W. Baltimore Pike, Media (891-3255).
Sacred Heart Medical Center, 9th and Wilson sts., Chester (874-1264).
Seashore House/Rheumatology Center, 3415 Civic Center Blvd. (578-1464).
St. Luke's Hospital, Cafeteria Conference Room, 801 Ostrum St., Bethlehem (865-4433).

*Link: Sponsored by the Eastern Pennsylvania Chapter of the Arthritis Foundation, providing phone support for arthritis sufferers.*
Bryn Mawr Rehabilitation Hospital, 414 Paoli Pike, Malvern (640-3900).
Sacred Heart Rehabilitation Center, 1430 DeKalb St., Norristown (278-8090).
1217 Sansom St., 4th Floor (574–9480, 800-322-9040).

**Bereavement:** *For those who have lost a loved one.*

Abington Memorial Hospital, 1200 Old York Rd., Abington (576–2700).
Delaware County Memorial Hospital, 501 N. Lansdowne Ave., Drexel Hill (284–8100).
Elkins Park Library. Specifically for adults who have lost a parent, not necessarily recently. Church Rd. near Old York Rd., Elkins Park (635–0176).
Fox Chase Cancer Center, 7701 Burholme Ave. (728–6900).
Hahnemann University Center for Families in Transition, 1427 Vine St. (246–5100).
Mercy Catholic, Fitzgerald Division, Lansdowne and Baily rds., Darby (237–4000).
Mercy Catholic, Misericordia Division, 5301 Cedar Ave., Philadelphia (748–9000).
Montgomery Cancer Center, 1330 Powell St., Suite 507, Norristown (270–2711).
Nazareth Hospital, 2601 Holme Ave. (335–7654).

**Breast Cancer:** *For patients and their partners.*
*A New Beginning.* A coed support group for any person who has had a bout with breast cancer. Families and friends invited. Abington School of Nursing, 1200 Old York Rd., Abington (646–4954).

*The Breast Cancer Support Group.* Support and information for those diagnosed with breast cancer. Montgomery Cancer Center, 1330 Powell St., Suite 308, Norristown (270–2700).
*Philadelphia Breast Cancer Support Group.* Two–hour programs, once a month, focusing on how individuals cope with breast

cancer during and after treatment. Graduate Hospital, Suite 901, Pepper Pavilion, 1800 Lombard St. (735–4699).

*American Cancer Society*
Albert Einstein Medical Center, York and Tabor rds. (728–2668).
Crozer–Chester Medical Center, 15th St. and Upland Ave., Chester (447–2646).
Fox Chase Cancer Center, 7701 Burholme Ave. (728–6900).
Hospital of the University of Pennsylvania, 3600 Spruce St. (662–6193).
Bryn Mawr Rehabilitation Hospital, 414 Paoli Pike, Malvern (642–0300).
Montgomery Hospital, 1330 Powell St., Suite 507, Norristown (270–2711).
North Penn Hospital, 100 Medical Campus Dr., Lansdale (361–4472).
Phoenixville Hospital, 140 Nutt Rd., Phoenixville (933–9281).
Pottstown Memorial Medical Center, 600 E. High St., Pottstown (327–7136).
Thomas Jefferson University Hospital, 111 S. 11th St. (955–8668).

**Breath of Fresh Air:** *Asthma education and support group.*
Underwood Hospital, Redbank Ave. and Broad St., Woodbury, NJ (609-478-6285).

**Cancer:** *I Can Cope. Run in conjunction with the American Cancer Society at nearly every hospital in the Delaware Valley. Contact your local hospital for details, including meeting dates and times. Certain hospitals offer more specialized support for various types of cancer; those are listed below.*

*Brain Cancer:*
Hospital of the Medical College of Pennsylvania, 3300 Henry Ave. (842–6453).

*Lymphoma–Leukemia:*
Albert Einstein Medical Center, York and Tabor rds. (456–7382).

*Ostomy Support Groups:*
Bucks–Mont Ostomy Support Group. Sites rotate among North Penn, Grand View, Doylestown and Quakertown hospitals (843–9761).
Central Montgomery County Ostomy Association (270–2000).
Fox Chase Cancer Center, 7701 Burholme Ave. (728–6900).
Lower Bucks Hospital, Bath Rd. at Orchard Ave., Bristol (785–9200).
Lower Merion Ostomy Group, Bryn Mawr Hospital, 130 S. Bryn Mawr Ave., Bryn Mawr (642–0300).
Philadelphia Ostomy Association, Logan Square East, 2 Franklintown Plaza (843–9761).
Pottstown Memorial Medical Center, 1600 E. High St., Pottstown (327–7149).

*Philadelphia Candlelighters:* For the families of children diagnosed with cancer. Meetings held at members' homes. For more information, call 884–0413.

*Prostate Cancer:*
Albert Einstein Medical Center, York and Tabor rds. (715–1613).

**CAPS (Children of Aging Parents):** *For middle–aged people with the problems of dealing with elderly parents.*
1609 Woodburn Rd., Suite 302A, Levittown (945–6900).

Medical College Hospital, Elkins Park Campus, 60 E. Township Line Rd., Elkins Park (663–6324).
Osteopathic Medical Center, City Avenue Campus, 4150 City Ave. (871–1000).

**Caregivers:** *For those caring for a disabled or elderly relative.*
Abington Memorial Hospital, Senior Care Center, 801 Easton Rd., Abington (784–9129).

**Coalition of Active Disabled of Chester County:** *For disabled people who can work or are able to go out. Advocacy, referral and support services.*
West Chester Municipal Bldg., Gay Street, West Chester (436–6502).

**Compassionate Friends:** *For parents who have lost a child.*
Einstein One, Room 111, 9880 Bustleton Ave. (742–5167, 745–3249).
Osteopathic Medical Center, City Avenue Campus, 4150 City Ave. (871–1000).
Temple University Hospital, Broad and Ontario sts. (221–2000).
Valley Forge Chapter, Lutheran Church of the Good Shepherd, 132 E. Valley Forge Rd., King of Prussia (265–4545).

*Sibling Group*— 1371 Varnum Dr., Wayne (688–1504).

**C.O.P.D.** *(Chronic Obstructive Pulmonary Disease): For people with emphysema, asthma, or any other chronic lung disease. Families and friends invited.*
Rancocas Hospital, Sunset Rd., Willingboro, NJ (609–835–3075).

**Cardiac Support Group:** *For those who have had angina, a heart attack, open–heart surgery or any cardiac disease. Families and friends invited.*
AMH Health Center, Willow Wood, 3901 Commerce Ave., Willow Grove (576–2204).

**Diabetes:** *For those suffering from juvenile or adult diabetes. Family and friends invited.*
Brandywine Health Services, 213 Reeceville Rd., Cain Township (383–8581).
Bryn Mawr Hospital, Boardroom, 130 S. Bryn Mawr Ave., Bryn Mawr (526–3409).
Chestnut Hill Hospital, 8835 Germantown Ave. (248–8160).
Children's Hospital, 34th St. and Civic Center Blvd. (590–3174).
Crozer–Chester Medical Center, 15th St. and Upland Ave., Chester (447–6595).
Delaware County Memorial Hospital, Room 113, 501 N. Lansdowne Ave., Drexel Hill (284–8393).
Frankford Hospital, Frankford Ave. and Wakeling St. (831–2122).
Germantown Hospital, One Penn Blvd. (951–8035).
Graduate Hospital, 1800 Lombard St. (985–2205).
Holy Redeemer Hospital, 1648 Huntingdon Pike, Meadowbrook (947–3000).
Hospital of the University of Pennsylvania, 3400 Spruce St. (662–2807).
Jeanes Hospital, 7600 Central Ave. (728–2296).
Jefferson Park Hospital, 3905 Ford Rd. (578–3419).
Lower Bucks Hospital, Bath Rd. at Orchard Ave., Bristol (785–9200).

Kennedy Memorial Hospital, Stratford Division, 18 E. Laurel Rd., Stratford, NJ (609–582–2500).
Kensington Hospital, 136 W. Diamond St. (426–8100).
Liberty Center for Independent Living, 919 Walnut St., 10th Floor, Philadelphia (627–0600).
Medical College Hospitals, Bucks County Campus, 225 Newtown Rd., Warminster (441–6662).
Medical College of Pennsylvania, 3300 Henry Ave. (842–6717).
Memorial Hospital of Burlington County, 175 Madison Ave., Mount Holly, NJ (609–267–0700)
Mercy Catholic Medical Center, Misericordia Division, 5301 Cedar Ave. (748–9420).
Methodist Hospital, 2301 S. Broad St. (925–9242).
Northeastern Hospital, 2301 E. Allegheny Ave. (291–3520).
Osteopathic Medical Center, 4150–90 City Line Ave. (871–1916).
Pennsylvania Hospital, 8th and Spruce sts. (829–6027).
Phoenixville Hospital, 140 Nutt Rd., Phoenixville (933–9281).
Philadelphia VA Hospital, Ambulatory Care Bldg., 38th St. and University Ave. (823–5800).
Pottstown Memorial Medical Center, 1600 E. High St., Pottstown (327–7000).
Presbyterian Medical Center of Philadelphia, 39th and Market sts. (662–8210).
Roxborough Memorial Hospital, 5800 Ridge Ave. (487–4318).
St. Agnes Medical Center, 1900 S. Broad St. (339–4100).
St. Christopher's Hospital for Children, Erie Ave. at Front St. (427–5173).
St. Joseph's Hospital, 16th St. and Girard Ave. (787–5077).
Thomas Jefferson University Hospital, 111 S. 11th St. (955–5077).

*Young Adult Diabetics:* Support group for those 18–40 years old.
Bryn Mawr Hospital, Barton Room, 130 S. Bryn Mawr Ave., Bryn Mawr (526–3409).
*Juvenile Diabetes Foundation*, 2200 Ben Franklin Parkway (567–4307).

**Epilepsy:** *Epilepsy Foundation of Philadelphia and New Jersey: For epilepsy patients, family and friends. Support, guest speakers, informative lectures.*
Graduate Hospital Comprehensive Epilepsy Center, 1800 Lombard St. (893–2440).
Kennedy Memorial Hospital, Cherry Hill Division, Chapel Ave. and Cooper Landing Rd., Cherry Hill, NJ (609–488–6500).

*Delaware Valley Parents of Children with Epilepsy: For the parents of epileptic children. Education and support.*
Bensalem Parents Support Group (741–0516).
Bryn Mawr Hospital, 130 S. Bryn Mawr Ave., Bryn Mawr (789–2142).

**Fibromylagia:** *For those suffering from this muscular disease. Families and friends invited.*
Abington Memorial Hospital, Widener Bldg., 4th Floor Day Room, 1200 Old York Rd. (745–3058, 782–1241).

**Foundation for Advancement in Cancer Therapy:** *Self–help for anyone who has*

had cancer. Information, private counseling, workshops and educational programming.
300 E. Lancaster Ave., Wynnewood (642–4810).

**Gay Men's Psychotherapy:** *A support group dealing with general issues confronting gay men.* By appointment; contact Dr. Dan Estes, 567–2260. Fee. Meets in Center City.

**Guillain–Barre Syndrome:** *For those suffering from this peripheral neurological disorder. Part of international group focusing on education, support and research. Family and friends invited.*
1234 Tyson Ave., Philadelphia (745–0773).
Osteopathic Medical Center, City Avenue Campus, 4150 City Ave. (871–1000).

**Huntington's Disease Society of America:** *For anyone suffering from the disease, family and friends.*
Montgomery Hospital, Cancer Center Conference Room, Fornance and Powell rds., Norristown (569–0536).
Osteopathic Medical Center, City Avenue Campus, 4150 City Line Ave. (871–1000).

**La Leche League:** *An international organization offering breast-feeding information and support for mothers.* For information about meeting times and locations, call 666–0359.

**Laryngectomee:** *For people who've had their larynxes removed.*
Cavalry Baptist Church, Marshall and Haws sts., Norristown (337–4677).
Delaware County Memorial Hospital, 501 N. Lansdowne Ave., Drexel Hill (259–7021).
Fox Chase Cancer Center, 7701 Burholme Ave. (728–6900).
Let's Talk Group of the Norristown Laryngectomy Club, Sacred Heart Hospital, 4th and Chew sts., Allentown (967–3021).
Speak Eazy Club of the Delaware Valley, Fox Chase Cancer Center, 7701 Burholme Ave. (739–1176).

**Lupus:** *For lupus sufferers, family and friends.*
Arthritis–Lupus Center of Hahnemann University, 221 N. Broad St. (448–3482).
Frankford Hospital, Torresdale Division, Knight and Red Lion rds. (934–4000).
Mercy Catholic Medical Center, Misericordia Division, 5301Cedar Rd. (747–5975).
Hahnemann University Hospital, 221 N. Broad St. (448–7000).
Lankenau Hospital, City and Lancaster aves. (448–3482, 743–7171).
Lupus Study Center, 221 N. Broad St. (448–3482, 743–7171).
Saint Mary Hospital, Langhorne–Newtown Rd., Langhorne (934–6723).
Trinity Church, 6901 Rising Sun Ave. (745–6114).
West Jersey Hospital, Rte. 73 and Brick Road, Marlton, NJ (609–767–3311).

**Multiple Sclerosis:** *For multiple sclerosis sufferers, family and friends.*
Abington Memorial Hospital, Widener Bldg., 4th Floor Conference Room, 1200 Old York Rd. (657–3762).
Bryn Mawr Rehabilitation Hospital, 414 Paoli Pike, Malvern (696–4811).
Doylestown Hospital, 275 S. Main

St., Doylestown (343–0573).
Good Shepherd Rehabilitation Hospital, 5th and St. John sts., Allentown (395–8121).
Grand View Hospital, 700 Lawn Ave., Sellersville (257–8214).
Kennedy Memorial Hospital, Cherry Hill Division, Chapel Ave. and Cooper Landing Rd., Cherry Hill, NJ (609–346–6000).
Lankenau Hospital, Lancaster and City aves. (645–2171).
Lower Bucks Hospital, Bath Rd. at Orchard Ave., Bristol (945–4758).
Moss Rehabilitation Center, 1200 W. Tabor Rd. (329–7166).
Nazareth Hospital, Physician's Office Bldg., Roosevelt Blvd. at Pennypack Circle (725–9746).
Riddle Hospital, 1068 W. Baltimore Pike, Media (874–6159).
Suburban General Hospital, 1548 DeKalb St., Norristown (631–5356).
Thomas Jefferson University Hospital, 111 S. 11th St. (955–6000).

**Narcotics Anonymous:** *For those ready to confront a narcotic addiction. Meets at over 50 area hospitals. Call your local hospital for meeting times.*

**Nar–Anon Family:** *Support group for relatives and friends of drug abusers.*
Huntington Hospital, Fitzwatertown and Welsh rds., Willow Grove (961–2851).

**National Depressive and Manic Depressive Association:** *An organization run by and for individuals with depression and manic depression. Family members, friends and health-care workers invited. Emphasis on support and advocacy.*
Belmont Center for Comprehensive Treatment, 4200 Monument Rd. (581–3838, 328–8412).

**Obsessive–Compulsive Behavior:**
Medical College of Pennsylvania, Eppi Conference Center, 3200 Henry Ave. (842–4010).

**Parkinson's Disease:** *For those suffering from the disease.*
Jeanes Hospital, 7600 Central Ave., Philadelphia (782–2082).
Sacred Heart Hospital and Rehabilitation Center, 1430 DeKalb Pike, Norristown (776–4500).

**Polio:**
Abington Memorial Hospital, Widener Bldg., Garden Cafe Room M, 1200 Old York Rd. (946–8567)
Rancocas Hospital, Sunset Rd., Willingboro, NJ (609–723–8314).

**Project SHARE:** *SHARE is currently the only national self–help clearinghouse run by mental–health patients. Provides support, information, referral and technical assistance to 20,000 patients nationwide. For information on meeting places and times, contact Beth Greenspan, 735–6367.*

**Recovery:** *An international organization for people with chronic depression, fatigue and nervousness, or mental illness. Offers a systematic method for curbing manic behavior. Call 332–0722 for information.*
Bryn Mawr Presbyterian Church, 625 Montgomery Ave., Bryn Mawr
Graduate Hospital, 1800 Lombard St.
Rhawnhurst Presbyterian Church, Loretta Ave. and Lansing St.

St. James Lutheran Church, Castor Ave. and Pratt St.
St. Joseph's College, 54th St. and Overbrook Ave.
St. Mary's Episcopal Church, Lancaster and Louella aves., Wayne.
St. Peter's Episcopal Church, 614 Easton Rd., Glenside.

**Scleroderma Association of Delaware Valley:** *Promotes awareness of Scleroderma. Sonsors fundraisers. Advocay and support.*
Jefferson Park Hospital, 3905 Ford Rd. (545-5807).

**Sjorgen's Syndrome:** *For victims of this autoimmune disease. Family and friends invited.*
Lower Bucks Hospital, Auditorium, Bath Rd. and Orchard Ave., Bristol (752–9347, 624–4577).

**Spinal Cord Injury:** *For those with any kind of spinal injury or disease.*
Abington Memorial Hospital, Rorer Bldg., Garden Cafe, 1200 Old York Rd., Abington (646–0335, evenings).
Bryn Mawr Rehabilitation Hospital, 414 Paoli Pike, Malvern (251–5400).
Moss Rehabilitation Hospital, 1200 W. Tabor Rd. (456–9900).

**Stroke:** *For people recovering from strokes. Family and friends invited.*
Abington Memorial Hospital, Rorer Bldg., Garden Cafe, 1200 Old York Rd., Abington (576–2570).
Bryn Mawr Hospital, Dining Rooms A and B, 130 S. Bryn Mawr Ave., Bryn Mawr (526–3212).
Bryn Mawr Rehabilitation Hospital, Volunteer Room, 414 Paoli Pike, Malvern (251–5599).
Crozer–Chester Medical Center, 15th St. and Upland Ave., Chester (447–2428).
Delaware County Memorial Hospital, 2nd Floor, 501 N. Lansdowne Ave., Drexel Hill (284–8908).
Mercy Catholic Medical Center, Fitzgerald Division, Lansdowne Ave. and Baily Rd., Darby (237–4000).
Moss Rehabilitation Hospital, 1200 W. Tabor Rd. (456–9900).
Pottstown Memorial Medical Center, 1600 E. High St., Pottstown (327–7000).
Sacred Heart Hospital and Rehabilitation Center, 1430 DeKalb Pike, Norristown (776–4500).
Saint Mary Hospital, Langhorne–Newtown Rd., Langhorne (750–2090).

**Survivors of Suicide:** *For those who have attempted suicide, their family and friends.*
Crozer–Chester Hospital, 15th St. and Puland Ave., Chester (586–5171).
Delaware Valley Medical Center, 200 Oxford Valley Rd., Langhorne (745–8247).
Graduate Hospital, 1800 Lombard St. (545–2242).
Northwestern Institute, 450 Bethlehem Pike, Fort Washington (745–8247).

**Tourette's Syndrome:**
Abington Memorial Hospital, Beardwood Classroom, 1200 Old York Rd. (343–9689).
Bryn Mawr Hospital, 414 Paoli Pike, Bryn Mawr (853–3798, 357–0159).

**Unite:** *For parents who've lost a baby during pregnancy or shortly after birth.*
Hospital of the University of Pennsylvania, 3400 Spruce St. (662–2616).
Jeanes Hospital, 7600 Central Ave. (728–3737).
Kennedy Memorial Hospital, Stratford Division, 18 E. Laurel Rd., Stratford (609–346–3600).
Lankenau Hospital, 120 E. Lancaster Ave., Wynnewood (645–2174).
Mercy Catholic Medical Center, Fitzgerald Division, Lansdowne Ave. and Baily Rd., Darby (237–4000).
Phoenixville Hospital, 140 Nutt Rd., Phoenixville (558–0272).
St. James Church, 3768 Germantown Pike, Collegeville (234–8216).
Saint Mary Hospital, Langhorne–Newtown Rd., Langhorne (968–6589).

**Widows & Widowers:**
*Widow and Widowers Counseling and Referral Service: For people who have lost a partner. Some hospitals may have support groups for widows/widowers of specific ages. For information call 635–4090.*
Christ Lutheran Church of Oreland, Pennsylvania Ave. below Ridge Ave. (886–4612).
North Penn Baptist Church, 26th St. and Haggart Rd. (229–2415).
Medical College Hospitals, Elkins Park Campus, 60 E. Township Line Rd., Elkins Park (663–2000).

**Zipper Club:** *For those who have had any sort of heart problem (heart attack, angioplasty, open–heart surgery, etc.). Support groups are run in conjunction with 38 area hospitals. For information call 887–6644. Family and friends invited.*

# MAGEE.

## 35 YEARS OF BUILDING ON STRENGTHS FOR INDEPENDENCE.

Magee Rehabilitation Hospital is one of the nation's leading centers for physical rehabilitation. We serve as part of the federally designated *Regional Spinal Cord Injury Center of Delaware Valley*. Magee's Brain Injury Rehabilitation Program was the first in the nation to be accredited by the Commission on Accreditation of Rehabilitation Facilities. Our annual Stroke Conference is recognized as one of the finest on the east coast.

Magee Rehabilitation Hospital's comprehensive inpatient and outpatient rehabilitation programs include:

- brain injury
- spinal cord injury
- stroke
- amputation
- orthopedics
- neurologic disorders
- pain management
- occupational health

### DISCOVER RECOVERY with MAGEE

**REHABILITATION HOSPITAL** • Six Franklin Plaza • Philadelphia, PA 19102 • 215-587-3000
**OUTPATIENT CENTER** • 1419 Oregon Avenue • Philadelphia, PA 19145 • 215-271-3050

Accredited by the Joint Commission on Accreditation of Healthcare Organizations (JCAHO) and the Commission on Accreditation of Rehabilitation Facilities (CARF).

# 33

# Getting Better

*A survey of rehab centers
from substance abuse to physical therapy.*

♥ In the world of health care, hospitals fall into two categories. General hospitals, as implied, treat a broad range of problems; specialized hospitals, on the other hand, deal with very specific needs. In this section, we focus on places geared to rehabilitation. Some concentrate on physical recovery from injury or debilitating illness, like a stroke. Others focus on recovery from alcohol and drug abuse. Because of the expanding need for this kind of care, we've included some for–profit centers that accept insurance. Many general hospitals also have units providing rehabilitation services, and you'll find those listed in chapters 7 and 10.

| | |
|---|---|
| 🛏 | **OVERNIGHT FACILITIES FOR FAMILIES** |
| 🙏 | **PASTORAL CARE** |
| 🏥 | **HOSPICE CARE** |
| 💈 | **BARBER** |
| ⚖ | **PATIENT ADVOCATE** |
| 🚭 | **SMOKE-FREE ENVIRONMENT** |
| 🎓 | **TEACHING HOSPITAL** |
| E | **EMERGENCY ROOM** |
| ✉ | **PREPAYMENT FOR DEDUCTIBLE REQUIRED** |

In addition, the region has many excellent private physical therapy clinics, such as Pat Croce's Sports Physical Therapists, that can be found in your local telephone directory. Choosing where to go for treatment may involve a combination of factors, from convenience to cost, so review all your options before deciding what's the best place for you.

## PHYSICAL REHABILITATION

### Bryn Mawr Rehabilitation Hospital

*414 Paoli Pike, Malvern, 251–5400.* Doctors on active staff: 8; number of beds: 21; accreditation: JCAHO, CARF.

Specialized treatment programs: the Brain Injury System, stroke and neurological disorders, spinal cord, multiple sclerosis, orthopedics.

Physical rehab services: aquatic, equestrian, recreational and horticultural therapy, cognitive redemption, rehab engineering.

Outpatient health and wellness programs: driver education, vocational rehab, amputee clinic, mild head injury.

Bryn Mawr Rehab has recently opened a new Horticultural Therapy facility that uses the psychological, physical and emotional benefits of gardening to treat depressed, physically handicapped, mentally retarded, and drug–addicted patients.

### Chestnut Hill Rehabilitation Hospital

*See Chapter 7.*

### Magee Rehabilitation Hospital

*Six Franklin Plaza, Philadelphia, 587–3000.* Doctors on active staff: 9 (100% board–certified); number of beds: 96; accreditation: JCAHO, CARF.

Specialized treatment programs: vision clinic; continence program; day hospital and community re-entry for brain injury survivors; pressure sore program; amputee day hospital and clinic.

Physical rehab services: spinal cord injury, brain injury, stroke, geriatrics, amputation, pain management, orthopedics, occupational health, work–hardening.

Outpatient health and wellness programs: Back School.

Magee's Brain Injury Rehab Program was the first in the country to be board–certified. Also serves as a federally designated regional Spinal Cord Injury Center for the Delaware Valley.

### Moss Rehabilitation Hospital

*1200 West Tabor Rd., Philadelphia, 456–9900.* Doctors on active staff: 79 (79% board–certified); number of beds: 152; 1.25 RNs per bed; accreditation: JCAHO, CARF.

Specialized treatment programs: Drucker Brain Injury Center, Moss Stroke Center, Regional Amputee Center, Kardon Center for Pediatric Rehabilitation, Regional Spina Bifida Center for Adults, Einstein–Moss Arthritis Center, Einstein–Moss Joint Replacement Center.

Physical rehab services: physical, occupational and speech therapy, therapeutic recreation, psychological services, electrodiagnostic center, gait analysis laboratory, motor control analysis, prosthetics and orthotics service, home adaptive designs service.

Outpatient health and wellness programs: fitness and exercise programs for people with physical disabilities, recreational programs.

Moss Rehab, a division of Albert Einstein Medical Center, is the region's largest provider of medical rehab services, and has outpatient centers in Olney, Northeast Philadelphia and Jenkintown.

## Mount Sinai Hospital

*4th and Reed sts., Philadelphia, 339–3456.* Doctors on active staff: 65 (90% board–certified); number of beds: 220; 1 RN per 2.2 beds; accreditation: JCAHO, CAP.

Specialized treatment programs: drug and alcohol programs (detox, residential, outpatient); psychiatry programs for geriatrics, adults and adolescents; skilled nursing facility.

Physical rehab services: Services patients recovering from stroke, head injury, amputation, arthritis, spinal cord injuries, chronic pain, and neurologic and orthopedic problems. In– and outpatient physical medicine and comprehensive rehab programs, including physical, occupational and speech therapy; EASY STREET (a therapy environment simulating a city street).

Outpatient health and wellness programs: family program series on substance abuse (topics include disease concept of addiction, progression of the disease concept, recovering family and relapse processes); fall and fracture prevention, pain clinic, free public health lectures.

Mount Sinai is a division of the Graduate Health System.

## Sacred Heart Hospital and Rehabilitation Center
*See Chapter 7.*

## SUBSTANCE ABUSE

### Abraxas Foundation, Inc.

*5401 Wayne Ave., Philadelphia, 848–3220.* For court-adjudicated adolescents with substance abuse problems. Provides re–entry programs, inpatient residential facilites located in Central Pennsylvania and intensive two–week programs for women. No detox.

### Advantage Recovery Network

*7901 Bustleton Ave., Suite 307, Philadelphia, 331–4800;* 24–hour number: 800–220–4801.

Licensed therapists on staff: 7; offices also in Center City Philadelphia and Swarthmore; all major insurance accepted.

An intensive eight–week outpatient program stressing individual and group sessions as well as fellowship meetings, such as AA, NA, CA. Also has a Prescription Freedom Program, a service which acts as an intermediary between the doctor and patient. Doctors give prescriptions directly to the program which fills them and delivers them to the patient's home.

### Alcohol and Mental Health Associates
*1200 Walnut St., 2nd floor, Philadelphia, 545–8078.* Provides methadone treatment for heroin addicts as well as outpatient drug and alcohol counseling.

### Bowling Green Brandywine
*495 Newark Rd., Kennett Square, 268–3588, 800–662–2438.* Medical director on staff 24 hours; number of beds; 60; detox services in acute cases; accepts most insurance plans.

Provides intensive outpatient programs for those who need help in overcoming a substance abuse problem without hospitalization. After–Work Recovery allows patients to live at home and continue to work while getting support and treatment. All entering patients receive medical, social and psychological assessment.

### Bridge Therapeutic Center
*8400 Pine Rd., 342–5000.* Residential drug and alcohol treatment facilities with schooling for teenagers 14–19.

Bridge Family & Youth offers outpatient drug and alcohol facilities for adults as well as teenagers. Those facilities are located at 1912 Welsh Rd.

### The Charter Fairmount Institute
*See Chapter 10.*

### Congreso
*704 W. Girard Ave., 625–0550, 229–4040* (Prevention Intervention for Youths). Offers outpatient drug and alcohol facilities and provides counseling on prevention for Hispanic inner–city adolescents.

### The Consortium
*26 S. 40th St., 3rd Floor, Philadelphia, 596–8011, 596–8083.* Outpatient drug and alcohol facilities at four area locations: 451 University Ave., 596–8084; 6408 Woodland Ave., 727–4420; 451 University Ave., 596–8277; 4219 Chester Ave., 596–8175 (for cocaine babies).

University Avenue location also has a methadone clinic for heroin addicts.

See Chapter 10 for additional information.

### Cora Services
Outpatient drug and alcohol facilities as well as counseling and referral.
See Chapter 10 for additional information.

### Diagnostic and Rehabilitation Center
*229 Arch St., Philadelphia, 625–2381, 625–8063 (for outpatient, residential and*

*detox), 223–1005 (shelter).* Has outpatient drug and alcohol as well as residential treatment facilities. Provides emergency care and detox services and acts as a homeless shelter.

### Eaglevile Hospital 🏥 🛏 ✉
*100 Eagleville Rd., Eagleville, 539–6000, 800–255–2019 (out–of–state).* Doctors on active staff: 15 (82% board–certified); number of beds: 159; 51 RNs; accreditation: JCAHO, PDH, PODAP; performs detox; accepts Blue Cross, Medicaid, Medicare.

Specialized treatment programs: Program for Employed Persons, a short–term intensive program for men and women; 30–day inpatient detox; men's inpatient program (focused on the special issues confronting chemically addicted men); women's inpatient program (a multidisciplinary approach for chemically addicted women); Continuum, a partial hospitalization program.

Eagleville is the only hospital in Pennsylvania licensed exclusively for drug and alcohol rehabilitation. It is one of the largest and most respected of its kind in the country.

### Gaudenzia House
*39 E. School House Lane, 849–7200.* Six area locations, each providing different services: Human Services Building, 1415 N. Broad St., Room 116, 235–5200, provides outpatient drug and alcohol treatment facilities; 1834 West Tioga St., 228–0644, provides residential treatment facilities; 1030 South Concord Rd., West Chester, 399–6929, provides residential treatment facilities and is a homeless shelter for women and children; 701 N. 63rd St., 447–0063, provides residential treatment facilities; 1300 Tulpehocken St., 924–6322, provides residential treatment facilities and is a homeless shelter; 2927 N. 5th St., 423–6766, provides prevention counseling.

### Hampton Hospital
*See Chapter 10.*

### Horizon House, Inc.
*120 S. 30th St., 386–3838.* Provides outpatient drug and alcohol treatment facilities, case management, and residential facilities, and acts as a homeless shelter.

See Chapter 10 for additional information.

### Malvern Institute
*940 King Rd., Malvern, 647–0330, 800–486–0017.* Doctors on active staff: 2; number of beds: 36; accreditation: JCAHO; detox available; accepts Independence Blue Cross, some HMOs, most commercial insurance carriers.

Specialized treatment programs: drug and alcohol rehab, dual diagnosis, free evaluation, inpatient rehab, family services, 12–step recovery groups.

Outpatient health and wellness programs: free evaluation and referral services, relapse prevention, continuing care, intervention (for those reluctant to get help).

A comprehensive addiction treatment facility, Malvern has been providing inpatient and intensive outpatient services for over 40 years.

### Mount Sinai Hospital
*See listing under Physical Rehabilitation.*

### Northeast Treatment Center
*2205 Bridge St., 289–2100.* Has outpatient drug and alcohol and residential treatment facilities.

### North Philadelphia Health Systems
*8th and Girard Aves., 787–2283.* Has outpatient drug and alcohol and residential treatment facilities, and a methadone clinic for heroin addicts. Provides counseling on prevention and performs detox.

### Penn Recovery Systems
*Mutch Building #4, 39th and Market sts., 386–4280* (24–hour phone service). Branches in Media, Fort Washington, Philadelphia and Pottstown. Doctors on active staff: 7; accreditation: JCAHO; detox available; accepts Independence BlueCross, HMO/PA and other insurance on

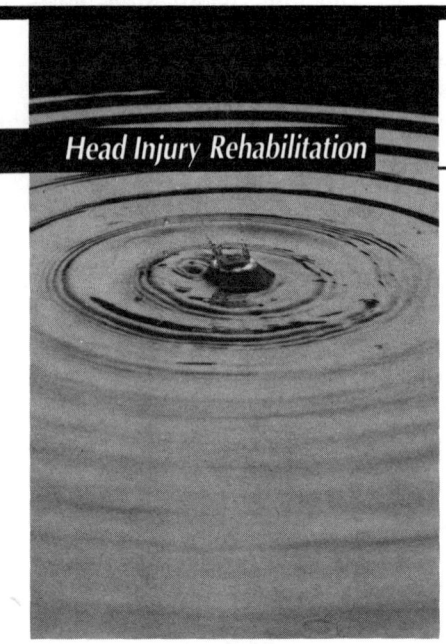

---

**Head Injury Rehabilitation**

## A Head Injury Only *Starts* With Your Head

*Then it affects every aspect of your life.*

It takes an enormous amount of courage and support to come back from a head injury. It also takes the right rehabilitation program.

ReMed Recovery Care Centers is recognized nationally for significant outcomes in its innovative post acute treatment programs. ReMed's uniquely trained staff use the community as the classroom to help survivors re-learn how to live, work and play.

ReMed is what other head injury programs try to be. Effective.

**ReMed**
RECOVERY CARE CENTERS
*Real-life Head Injury Rehabilitation*

*CARF accredited • Residential • Outpatient • Homebased Programs*
**625 Ridge Pike Building C • Conshohocken, PA 19428 • 1-800-84-ReMed**

a flexible basis.

A private health-care organization providing direct and supportive in- and outpatient services. Specializes in chronic drug and alcohol abuse. Stresses 12-step program groups such as AA, NA and CA. Admission to outpatient program is based on the following criteria: regular substance abuse for less than six months; frequency of abuse no more than twice weekly; minimal impairment of occupational and social functioning; absence of significant psychosocial stressors; presence of positive social support system; willingness and ability to attend 12-step program meetings such as AA, NA and CA.

### ReEnter
*3331 Powelton Ave., Philadelphia, 222-2770.* One physician always on staff; 15 beds; no detox; accepts any drug and alcohol policy; no emergency room.

A therapeutic inpatient recovery home for males between the ages of 18 and 60 struggling with substance abuse. Patients must be ambulatory, and substance-free for a minimum of five to seven days prior to admission. Minimum stay: three months; maximum stay: 12 months.

Clinical services: history and physical examination, diagnostic and psychiatric evaluation, relapse prevention program, individual and group psychotherapy, family education and group therapy program, random drug screens.

# Step By Step

Offering a continuum of care to meet the rehabilitation needs of the Delaware Valley

- Physical Medicine and Rehabilitation
- Mental Health Programs
- Skilled Nursing Facility
- Substance Abuse Rehabilitation

*Step By Step Mt. Sinai Hospital is taking rehabilitative care to new heights. Combining resources for the treatment of Adolescents, Adults and Older Adults.*

**MT. SINAI HOSPITAL**
Fourth and Reed Streets
Philadelphia, PA 19147
215/339 3456

Graduate Health System

### Valley Forge Medical Center and Hospital
*1033 W. Germantown Pike, Norristown, 539–8500.* Three psychiatrists and 4 MDs on staff; number of beds: 70; detox available; accepts all major insurance and some MAs.

Specializes in drug, alcohol and gambling rehabilitation on an in– and outpatient basis. Special programs: psychological testing (for gambling patients), individual therapy, group therapy, guided imagery group, marriage and family counseling, financial management consultation, biofeedback and stress management, AA and NA meetings.

### Woodside Hall Addiction Treatment Program
*4200 Monument Ave., 581–5445.* See Belmont Center for Comprehensive Treatment, Chapter 7.

---

*Take good care of yourself . . .*

visit the Breast Care Center
for a comprehensive breast evaluation
and treatment options available from a multidisciplinary team of specialists

*you belong to you . . .*

for more information or
to make an appointment, call
**544-1040**

the Breast Care Center
a Program of the Taylor Health System

at the Springfield Medical Imaging Center
Baltimore Pike and Andrew Road
Springfield, Pennsylvania 19064

# 34 Hot Numbers

*A potpourri of hot lines and resources for health-related problems.*

## 800 NUMBERS

*These are some of the more widely used national 800 numbers. Use them if you are looking for information, referrals, counseling or technical assistance.*

### Aging
Medicare Telephone Hotline, 800–638–6833.
National Council on Aging, 800–424–9046.

### AIDS
AIDS, 800–Trials–A.
National AIDS Hotline, 800–342–AIDS.
National AIDS Information Clearinghouse, 800–458–5231.

### Alzheimer's
Alzheimer's Disease and Related Disorders Association, 800–621–0379.

### Arthritis
Arthritis Foundation Information Line, 800–283–7800.

### Alcoholism and Drug Dependence
Alcoholism and Drug Addiction Treatment Center, 800–447–3447.
American Council on Alcoholism and Drug Dependence, Inc., 800–NCA–CALL.

### Cancer
American Cancer Society Cancer Response Line, 800–ACS–2345.
American Institute for Cancer Research, 800–843–8114.
AMC Cancer Information, 800–525–3777.
Cancer Information Service, 800–4–CANCER.

### Children
American SIDS Institute, 800–232–SIDS.
National Child Abuse Hotline, 800–422–4453.
National Resource Center on Child Abuse and Neglect, 800–2–ASK–AHA.

### Cystic Fibrosis
Cystic Fibrosis Foundation, 800–344–4823.

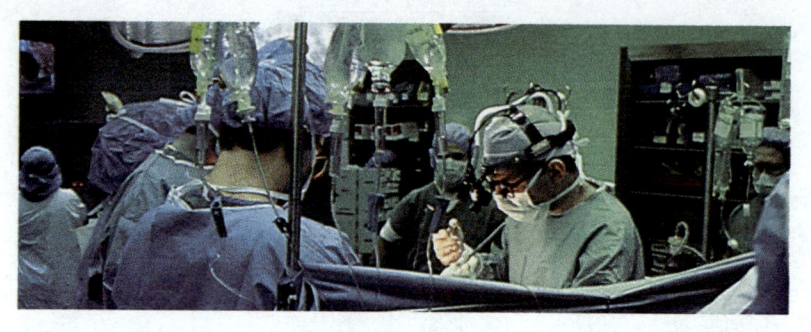

## Introducing the Delaware Valley's Newest Health System...
## Medical College Hospitals

The **Medical College Hospitals** system combines the skills of community hospitals and community-based specialists with the sophisticated technologies and respected faculty of an academic medical center.

We are particularly recognized for our comprehensive programs in:
- Cardiovascular Services
- Geriatrics
- Women's Services
- Rehabilitation
- Occupational Health
- Psychiatric Services

For more information on our services, programs or physicians, or to make an appointment, call **1-800-PRO-HEALTH.***

*\*1-800-776-4325*
*Medical College Hospitals, the Medical College of Pennsylvania and St. Christopher's Hospital for Children are the Delaware Valley members of Allegheny Health, Education and Research Foundation.*

**Medical College Hospitals, Main Clinical Campus**
*formerly Hospital of the Medical College of Pennsylvania*

**Medical College Hospitals, Eastern Pennsylvania Psychiatric Institute**
*formerly Medical College of Pennsylvania/Eastern Pennsylvania Psychiatric Institute*
3300 Henry Ave.
Philadelphia, PA 19129

**Medical College Hospitals, Bucks County Campus**
*formerly Warminster General Hospital*
225 Newtown Rd.
Warminster, PA 18974

**Medical College Hospitals, Elkins Park Campus**
*formerly Rolling Hill Hospital*
60 E. Township Line Rd.
Elkins Park, PA 19117

**MEDICAL COLLEGE HOSPITALS**

**Diabetes**
*American Diabetes Association,*
800–ADA–DISC.
**Down's Syndrome**
*National Down's Syndrome Congress,*
800–232–6372.
**Hearing Problems**
*Deafness Research Foundation,*
800–535–3323.
*Ear Foundation,* 800–545–4327.
*Hearing Helpline,* 800–327–9355.
*National Hearing Aid Helpline,*
800–521–5247.
**Liver and Kidney**
*American Liver Foundation,*
800–223–0179.
*National Kidney Foundation,*
800–622–9010.
**Lung Illness**
*Asthma and Allergy Foundation of America,* 800–7–ASTHMA
*Asthma Information Line,*
800–822–ASMA.
**Lupus**
*American Lupus Society,*
800–331–1802.
*Lupus Foundation of America,*
800–558–0121.
**Mental Illness**
*National Foundation for Depressive Illness,* 800–248–4344.
*National Mental Heath Association,*
800–969–6642.
**Multiple Sclerosis**
*National Multiple Sclerosis Society,*
800–624–8236.
**Miscellaneous Diseases**
*American Narcolepsy Association,*
800–222–6085.
*Amyotrophic Lateral Sclerosis Association,* 800–782–4747.
*Huntington's Disease Society of America,* 800–345–4372.
*National Organization for Rare Diseases,* 800–999–6673.
*United Cerebral Palsy Association,*
800–USA–1UCP.
**Sexual Problems**

*Impotence Information Center,*
800–843–4315.
*STD Hotline,* 800–227–8922.
**Sickle–Cell Anemia**
*National Association for Sickle–Cell Disease,* 800–421–8453.
**Stroke**
*Courage Stroke Network,*
800–553–6321.
*National Stroke Association,*
800–223–2732.
**Tourette Syndrome**
*Tourette Syndrome Association,*
800–237–0717.
**Vision Problems**
*National Center for Sight,*
800–221–3004.
**Women**
*International Childbirth Education Association,* 800–624–4934.
*PMS Access,* 800–222–4767.
*50th Ward Community Ambulance Association,* 924–1331.

## AMBULANCE SERVICES

*Bridesburg Civic Association Community Ambulance,*
288–6606.
*Burholme FirstAid Corps,* 745–1550.
*Healthtech–South Jersey Division,*
609–365–1911.
*Lindenwold Transportation, Inc.,*
609–784–8583.
*Medical Transport Company,*
609–488–1611.
*Metropolitan Ambulance, Inc.,*
609–661–8176
*Northeast First Aid Corps,* 624–7024.
*Northwest Community Ambulance Corps,* 537-2120.
*Olney Community Ambulance, Inc.,*
549–4848.
*Rhawnhurst Bustleton Ambulance Association,* 698–9111.
*Wissahickon Community Ambulance Association,* 482–6400.

Wissonoming First Aid Corps, Inc., 332–1509.
Wynne–Brook Community Ambulance Association, 473–4043.

## DISEASES & DISORDERS

### LOCAL ORGANIZATIONS

Action AIDS, 981–0088.
Alzheimer's Association, 568-6430.
American Anorexia and Bulimia Association, 567–2255.
American Cancer Society, 665–2900.
American Diabetes Association, 557–8070.
Arthritis Foundation, 574–9480.
Asthma and Allergy Foundation, 825–0582.
Center for Advancement of Cancer Therapy, 642–4810.
City of Hope, 854–8400.
Community AIDS Hotline, 985–2437.
Crohn's and Colitis Foundation of America, 742–1800.
Cystic Fibrosis Research Foundation, 238–8500.
Delaware Valley Transplant Program, 800–543–6391.
Easter Seals Society for Handicapped Children and Adults, 879–1000.
Elm LifeLine (cancer counseling and support programs), 609-654-4044.
Epilepsy Foundation of Philadelphia, 667–7478.
Epilepsy Network, 567–1306.
Guillain–Barre Syndrome Foundation International, 667–0131.
Heart Association, 735–3865.
Hemifacial Microsomia/Goldenhar Syndrome Family Support Network, 667–4787.
Hemophilia Foundation, 732–3030.
Juvenile Diabetes, 567–4307.
Lupus Foundation of Delaware Valley, 649–9202.
Lupus Foundation of Philadelphia, 743–7171.

National Multiple Sclerosis Society, 963–0200.
National Kidney Foundation, Delaware Valley Chapter, 923–8611.
Northeastern Alopecia Areata Research, 943–8493.
Operation VENUS (venereal disease), 567–6969.
Ostomy Information Line, 884–8348.
Overeaters Anonymous, 848–3191.
Pennsylvania Tourette Syndrome Association, 800–446–6356.
Parkinson's Disease Center, 545–8406.
Philadelphia Community Health Alternatives (VD screening and treatment), 545–8686.
Philadelphia Help Group (herpes), 763–2247.
Reye's Syndrome Foundation, 677–1730.
Scleroderma Association of the Delaware Valley, 545–5807.
Sickle–Cell Anemia, Volunteers in Aid of, 877–3485.
Spina Bifida Associaton,676-8950.
United Cerebral Palsy, 242–4200.
Zipper Club (cardiac surgery and heart information), 887–6644.

## DRUG & ALCOHOL

Alcoholics Anonymous, 574-6900.
Al–Anon, 222–5244; 609–547–0855
Al–Assist, 592–4241.
ALACALL, 609–547–0855.
Alcoholism HELP, 800–322–5525 (toll–free in New Jersey).
CODAAP (Coordination Office for Drug and Alcohol Abuse Program), 592–5403.
Family Center (pregnant addicts), 955–8577.
Greater Philadelphia Health Action, Inc., 288–9200.
Jewish Family and Vocational Services, 236–0100.

Jewish Employment and Children's
  Agency, 698–9950.
Narcotics Anonymous, 496–2826.
School District of Philadelphia,
  875–3975.
Teen Challenge Center, 849–2054.
Women in Transition, 922–7177.

## HOSPICE PROGRAMS

Albert Einstein Medical Center
  Hospice, 456–7155.
Bryn Mawr Hospital Hospice Program,
  526–3265.
Holy Redeemer Hospice, 671–9200.
Home Health Care Referral and
  Consultants, Inc., 627–3037.
Hospice of Pennsylvania Hospital,
  829–5335.
Hospice of Presbyterian Medical Center,
  662–8996.
Hospice of the University of
  Pennsylvania Hospital, 662–3927.
Lankenau Hospital Hospice Program,
  645–2022.
Wissahickon Hospice, 247–0277.

## SUICIDE

CONTACT, 879–4402;
  609–667–3000.
Suicide and Crisis Intervention Center,
  686–4420.
Survivors of Suicide, 545–2242.

## VISUAL IMPAIRMENT

Associated Services for the Blind,
  627–0600.
Blindness and Visual Services,
  560–5700.
Blind Relief Fund of Philadelphia,
  627–2333.
Federation of the Blind of
  Pennsylvania, 988-0888.
Fight for Sight of Greater Philadelphia
  (children's eye clinic),
  928–3240.

Helen Keller National Center
  (deaf–blind youths and children),
  237–1575.
Library for the Blind and Visually
  Handicapped, 925–3213.
Lions Eye Bank of Delaware Valley,
  Inc., 627–0700.
Pennsylvania Association for Blind
  Athletes, 525–3399.
Pennsylvania Council for the Blind,
  238–1410.

## WOMEN'S SERVICES

Alpha Pregnancy Services, 735–6028.
Birthright, 877–7070.
Childbirth Education Association of
  Greater Philadelphia, 828–0131.
Choice Hotline, 985–3300.
Covenant House, 844–1020.
Domestic Abuse Project of Delaware
  County, 565–4590.
Domestic Violence Program,
  739–9999.
Elizabeth Blackwell Center for Women
  (gynecological services; counseling),
  923–7577.
HERS Foundation (Hysterectomy
  Educational Resources and Services),
  667–7757.
Lamaze Educators of Southeastern
  Pennsylvania, Inc.,
  800–368–4404.
My Sister's Place (cocaine–addicted
  pregnant women and their
  children), 727–1640.
Planned Parenthood, 361–5560.
Pregnancy Hotline, 829–5437.
Resolve (Infertility), 849–3920.
Spectrum Health Services, 471–2750.
WOAR (Women Organized Against
  Rape), 985–3333.
Women Against Abuse, 386–7777.
Women in Transition (in–house
  counseling for domestic violence and
  substance abuse), 922–7500.
Women's Suburban Clinic,
  647–1344.

## MISCELLANEOUS

*Breast Health Institute,* 1015 Chestnut St., 627-4447. A Nonprofit center dedicated to raising money for breast cancer research. Provides educational material, public seminars and research grants. Gives vouchers to uninsured, low-income women for mammogram services at Hahneman University Hospital. Sponsors the Race for the Cure, a fundraising drive for breast cancer research which takes place on Mother's Day at the Philadelphia Art Museum.

*Center for Advancement in Cancer Education,* Suite 100, 300 East Lancaster Ave., Wynnewood, 642-4810. A nonprofit cancer information, counseling and referral center for people interested in nontoxic alternatives to conventional cancer treatments. It collects, evaluates and distributes information on biological cancer therapies, provides educational programs and functions as a clearinghouse for data on clinical nutrition, immuno-therapeutics, botanical medicine and psychoneuroimmunology.

*CONTACT,* 879-4402; 609-667-3000. A telephone support service using trained volunteers to help people in emotional crisis. Offers referrals.

*Couples Learning Center,* Benson East, Township Line and York rds., Jenkintown, 884-4664. Helps men and women confront and resolve their relationship problems. It offers private counseling for individuals, couples and families, and designs and conducts on-site programs for business, professional and community groups.

*ELM LifeLines,* 23 S. Main Street, Medford, NJ, 609-654-4044. A private nonprofit outpatient group providing cancer counseling and a support program. Offers weekly two hour sessions, emotional support, relaxation and visualizations, nutrition and exercise, stress management, coping strategies, and health, healing and wellness materials.

*Linda Creed Foundation,* 118 South 11th St., 955-4354. Dedicated to the early detection and treatment of breast cancer, this is a nonprofit organization sponsored by Jefferson Hospital, offering seminars, advocacy and referrals. Operates free mammography services and free breast cancer screenings at Jefferson Park Hospital, Methodist Hospital and Jefferson Hospital. Provides educational programs through businesses and high schools on breast self–examination, risk factors, and disease protection. Also runs a ten–week support workshop for breast cancer patients.

*The Poison Control Center,* One Children's Center, 386-2100. The purpose of the group is to reduce the morbidity, mortality, costs and occurrence of poisoning in Southeastern Pennsylvania by providing an around–the–clock emergency hot line service, coordinating and promoting public education, training health-care professionals, and pursuing research related to poisonings.

# PROFESSIONAL DIRECTORY

♥ *As an additional source to our readers the following health professionals have elected to list their services.* ♥ *These listings are paid advertisements and the information they contain has been furnished by the doctors and other medical practitioners. Philadelphia Magazine is not responsible for the credentials, affiliations, associations or other claims provided and does not endorse or recommend any medical professionals on the basis of their advertisement in this space. The listings appear in alphabetical order by specialty and name.*♥

*Special Advertising Section*

## ACUPUNCTURE

**ACUPUNCTURE SOCIETY OF PENNSYLVANIA**
P.O. Box L–640, Langhorne, PA 19047; (215)292–4572.
The ancient Chinese art of acupuncture has worked for people all over the world for centuries. Call for referral to an acupuncturist in your locality.

**MURRAY L. DORFMAN, M.D.**
1001 City Ave. WA 105, Wynnewood, PA 19096; (215)649–5667.
President, Acupuncture Society of Pennsylvania. Traditional, auricular therapy, meridian balancing. Needle and non–needle technique. Chronic pain, arthritis, weight reduction, smoking addiction. Descriptive literature on request.

**MARSHALL H. SAGER, D.O.**
One Bala Plaza, Suite 133, Bala Cynwyd, PA 19004; (215)668–2400.
University trained, certified medical acupuncture physician combining acupuncture, osteopathic manipulation, and Western medicine. Smoking, pain control, arthritis, backs, migraines, allergies, tendonitis, colitis, PMS, fatigue, stress.

## ALLERGY

**LINDA D. GREEN, M.D.**
*Allergy and Immunology*
Falcon Center, Suite 102B, 525 West Chester Pike, Havertown, PA 19083; (215)446–4844.
Take control of your allergies! Specializing in comprehensive diagnosis and treatment of children and adults with asthma, hay fever, sinus problems, eczema, hives and more.

**GEORGE L. MARTIN, M.D.**
**SHARON L. SHELANSKI, M.D.**
Suite 237, Lankenau Hospital Medical Bldg. West, 100 Lancaster Ave. Wynnewood, PA 19096; (215)649–9300.
Board-certifed, specializing in adult–pediatric allergy, asthma, hay fever, sinus problems and hives; treated with personal attention by physicians who care. Day and evening hours. Accept insurance.

**ROBERT J. PERIN, M.D., P.A.**
*Immunology and Asthma*
630 Salem Ave., Woodbury, NJ 08096; (609)845–8300.
We stress preventive medicine and patient education. All types of allergies treated. Specialize in cough and asthma evaluation. Spanish and French spoken.

**SHERYL TALBOT, M.D.**
822 Pine Street, Suite 2A, Philadelphia, PA 19107; (215)922–7200.
Chief, Section of Allergy, Pennsylvania Hospital, specializing in all types of allergy, allergic and non–allergic asthma, and sinus problems, in patients 12 or older.

## ARTHRITIS/RHEUMATISM

**ARTHRITIS ASSOCIATES PRESBYTERIAN MEDICAL CENTER**
*Arthritis and Rheumatism*
39th and Market sts., Philadelphia, PA 19104; (215)662–9292.
Drs. Warren A. Katz, Fredrick B. Vivino, Lawrence J. Leventhal, experienced board-certified specialists in multidisciplinary approaches to all forms of arthritis, connective tissue diseases, lower back problems, gout, and fibrositis.

**ARTHRITIS ASSOCIATES**
**DR. BRUCE I. HOFFMAN**
**DR. LAWRENCE J. LEVENTHAL**
Klein Professional Bldg., 5401 Old York Rd., Philadelphia, PA 19141; (215)456–1400.
Experienced board-certified specialists in multi-disciplinary approaches to all forms of arthritis, connective tissue diseases, lower back problems, gout, fibrositis.

**HELENE J. CASSELLI, M.D.**
*Internal Medicine*
Roxborough Medical Bldg., Suite 102, 5735 Ridge Ave., Philadelphia, PA 19128; (215)483–1675, and Klein Professional Bldg., Suite 207, 5401 Old York Rd., Philadelphia, PA 19141.
Treating arthritis, rheumatism of the adult, and all connective-tissue diseases of muscles and bones.

*Special Advertising Section*

**PENNSYLVANIA RHEUMATOLOGY ASSOC., P.C.**
**BARRY M. SCHIMMER, M.D., F.A.C.P., F.A.C.R.**
**ALAN L. EPSTEIN, M.D., F.A.C.P., F.A.C.R.**
Pennsylvania Hospital, Suite 1–C, 822 Pine St., Philadelphia, PA 19107;(215)829–5358.
Specializing in the evaluation and treatment of adult rheumatic disorders, including arthritis, connective-tissue diseases, osteoporosis, and all forms of musculoskeletal pain, especially as it pertains to general internal medicine.

**ANTONIO J. REGINATO, M.D.**
Cooper Hospital/University Medical Center
3 Cooper Plaza, Suite 215, Camden, NJ 08103; (609)342–2439.
Specialists in lupus, rheumatoid arthritis, scleroderma, gout, degenerative arthritis, osteoporosis and back pain, as well as the evaluation of patients with undiagnosed musculoskeletal symptoms.

## CARDIOLOGY

**BRANDYWINE VALLEY CARDIOVASCULAR ASSOCIATES**
3456 E. Lincoln Hwy., Thorndale, PA 19372; (215)384–2211.
Cardiovascular disease, interventional cardiology, critical-care medicine, internal medicine. Arthur B. Hodess, M.D., FACC, Thomas S. Metkus, M.D., FACC, David J. Bernbaum, M.D., FACC, Alan D. Troy, M.D., FACC, Donald V. Ferrari, DO, FACC.

**MARK D. BURGER, M.D.**
Pennsylvania Cardiology Associates, Pennsylvania Hospital, 801 Spruce St., Philadelphia, PA 19107; (215)829–5064.
Interventional cardiology, cardiac catheterization, coronary angioplasty, stress echocardiography; Clinical Assistant Professor of Medicine, University of Pennsylvania, Clinical Assistant Pennsylvania Hosptial, board-certified internal cardiovascular medicine.

# Innovations in Treatment: Nose and Sinus, Head and Neck, Hearing

The internationally recognized physicians of **Penn's Department of Otorhinolaryngology—Head and Neck Surgery** have expertise in a broad range of services. Our faculty physicians have developed many of today's innovative techniques in endoscopic sinus surgery and head and neck reconstructive surgery.

Specialties include:

- Nasal and Sinus Surgery
- Microsurgery of the Ear
- Speech and Hearing Center - a full range of audiologic and speech therapy services.
- Head and Neck Cancer
- Reconstructive and Cosmetic Head and Neck Surgery
- Microvascular Surgery

For information about our physicians and services, please call **Penn's referral counselors, 215-662-PENN (7366)**

**UNIVERSITY OF PENNSYLVANIA MEDICAL CENTER**
University of Pennsylvania School of Medicine
Hospital of the University of Pennsylvania

# Ugly feet?

If you're ashamed to have people see your feet because of unsightly, painful bunions, hammertoes or other problems call The Foot Center today! Using the newest techniques of orthopedic/podiatric and plastic surgery, including lasers and liposuction, Dr. Edward Chairman* can eliminate those painful conditions, reshape your feet, make them more attractive and more comfortable than you ever thought possible! And most procedures are done *without* a hospital stay and are covered by insurance. Don't stand for ugly, painful feet another minute...call The Foot Center at **732-0200** today for details or an appointment.

*Dr. Edward Chairman*

## The Foot Center

Suite 604, Pepper Pavilion, One Graduate Plaza
Philadelphia, PA 19146   215-732-0200
*Diplomate, American Board of Podiatric Surgery; Fellow, American College of Foot Surgeons

*Special Advertising Section*

**JOHN R. FILIP, M.D.**
1073 Montgomery Ave., Narberth, PA 19072; (215)667–7000.
Assessing the risk of heart attack, advice on cholesterol reduction. Heart disease and chest pain evaluation, education program. University affiliated, board-certified.

**WILLIAM S. FRANKL, M.D.**
**HERBERT A. FISCHER, M.D.**
**JOHN G. IVANOFF, M.D.**
Medical College of Pennsylvania and Medical College Hospitals, Main Clinical Campus, 3300 Henry Ave., Philadelphia, PA 19129; (215)842–7520.
Announcing the relocation of our cardiovascular practice to the Delaware Valley's newest health system—Medical College Hospitals, where Dr. Frankl is Director, regional cardiovascular program.

**JONATHAN GOMBERG, M.D., F.A.C.C.**
*Cardiovascular Disease*
Cardiology Associates of Chestnut Hill, 8200 Flourtown Ave., Suite 7, Wyndmoor, PA 19118; (215)836-1450.
We are board-certified cardiologists dedicated to thoughtful, thorough and personal care 24 hours a day. Our practice encompasses office, community and university hospital settings.

**GRADUATE CARDIOLOGY CONSULTANTS, INC.**
*Cardiovascular Disease*
Graduate Hospital, Pepper Pavillion, 1800 Lombard St., Philadelphia, PA 19146; (215)893-2495 or (215)893-7478.
Patient-centered cardiology services providing inpatient and outpatient cardiac catheterization, balloon angioplasty, electrocardiography, echocardiology, Holter monitoring, and stress thallium testing. Electrophysiology laboratory for cardiac arrhythmias.

**MICHAEL KIRSCHBAUM, M.D.**
*Cardiovascular Medicine*
G.S.B. Bldg., Suite 400, City and Belmont aves., Bala Cynwyd, PA 19004; (215)667–8558.
Board-certified, Deborah trained, Fellow American College of Cardiology, textbooks published, nationally known, highest quality support staff. Consultation, stress testing, treatment of all cardiovascular problems. Weekdays, evenings.

**FRED K. NAKHJAVAN, M.D., FACC**
*Invasive and Interventional Cardiology*
Klein POB, Suite 404, 5401 Old York Rd., Philadelphia, PA 19141; (215)456–7023.
Board-certified cardiologist specializing in diagnostic and interventional procedures: cardiac catheterization, angioplasty, atherectomy, valvuloplasty and all newer FDA-approved cardiology techniques.

**GREGG J. REIS, M.D.**
Pennsylvania Cardiology Associates, Pennsylvania Hospital, 801 Spruce St., Philadelphia, PA 19107; (215)829–5064.
Interventional cardiology, cardiac catheterization, atherectomy, Clinical Assistant Professor, University of Pennsylvania; cardiology fellowship Harvard Medical, affiliation with Presbyterian Hospital, board-certified internal and cardiovascular medicine.

**JACOB ZATUCHNI, M.D.**
Pennsylvania Cardiology Associates, Pennsylvania Hospital, 801 Spruce St., Philadelphia, PA 19107; (215)829–5064.
Heart failure, electrocardiology. Director, clinical services cardiovascular section, Senior Diagnostician at Pennsylvania Hospital; Clinical Professor University of Pennsylvania, board-certified internal and cardiovascular medicine.

**DAVID S. POLL, M.D.**
Pennsylvania Cardiology Associates, Pennsylvania Hospital, 801 Spruce St., Philadelphia, PA 19107; (215)829–5064.
Director, heart station electrophysiology laboratories Pennsylvania Hospital, Clinical Assistant Professor of Medicine University of Pennsylvania, affiliation with Presbyterian Hospital, board-certified internal and cardiovascular medicine.

**JOSEPH R. DESANTOLA, M.D.**
Pennsylvania Cardiology Associates, Pennsylvania Hospital, 801 Spruce St., Philadelphia, PA 19107; (215)829–5064.

Cardiac catheterization, interventional cardiology, transesophageal echocardiography, Clinical Assistant Professor of Medicine University of Pennsylvania, affiliated with Presbyterian Hospital. Board-certified internal and cardiovascular medicine.

**PHILADELPHIA CARDIOLOGY ASSOCIATES**
**BERNARD L. SEGAL, M.D.**
**AMI E. ISKANDRIAN, M.D.**
**MARIELL JESSUP, M.D.**
**MARK W. PREMINGER, M.D.**
Medical Arts Bldg., Suite 119, 39th and Market sts., Philadelphia, PA; (215)662-5050, and 8001 Roosevelt Blvd., Suite 502; (215)552-5050.
University-affiliated and board-certified specialists in the diagnosis and treatment of angina, hypertension, high cholesterol and heart failure.

**STANLEY SPITZER, M.D.**
**TED PARRIS, M.D.**
**GARO GARIBIAN, M.D.**
**RICHARD NAIMI, M.D.**
*Cardiovascular Disorders*
227 N. Broad St., Philadelphia, PA 19107; (215)564-3050.
Cardiology group practice based at Hahnemann University Hospital and Jeanes Hospital. Able to provide treatment for complex cardiovascular problems, including catheterization, angioplasty and atherectomy procedures.

**HOSPITAL OF THE UNIVERSITY OF PENNSYLVANIA CARDIOVASCULAR DIVISION**
3400 Spruce St., Philadelphia, PA 19104; (215)662-3140.
Clinical cardiologists and programs available in all areas of cardiology, including cardiac catheterization, angioplasty and valvuloplasty, electrophysiology, heart failure, heart transplantation, MRI and echocardiography.

**HARVEY L. WAXMAN, M.D.**
Cooper Hospital/University Medical Center, 3 Cooper Plaza, Suite 311, Camden, NJ 08103; (609)342-2604.
Cardiology consultation by 11 faculty cardiologists, cardiac catheterization, laser coronary angioplasty, arrhythmia management including EPS and radio-frequency ablation, transesophageal and routine echocardiography and thallium stress testing.

## CARDIOTHORACIC SURGERY

**CTS CARDIAC AND THORACIC SURGEONS PC**
Hahnemann University Hospital, Broad and Vine sts. M.S. 111, Philadelphia, PA 19102-1192; (215)762-7802.
Drs. Brockman, Strong, Grunewald, Kuretu, Morris, and Alpern. A full-service adult practice providing all aspects of thoracic, cardiac, and open-heart surgery, including transplantation.

**ARTHUR A. HELLMAN, M.D.**
**JOHN BELL-THOMPSON, M.D.**
**RICHARD HIGHBLOOM, M.D.**
The Open Heart Institute, 301 South 8th St., Philadelphia, PA 19106; Contact: Ms. Elle Bard (215)829-7120.
Premier cardiac surgeon teams. Skill and expertise with high-risk surgery. Uncompromising pursuit of perfect results. World-class training and experience.

**MAIN LINE CARDIOTHORACIC SURGEONS, P.C.**
**SCOTT M. GOLDMAN, M.D., F.A.C.S.**
**FRANCIS P. SUTTER, D.O., F.A.C.S.**
Lankenau Medical Bldg., East, Suite 558, 100 Lancaster Ave., Wynnewood, PA 19096; (215)896-9255.
Board-certified. State of the art techniques include heart valve repair vs. replacement, surgery without blood supply interruption to the heart, blood conservation preventing transfusions.

## CHIROPRACTIC

**MARC BELITSKY, D.C.**
2633 West Chester Pike, Broomall, PA 19008; (215)353-2220.
Modern family practice that combines wellness care and health maintenance with the prevention and treatment of health problems, including sports, automobile and work injuries.

*Special Advertising Section*

**CATHERINE E. CANTY, R.N., D.C.**
**CHIROPRACTOR**
1029 Bridge St., Philadelphia, PA 19124; (215)533–9001.
Education: University of Pennsylvania, Palmer College of Chiropractic. Comprehensive family care—infants to senior citizens. Emphasis on neuro–musculoskeletal conditions and sports injuries. Day and evening appointments.

**ALAN D. HORWITZ, M.D.**
**SOUTHAMPTON CHIROPRACTIC ASSOCIATES**
707 Lakeside Drive, Southampton PA 18966-4020; (215)357–9036.
Offering over 10 years experience diagnosing and carefully treating back/neck pain, headaches, arthritis, scoliosis, disc herniations. Massage therapy available. Most insurances accepted, complimentary first visit.

**DR. ANDREW INDRISO**
1421 Spruce St., Philadelphia, PA 19102; (215)735–2997.
A method of health care which is conservative, gentle, and does not utilize drugs or surgery. We have been successful in many cases where other treatment has failed.

**DAVID W. NADLER, D.C.**
*Back and Neck Specialist*
3217 West Chester Pike, Suite A, Newtown Square, PA 19073; (215)353–3888.
Board-certified—National Board of Chiropractic Examiners. Advanced methods, non–surgical and drug-free approach; gentle, safe adjustments, state of the art therapy equipment.

**ROBERT S. STEIN, M.A., D.C.**
**ADVANCED CHIROPRACTIC CENTER, P.C.**
Lawrence Park Shopping Center (rear), 580 Reed Rd., Suite 8A, Broomall, PA 19008; (215)356–2300. We're committed totally to our patients' well–being and treat everyone like family. Diversified techniques. Most insurance accepted, Blue Shield provider. Near Blue Route, Exit 4.

# OBSTETRICS & GYNECOLOGY
## Jefferson Center For Women's Medical Specialties

*Chairman*
*Richard Depp, M.D.*

Benjamin Franklin House
834 Chestnut Street
Suite 300
Philadelphia, PA 19107

**(215) 955-5000**

### GENERAL OBSTETRICS & GYNECOLOGY
Hee-Ok Park, M.D
Cynthia G. Silber, M.D.
Howard L. Kent, M.D.
Anthony DelConte, M.D.
Joanne Armstrong, M.D.

### GYNECOLOGIC ONCOLOGY
John A. Carlson, Jr., M.D.
Charles Dunton, M.D.
George C. Lewis, M.D.

### HIGH-RISK OBSTETRICS/GENETICS/PRENATAL DIAGNOSIS
Ronald J. Wapner, M.D.
Linda Chan, M.D.
Neil Silverman, M.D.
Richard Depp, M.D.
George H. Davis, D.O.
Kathleen A. Kuhlman, M.D.
Anthony Johnson, D.O.
Jodi F. Abbott, M.D.

### ENDOCRINE & INFERTILITY
Craig A. Winkel, M.D.
Gregory T. Fossum, M.D.
Alvin F. Goldfarb, M.D.
Chung H. Wu, M.D.
Michael I. Sobel, D.O.

**IN-VITRO FERTILIZATION**
Gregory T. Fossum, M.D.

**ULTRASOUND**
Kathleen A. Kuhlman, M.D.

**URINARY INCONTINENCE**
Joseph Montella, M.D.

~~~~~~~~~~~~~~~~Complete Ob/Gyn Laboratory & Diagnostic Services~~~~~~~~~~~~~~~~

*Special Advertising Section*

**JAMES A. STILLEY, D.C., C.C.S.P.**
*Sports Physician*
814 E. Germantown Pike, Norristown, PA 19401; (215)279–1215. X–ray and therapy on premises. Pediatric cases accepted; referred to by medical doctors. Offices located 1 1/4 miles west of Norristown/West Germantown Pike Exit, I–76/476.

**STUART B. TOLLEN, D.C.**
*Chiropractor*
435 Johnson St., Jenkintown, PA 19046; (215)885–8730.
Jenkintown Chiropractic Center, Inc. takes the holistic approach to health care, including: spinal manipulation, massage therapy, sports medicine, preventive care, nutritional counseling and homeopathic supplementation.

**DR. GEOFFREY S. ZWERLING**
Suite 518, Benjamin Fox Pavillion, Jenkintown, PA 19046; (215)886–8340.
A gentle healing professional: holistic, nutrition, pain relief, stress management, pediatrics, sports injuries, drug-free, exercise, headaches, menopausal distress, geriatrics, massage. Most insurances, payment plans available.

## COLON/RECTAL SURGERY

**RICHARD S. GOLDSTEIN, M.D., F.A.C.S.**
**ANNE–MARIE MARCOUX, M.D.**
Oxford Square, Suite 612, 390 Middletown Blvd., Langhorne, PA 19047; (215)741–4910.
Board-certified. Specialists in the diagnosis and treatment of diseases of the colon, rectum and anus, including colonoscopy, laparoscopy and laser surgery.

**RICHARD H. GREENBERG, M.D.**
Albert Einstein Medical Center
5501 Old York Rd., Klein Bldg., Suite 501, Philadelphia, PA 19141; (215)457–4444.
Board-certified in colo–rectal surgery. Office and laser management of hemorrhoid/anorectal problems. Colonoscopy, cancer screening, and treatment. Laparoscopic and sphincter-saving surgery for colo–rectal cancer.

**DR. LOWELL MEYERSON**
*Proctology*
7516 City Line Ave., Philadelphia, PA; (215)–877–3639.
Board-certified. Emphasis on office procedures for hemorrhoid treatment and cancer screening of colon and rectum. Laser surgery. 2nd office: Medical College of PA, Township Line Rd.; (215)379–0444.

**ROBIN ERIC ROSENBERG, M.D. F.A.C.S., F.A.C.R.S.**
Surgical Services, Ltd., Moss Plaza-Suite 206, 9892 Bustleton Ave., Philadelphia, PA 19115; (215)673–0343.
Specializing in colon proctology, colo–rectal cancer detection and management, office proctology, laparoscopic–endoscopic surgery for intestine, biliary and hernia procedures. Board-certified.

## DENTAL

**ABOUT YOUR SMILE, P.C.**
**GLENN A. BROWN, D.M.D.**
**STEPHANIE CLARK, D.M.D.**
**PAYAM HARIRI, D.M.D.**
6772 Market St., Upper Darby, PA 19082; (215)734–0666.
Comprehensive dentistry for Delaware and Philadelphia residents. Implants, gum treatment, crowns, dentures, endodontics, cosmetic dentistry. HMO–PA and Blue Shield-HMO. Patients of all ages are welcome.

**JOSEPH B. BREITMAN, D.M.D. AND ASSOCIATES**
*Prosthodontics, Implant Reconstruction and Adult Restorative Dentistry*
8021–B Castor Ave., Philadelphia, PA 19152; (215)728–1696.
Bonding, crowns, bridges, dentures, TMJ therapy, and implant reconstruction. Day and evening hours and Sat. a.m.; qualified specialists.

**CENTER CITY DENTAL HEALTH GROUP, LTD.**
**HENRY C. HURWITZ, D.D.S.**
**ALAN M. ATLAS, D.M.D.**
**GERALD P. WEGER, D.D.S.**
1616 Walnut St., Suite 1000, Philadelphia, PA 19103; (215)732–9376.

*Special Advertising Section*

All phases of denistry including implants. State of the art sterilization methods. Past and present University of Pennsylvania faculty members. Committed to comfortable, quality dental health care.

**CHILLEMI DENTAL CARE.**
**RICHARD CHILLEMI, D.D.S.**
**RICHARD CHILLEMI II, D.M.D.**
**SHARON BELEILER, D.M.D.**
*Dentistry*
1707 W. Passyunk Ave., Philadelphia, PA 19145; (215)271-7259.
At Chillemi Dental Care all phases of state of the art dentistry are offered at one convenient location. Smile with confidence. Excellence is a family tradition.

**A.S. CHINAPPI JR., D.D.S.**
**K.W. LAUDENBACH, D.D.S.**
220 S. 16th St., Philadelphia, PA; (215)985-4337, and 43 E. Main St., Marlton, NJ; (609)983-5559.
Coordinated care of patients experiencing head/neck pain and TMJ symptoms through an integration of restorative dentistry and adult orthodontics.

**THE FAMILY DENTAL GROUP**
**HOWARD A. JONES, D.M.D.**
**ERNESTO A. LEE, D.M.D.**
**EDWARD A. SOLOMON, D.M.D.**
**LYNANN M. MASTAJ, D.M.D.**
**ERIC G. GOLDBERG, D.D.S.**
*Multi–Specialty Center.*
1599 Paoli Pike, West Chester, PA 19380; (215)692–1808.
Complete multi–specialty center providing comprehensive dental treatment in one location. Advanced restorative and surgical implant therapy by experienced university-affiliated professionals. Complimentary inital consultation.

**DR. PETER HUNT AND ASSOCIATES IN DENTISTRY, PC**
116 S. 18th St., Philadelphia, PA; (215)564–0408.
Dr. Peter Hunt provides the full range of

# Center for Human Appearance

Our physicians and surgeons are internationally known and board-certified in their fields of specialization. Supported by the resources of a world-renowned academic medical center, they provide evaluation and treatment for cosmetic and reconstructive problems which affect appearance.

*Plastic Surgery*
Linton A. Whitaker, MD
Scott P. Bartlett, MD
Ralph Hamilton, MD
Don LaRossa, MD
David W. Low, MD
Peter Randall, MD

*Oral/Maxillofacial Surgery*
Peter Quinn, DMD, MD
Robert Seckinger, DMD, MDS
Kenneth Kent, DMD

*Dermatology*
James Leyden, MD

*Ophthalmology*
James Katowitz, MD

*Psychiatry*
Penn's faculty specialists

Some of our physicians also see patients at **Penn Medicine at King of Prussia.**

For information and appointments, please call the **Center for Human Appearance, 215-662-7095** or Penn's referral counselors at **215-662-PENN (7366).**

**UNIVERSITY OF PENNSYLVANIA MEDICAL CENTER**
University of Pennsylvania School of Medicine
Hospital of the University of Pennsylvania

*Special Advertising Section*

modern aesthetic and reconstructive dental procedures, including implants, in an ultra-modern facility located in Center City.

**MORTON A. LANGSFELD, III, D.D.S.**
**ROBERT S. KRAVITZ, D.D.S.**
**RANDE S. KAMINSKY, D.M.D.**
*General and Cosmetic Dentistry*
1608 Walnut St., Suite 200, Philadelphia, PA 19103; (215)545–0055.
Providing general and cosmetic dentistry, including implants, with the latest, most sophisticated sterilization and infection-control techniques. Establishing individual, personal relationships with our patients for over 90 years.

**K.W. LAUDENBACH, D.D.S., LTD.**
220 S. 16th St., Suite 1100, Philadelphia, PA 19102; (215)985–4337.
Integrated fine dentistry for adults: oral dentistry, periodontal prosthesis dental implants, coordinated care of patients experiencing head/neck pain.

**MANSOOR MADANI, D.M.D.**
*Oral and Maxillofacial Surgery*
Klein Professional Bldg., Suite 204, 5401 Old York Rd., Philadelphia, PA 19141; (215)456–7328.
Board-certified. Specializing in wireless jaw surgery for functional or cosmetic reasons, dental implants, TMJ disorders, removal of teeth, facial injuries, inpatient–outpatient surgeries, emergencies.

**MODERN DENTAL CONCEPTS**
*Complete Dental Care*
(1-800)427-7100. 16 locations throughtout Center City, the Northeast, Bucks, Montgomery, Delaware counties and N.J. Implants, cosmetic dentistry, root canal, extractions, periodontics, TMJ, braces (standard, designer, color, invisible). Evening and weekend hours. No down payment/low monthly plans. All major insurance plans accepted. HMO participant.

**BRIAN MOSCOW, D.M.D., F.A.D.S.A.**
*Dental Anesthesiology*
300 E. Lancaster Ave., Wynnewood, PA 19096; (215)642–0336.
Specializing in the treatment of dental phobics. Offering general anesthesia and I.V. sedation to provide pain–free restorative dentistry in a state of the art private practice.

**PROSTHODONTICS INTERMEDICA**
**THOMAS J. BALSHI, D.D.S., F.A.C.P.**
**CHARLES F. HERTZOG, D.M.D.**
**GERALD J. O'KEEFE, D.M.D.**
*Implant Prosthodontics*
467 Pennsylvania Ave., Suite 201, Fort Washington, PA 19034; (215)646–6334.
Spearheaded by Thomas J. Balshi, board-certified prosthodontist, avid researcher and international lecturer; this comprehensive implant center achieves patient confidence, technical excellence and artistic, restorative detail.

**DONALD G. REBHUN, D.M.D.**
*Oral and Maxillofacial Surgery*
Pavilions of Voorhees, 2301 Evesham Rd., Suite 211, Voorhees, NJ 08043; (609)772–1500.
Specializing in diagnosis and treatment of facial and oral diseases, dental implants, impacted teeth, traumatic injuries. Board-certified, American Board of Oral and Maxillofacial Surgery.

**DONALD L. ROBBINS, D.M.D.**
*TMJ, Headache and Neck Pain*
340 North Rte. 100, Exton, PA 19341; (215)363–1980.
Non–surgical conservative treatment and diagnosis of TMJ syndrome, head, neck and facial pain, including automobile, accident and trauma cases. Expert opinion and legal testimony.

**P. MICHAEL SCHELKUN, M.D., D.D.S.**
**LEWIS J. SCHWARTZ, D.M.D.**
*Oral and Maxillofacial Surgeons*
Brownstone Office Complex, 853 Second Street Pike, Suite A–106, Richboro, PA 18954; (215)355–4500.
Specialists in facial corrective and reconstructive surgery, TMJ arthroscopy, dental implants, wisdom teeth, facial trauma, head and neck tumors and general anesthesia.

**LEWIS J. SCHWARTZ, D.M.D.**
**P. MICHAEL SCHELKUN, M.D., D.D.S.**
*Oral and Maxillofacial Surgeons*

158 York Rd., Warminster, PA 18974; (215)672–6560.
Specialists in facial corrective and reconstructive surgery, TMJ arthroscopy, dental implants, wisdom teeth, facial trauma, head and neck tumors and general anesthesia.

**STEVEN W. SEITCHIK, D.M.D.**
Pennsylvania Hospital, 700 Spruce St, Suite 505, Philadelphia, PA 19106; (215)627–6400.
Fellowship in Academy of General Dentistry. Thirteen years teaching at University of Pennsylvania Dental School. Emphasis on restorative, cosmetic, reconstructive dentistry—including implants. Bala Cynwyd office.

**PHILIP T. SIEGEL, D.D.S.**
**MICHAEL A. CICHETTI, D.M.D.**
*Orthodontics*
Medical/Dental Bldg., 6404 Roosevelt Blvd., Philadelphia, PA; (215)743–3700, and 6801 Ridge Ave. (Roxborough) Philadelphia, PA; (215)483–6633.
Board-certified. Dr. Siegel is also board-certified in pediatric dentistry, one of only two dentists holding this distinction.

**OTTO F. TIDWELL, D.D.S.**
*Oral and Maxillofacial Surgery*
1601 Walnut St. Suite 215, Philadelphia, PA; (215)–557–7949.
Specialty care includes: removal of wisdom teeth, non–restorable teeth (awake/asleep), dental implants, services for handicapped. General anesthesia for general dentistry. Brochure available upon request.

## DERMATOLOGY

**ARTHUR K. BALIN, M.D., PH.D.**
2129 Providence Ave., Chester, PA 19013; (215)876–0200.
Skin cancer and aging skin specialist. Cosmetic skin surgery. Board-certified in dermatology, dermatopathology, internal medicine, geriatric medicine, and Mohs micrographic surgery and cutaneous oncology.

---

"I WAS CONCERNED MY SYMPTOMS INDICATED A MORE SERIOUS CONDITION....

...but Dr. Meyerson assured me that relief from hemorrhoids is often quick and painless."

Ask about our simple procedure which is done right in our office.

*(As recently heard on Dr. Jim Corea's "The Doctor Is In" show on WWDB-FM.)*

**PROCTOLOGY & COLONOSCOPY**
- Screening for Rectal & Colon Cancer
- Laser Surgery
- Infrared and Rubberband Treatment for Hemorrhoids

# DR. LOWELL D. MEYERSON

BOARD CERTIFIED PROCTOLOGIST

*Participation in Medicare, Blue Shield, Private Insurances, HMO's....*

**MAIN LINE:** 7516 City Line Ave., Suite #2, Phila. • 215-877-3639
**ELKINS PARK:** *Medical College Hospital*, 60 E. Township Line Rd. • 215-379-0444

# What is Mohs Surgery?

Mohs micrographic surgery, **the most effective technique for treating skin cancers**, involves shaving off cancerous tissue one layer at a time for immediate examination under a microscope. The in-office procedure, performed under local anesthesia, is repeated until healthy tissue is reached, thus ensuring that no cancerous roots are left behind. This method provides the highest assurance of complete cancer removal while minimizing damage to surrounding healthy skin.

## ARTHUR K. BALIN, M.D., Ph.D.
### SKIN CANCER SPECIALIST

Dr. Balin practices dermatology (treatment of problems of the skin, hair, and nails), while specializing in the treatment of skin cancer. He has been involved in pioneering new treatments for skin diseases.

**About Dr. Balin:** Dr. Balin received his M.D. and Ph.D. degrees from the University of Pennsylvania. He received his training in Internal Medicine at the Hospital of the University of Pennsylvania; in Dermatology and Dermatopathology at the Yale-New Haven Hospital; in Mohs Surgery at Baylor University. Dr. Balin is Board Certified in five medical specialties: Dermatology; Dermatopathology; Internal Medicine; Geriatric Medicine; and Mohs Micrographic Surgery and Cutaneous Oncology.

■ Dr. Balin's Ph.D. degree is in Biochemistry. He has been actively engaged in research designed to understand the basic mechanisms of the aging process along with authoring numerous papers on aging research, nutrition, wound healing, and clinical and experimental dermatology.

■ Dr. Balin spent nine years in academic medicine. He was a full-time faculty member of the Rockefeller University in the Laboratory of Investigative Dermatology and was on the faculty of Cornell University Medical School and the New York Hospital.

■ He is past president of the American Aging Association, serves on the editorial and scientific advisory boards of numerous journals and organizations, and has received many academic and scientific awards. Dr. Balin has written the sections on 'skin' for two of the major textbooks in Geriatric medicine, the *Principles of Geriatric Medicine and Gerontology*, and the *Oxford Textbook of Geriatric Medicine*, and edited the medical text *Aging and the Skin* along with Albert Kligman, M.D.

## LORETTA PRATT, M.D.
### COSMETIC DERMATOLOGY SPECIALIST

**About Dr. Pratt:** Joining Dr. Balin in practice is Board Certified dermatologist Loretta Pratt, M.D., who specializes in the treatment of women's skin problems. Dr. Pratt specializes in cosmetic dermatology, including collagen injections, liposuction, dermabrasion, sclerotherapy for leg veins, chemical peels, and individual complexion evaluations.

## ARTHUR K. BALIN, M.D., Ph.D., P.C.
## LORETTA PRATT, M.D.

2129 Providence Avenue ■ Chester, PA 19013
Easily accessible via I-95 or Blue Route
Telephone: (215) 876-0200

*Special Advertising Section*

**MERLE BARI, M.D.**
*Dermatological Surgery*
Corner of Youngsford and Merion Square rds., Gladwyne, PA 19035; (215)649-5001.
With the eye of a fine diagnostician, the hands of a surgeon, this high-tech dermatologist welcomes people in search of a talented, gentle, female physician.

**HAROLD F. FARBER, M.D.**
*Dermatologic Surgery*
140 Montgomery Ave., Bala Cynwyd, PA; (215)664-4433, and 9892 Bustleton Ave., Suite 302, Philadelphia, PA; (215)676-2464.
Board-certified, Jefferson Hospital. Specializing in treatment of skin, hair and nail disorders; skin surgery. Skin-cancer screening and treatment of acne, rashes, moles, warts, growths, psoriasis, ultraviolet therapy, hair loss, wrinkles, scars, chemical peels, spider veins, earlobe repairs. Bala Cynwyd, Northeast and Center City offices. Evening and weekend hours available.

**JEROME GOLDSTEIN, M.D.**
10151 Bustleton Ave., Philadelphia, PA 19116; (215)677-1155.
Philadelphia hospital-traind in skin and cancer care–completed residency 1961. Private practice of dermatology and dermatological surgery. Insurance plans accepted.

**PAUL R. GROSS, M.D.**
*Cosmetic Dermatology, Dermatopathology*
220 S. 8th St., Philadelphia, PA 19107; (215)829-3576.
Recognized in the *Philadelphia Magazine*'s "Top Doctors" issues, Dr Gross is Chief of Dermatology at the Pennsylvania Hospital and Clinical Professor of Dermatology at the University of Pennsylvania.

**WARREN R. HEYMANN, M.D.**
Cooper Hospital/University Medical Center, 3 Cooper Plaza, Suite 215, Camden, NJ 08103; (609)342-2439.
Specializing in diagnostic problems of the skin, hair, nails and mucous membranes and the evaluation of generalized illnesses with dermatologic manifestations in adults and children.

**MARLENE MASH, M.D.**
919 E. Germantown Pike, Suite 3, Norristown, PA 19401; (215)279-1500.
A board-certified dermatologist, dermatologic surgeon, and laser surgery specialist who treats skin cancers, repairs torn ear lobes and performs sclerotherapy (destruction of unwanted veins).

**DREW MCCAUSLAND, M.D.**
*Dermatology*
606 E. Marshall St., Suite 107, West Chester, PA 19380; (215)436-8440.
Dr. McCausland, a board-certified dermatologist practicing for 20 years, has extensive experience with skin surgery and acne treatment. All procedures are performed in office.

**HAROLD J. MILSTEIN, M.D.**
**STEPHEN M. SCHLEICHER, M.D.**
**LEG ULCER AND VEIN CENTERS OF AMERICA**
The Jamestown Medical Bldg., 525 Jamestown Ave., Suite 206, Philadelphia, PA 19128; (215)483-3666.
Board-certified physicians specializing in all aspects of wound care and healing, varicose veins, and sclerotherapy (nonsurgical destruction of unsightly leg veins).

**LORETTA PRATT, M.D.**
2129 Providence Ave., Chester, PA 19013; (215)876-0200.
Specializing in treatment of women's skin problems, acne, aging skin. Individual complexion evaluation. Sclerotherapy, liposuction, lipoinjection, chemical peels, collagen injection are performed in the office.

**WILLIAM K. SHERWIN, M.D., PH.D.**
**HERBERT GOLDSCHMIDT, M.D.**
**F.A.C.P.**
**MARCIA R. TAYLOR, M.D.**
*Dermatological Surgery*
Suite 620, One Bala Plaza, Bala Cynwyd, PA 19004; (215)664-3300.
The longest continuing dermatology office in the Philadelphia and Main Line area, with special expertise and equipment for treatment of skin cancers and precancerous tumors. Some evening and Saturday hours. Hospital affiliations: Lankenau, University of Pennsylvania. Accept providers

*Special Advertising Section*

Medicare, Pennsylvania Blue Shield and several private insurance companies.

**SUSAN C. TAYLOR, M.D.**
**SOCIETY HILL DERMATOLOGY**
*Dermatologic Surgery*
932 Pine St., Philadelphia 19107; (215)829–6861.
Harvard-educated, board-certified. Brings the strength of individualized care to her practice. General dermatologic care and surgery for patients expecting quality guidance and education.

## DIABETOLOGY

**SETH BRAUNSTEIN, M.D.**
*Internal Medicine*
Ravdin Bldg., 3rd floor. Hospital of the University of Pennsylvania, 3400 SpruceSt., Philadelphia, PA 19104; (215)662–7280.
Dedicated to excellence in diabetes care, applying latest therapy developments to management. Coordinated care of complications, including eye, cardiac, vascular, renal, neurological and skin problems.

**ALAN B. SCHORR, D.O.**
*Endocrinology/Metabolic Diseases*
Suite 710, 380 Middletown Blvd. Langhorne, PA 19047; (215)750–1691.
Board-certified, endocrinology/diabetes specialized care, and treatment of disorders endocrine (hormonal) system. Area of expertise is insulin pumps in diabetes care. Hours by appointment only.

## FAMILY MEDICINE

**VINCENT E. BALDINO, D.O., P.C.**
1701 Ritner St., Philadelphia, PA 19145 and 5737 Chester Ave., Philadelphia, PA 19143; (215)336–2145.
Specializing in family/general medicine – all ages accepted. Please call for appointment—evening hours available Monday through Thursday.

**GEORGE W. BRADFORD, M.D.**
Academy House Professional Offices, Suite 200, 1420 Locust St., Philadelphia, PA 19102; (215)545–6735.
Personalized care for adults and children

12 and over. Accessible Center City location next to the Academy of Music, convenient to offices and public transportation.

**ALEXANDER BUNT, JR., D.O.**
422 E. 22nd St., Chester, PA 19013; (215)872–2200.
Board-certified, complete family health care, women's health care, colds, allergies, sports injuries; pain control center, manipulative therapy, x–rays on premises. Most insurance accepted.

**FEASTERVILLE FAMILY HEALTH CARE CENTER**
**STEVEN ROSENBERG, D.O.**
**BARBARA SARACINO, D.O.**
**ROB DANOFF, D.O.**
1665 Bustleton Pike, Feasterville, PA 19053; (215)355–9770.
Board-certified. Office hours daily, Saturday and evenings. On-site x–rays, laboratory, physical therapy, echocardiography, diagnostic ultrasound. House calls available. Friendly, courteous staff. We care.

**THE NELSON MEDICAL GROUP, P.C.**
*Internal Medicine*
255 S. 17th St., Suite 2001, Philadelphia, PA 19103; (215)546–7049.
A health organization comprised of six community–based office sites providing comprehensive health care to infants, children, adults, the chronically ill and elderly in Philadelphia.

**RICHARD M. PAPA, D.O.**
1101 Snyder Ave., Philadelphia, PA 19148; (215)463–0330, and 257 N. 52nd St., Philadelphia, PA 19139; (215)474–3400.
Board-certified in general practice and pain management.

**RUSSELL V. SILVERMAN, D.O.**
Haverford and Malvern aves., Overbrook Park, Philadelphia, PA 19151; (215)878-2220.
Board-certified. Dedicated to personal care. Holistic, acute, preventive. In-house lab, physical therapy. House calls. Medicare, Blue Shield, Keystone accepted, new patients welcome.

*Special Advertising Section*

**WEATHERVANE FAMILY PRACTICE ASSOCIATES**
*Family Practice*
202 Weathervane Office Commons, Almshouse Rd., Richboro, PA 18954; (215)364-4141.
Board-certified; MCH–BUCKS, Doylestown Hospital; home care, preventive medecine, personal injury, manipulation therapy, office surgery. Day, evening, weekend hours. Emergency coverage. BS, MC, HMO, HPO, 1992 recipients United Way Medical Humanitarian Award.

## GASTROENTEROLOGY

**PHILIP J. DIGIACOMO JR., M.D.**
**JERALD C. FINGERUT, M.D.**
1330 Powell St., Suite 310, Norristown, PA 19401; (215)277-2635.
Endoscopy in office, colon cancer screening. Diseases of stomach (ulcers), liver, bowels, gall bladder, pancreas evaluated, and treatment of nutrition, gas, digestive problems. Patients 10 and older.

**L. EHRLICH, M.D.**
**S. NACK, M.D.**
**E. GOOSENBERG, M.D.**
2303 N. Broad St., Colmar, PA. 18915; (215)997-9377, and 8815 Germantown Ave., Suite 12, Philadelphia, PA 19118; (215)247-4604.
Experts at the diagnosis and treatment of diseases of the gastrointestinal tract, liver, bile ducts, and pancreas. Experience at endoscopic procedures, including colonoscopy, endoscopy.

**GRADUATE HOSPITAL GASTROENTEROLOGY ASSOC. P.C.**
19th and Lombard sts, Suite 100, Philadelphia, PA 19146; (215)893-2532.
Julius Deren, M.D., Steven Greenfield, M.D., Jeffrey Retig, M.D., Donald Castell, M.D., George Ahtaridis, M.D., S. Philip Bralow, M.D., Anthony Infantolino, M.D., David Katzka, M.D.

**JULIAN KATZ, M.D.**
*Internal Medicine*

---

## New hope for wounds that won't heal.

For someone with diabetes or poor circulation, the pain and discomfort of a simple wound can have a devastating impact on their life.

The Graduate Hospital Wound Care Center specializes in treating non-healing wounds, using some of the most advanced techniques.

Our unique team approach has successfully treated hundreds of patients.

If you have a wound that won't heal, ask your doctor about The Graduate Hospital Wound Care Center.

OR CALL US: **215-893-7655.**
Graduate Health System

*"I tried everything, but nothing worked...until I found Graduate's Wound Care Center."* — Maureen Ince

**THE GRADUATE HOSPITAL**
## Wound Care Center
1740 South Street  Suite 306  Philadelphia, PA 19146

2 Bala Plaza, Suite IL–22, Bala Cynwyd, PA 19004; (215)664–9700 or (215)632–3500. Diseases of the digestive tract and liver. Special qualifications in geriatric medicine. Clinical Professor of Medicine, Medical College of Pennsylvania and Jefferson Medical College.

**STEVEN R. PEIKIN, M.D.**
Cooper Hospital/University Medical Center, 3 Cooper Plaza, Suite 215, Camden, NJ 08103; (609)342–2439.
Comprehensive consultations, upper and lower endoscopy, motility studies, care of ileitis and colitis, irritable bowel, gastroesophageal reflux, peptic ulcers and gallbladder disease.

**ALAN J. SEARS, M.D., P.C.**
**RITA L. RITSEMA, M.D.**
2100 Keystone Ave., Suite 405, Drexel Hill, PA 19026; (215)626–2400.
Comprehensive services: laser therapy, diagnosis/therapy heartburn; ulcers, inflammatory bowel disease treated; colonoscopies for cancer screening to find and remove colon growths to prevent invasive cancer.

**GARY A. NEWMAN, M.D., P.C.**
**MARC A. ZITIN, M.D.**
*Gastroenterologists*
366 Lankenau Medical Bldg. East, Wynnwood, PA 19096; (215)896–8335. Specializing in diseases of the tract and liver. Accepting all major insurance plans. Office hours by appointment.

## HAND SURGERY

**STEPHEN L. CASH, M.D.**
Suite 253, Lankenau Hospital, Wynnwood, PA 19096; (215)642–8823. Board-certified orthopedic surgery, certificate-qualified surgeon of the hand. Specializing in hand, upper extremity and microsurgery. Including new arthroscopic and endoscopic techniques.

**A. LEE OSTERMAN, M.D., A.B.O.S., A.O.S., A.S.M.**
Penn Towers, 8th floor, 34th St. and Civic Center Blvd., Philadelphia, PA 19104, University of Pennsylvania; (215)662–3345; King of Prussia: (215)354-0540; Lansdowne: (215)534-6192; Childrens' Hospital of Philadelphia: (215)662–3345. Specialty practice with emphasis on hand, wrist, elbow problems, wrist arthroscopy; upper extremity joint replacements; childrens' hand and arm problems of both congenital and injury nature; microsurgery, nerve injury repair; hand rehabilitation. Chief of orthopedic hand surgery CHOP. Assoc. Professional Orthopedic Surgery at University of Pennsylvania.

**STUART L. TRAGER, M.D.**
*Microsurgery*
Department of Orthopedic Surgery, Suite 802, Pepper Pavilion, One Graduate Plaza, Philadelphia, PA 19146; (215)893–0132. Specializing in the treatment of hand and wrist injuries, degenerative and rheumatoid arthritis, vascular diseases of the upper extremities, nerve compression, and cummulative trauma disorders.

## INFECTIOUS DISEASE

**M. PIA DEGIROLAMO, M.D.**
**ABBY I. HUANG, M.D.**
*Travel Medicine*
712 Lawn Ave., Sellersville, PA 18960; (215)257–8450.
Trained at Temple Hospital, Hospital of the University of Pennsylvania specializing in general infectious diseases, HIV, Lyme, travel immunizations. Affiliated with Grand View, North Penn, Quakertown hospitals.

**KATHLEEN M. GEKOWSKI, M.D.**
Cooper Hospital, University Medical Center, 3 Cooper Plaza, Suite 215, Camden, NJ 08103; (609)342–2439.
Comprehensive services for patients with Lyme disease, sexually transmitted infections including AIDS and all other types of infections, bacterial, viral, yeast, and parasitic.

**MATTHEW E. LEVISON, M.D.**
**DONALD KAYE, M.D.**
**OKSANA KORZENIOWSKI, M.D.**
**CAROLINE JOHNSON, M.D.**
**SANDRA HARRIS, M.D.**
**ALLAN TUNKEL, M.D.**
Medical College of Pennsylvania and

# SEEK AND WE SHALL FIND.

With so many physicians and dentists to choose from in the Delaware Valley, which one would you choose? Who can you call to help you make an informed choice?

By dialing 1-800-DOCTORS you'll reach Prologue, the service that well over 4 million people, in your same situation, have turned to.

A Prologue counselor will give you the crucial information you need on 2,338 doctors, covering 35 medical and dental specialties; from their hospital affiliation and medical training, to their hours, fees, and even the insurance plans they accept.

Prologue is a free and objective service supported by leading hospitals throughout Delaware Valley.

So call 1-800 DOCTORS. We can help you find what you're looking for.

## Prologue℠

### AMERICA'S MOST COMPLETE INFORMATION SOURCE ON PHYSICIANS AND DENTISTS.

## 1-800-DOCTORS

Please mention you saw this ad when you call Prologue and we'll send you a list of 20 questions to ask when you select a new physician or dentist, free!

Medical College Hospitals, Main Clinical Campus, 3300 Henry Ave., Philadelphia, PA 19129; (215)842–6975.
Internationally recognized infectious disease specialists available for consultation for services, which include Lyme Disease Center, Travel Health Center (immunizations, health conditions abroad) and HIV clinic.

**JEROME SANTORO, M.D.**
**MARK INGERMAN, M.D.**
**LAWRENCE L. LIVORNESE JR., M.D.**
*Travel Health*
Lankenau Medical Bldg. East, Suite 467, Wynnewood, PA 19096; (215)896–0210.
Three-member group practice of board-certified infectious disease specialists with special interest in travel health, immunization, Lyme disease, and diseases caused by infectious agents.

**JOAN C. WALLER, M.D.**
**MARGARET TREXLER HESSEN, M.D., F.A.C.P.**
*Internal Medicine*
5101 Township Line Rd., Drexel Hill, PA 19026; (215)446–5550, and 875 County Line Rd., Bryn Mawr, PA 19010; (215)527–9490.
Infectious disease, travel medicine, internal medicine. Board-certified. Infectious disease consultation, travel immunizations, internal medicine.

## INFERTILITY

**JEROME H. CHECK, M.D.**
*Reproductive Endocrinology*
Reproductive and Medical Endocrine Assoc., PC, 7447 Old York Rd., Melrose Park, PA 19126; (215)635–4400.
Dedicated, caring, and knowledgeable staff. Hours convenient to patients. Dr. Check is world-renowned for his achievements in achieving successful pregnancies and in research.

**MARTIN F. FREEDMAN, M.D.**
**MARIA PIA PLATIA, M.D.**
1300 Old York Rd., Bldg. E–4, Abington, PA 19046; (215)572–1515, and 1650 Huntingdon Pike, Suite 154, Meadowbrook, PA 19046; (215)938–1515.
Board-certified, university affiliated. Specializing in all forms of infertility treatment; IVF, ovulation induction, operative laparoscopy and hysteroscopy.

**MICHAEL E. TOAFF, M.D.**
*Gynecology/Reproductive Endocrinology*
1201 County Line Rd., Bryn Mawr, PA 19010; (215)525–9999.
Bryn Mawr Hospital board-certified, fellowship-trained. Microsurgery; tubal ligation, endometriosis, malformations, lutratubal insemination (lower–cost GIFT alternative). Major gynecological surgery; fibroids, prolapse.

## INTERNAL MEDICINE

**MICHAEL BAIME, M.D.**
**LYNNE KOSSOW, M.D.**
**DONALD LISS, M.D.**
**ELIOT NIERMAN, M.D.**
**KEVIN ZAKRZEWSKI, M.D.**
Internal Medicine Associates, Graduate Hospital, Suite 503, Pepper Pavilion, 1800 Lombard St., Philadelphia, PA 19146; (215)893–4150.
Compassion and expertise in primary care and consultative internal medicine.

**RONALD S. BANNER, M.D.**
*Clinical Preventive Medicine, Psychosomatic Medicine*
2050 Welsh Rd., Philadelphia, PA 19115; (215)969–0887.
Board-certified, internal medicine, 1973. Comprehensive medical examinations. Personal, thorough, and humanistic health care emphasizing doctor–patient relationship, shared decision-making, and mutual participation and respect.

**GENE BETH BISHOP, M.D.**
*Geriatrics*
Suite 260, Medical Office Bldg., Presbyterian Medical Center, 51 N. 39th St., Philadelphia, PA 19104; (215)662–8870.
General adult internal medicine with special interest in women's health. Comprehensive care, attentive listening, "on time" office in a caring environment.

nose contouring

facelift

breast
sculpturing

liposuction

spider vein
removal

Cosmetic Surgery should be natural looking and give the feeling of confidence. Dr. DiMario, a board certified surgeon, combines surgical skill and experience with the talent of an artist.

# Dr. Carmen DiMario
## 215-667-2005

Bala Cynwyd • Chadds Ford • Philadelphia • Yardley

Board Certified Cosmetic Surgery ABCS • Board Certified Facial Plastic Surgery AOBOO

*Special Advertising Section*

**BUCKLEY MEDICAL ASSOCIATES**
**R. MICHAEL BUCKLEY, M.D.**
**MICHAEL N. BRAFFMAN, M.D.**
**JOHN J. STERN, M.D.**
*Internal Medicine/Infectious Diseases*
Pennsylvania Hospital, 822 Pine St., Philadelphia, PA 19107; (215)925–8010.
Sees adults for general medical problems and preventive care. Advises, immunizes patients prior to international travel. Diagnoses and treats complicated infections.

**H. BUSCHIAZZO, M.D.**
**A. FERREIRA M.D., P.C.**
*Geriatrics*
4955 Frankford Ave., Philadelphia, PA 19124; (215)831–9663.
Specializing in house calls for senior citizens in Northeast Philadelphia, Cheltenham, and Frankford. Nursing home and hospital placements. Arrangements for nursing and in–home testing and therapy.

**DRY MOUTH CENTER**
*Dry Mouth disorders*
Presbyterian Medical Center, 39th and Market sts., Philadelphia, PA 19104; (215)662–9211.
Frederick B. Vivino, M.D. is Director of this Center dedicated to diagnosing and managing Sjoren's Syndrome and other dry mouth conditions, using innovative and traditional techniques.

**ELIZABETH L. FABENS, M.D.**
*Geriatrics*
345 E. Mount Airy Ave., Philadelphia, PA 19119; (215)242–5000.
Neighborhood practice caring for patients 14 and older with minor to critical illnesses. Convenient hours. On staff at Medical College of Pennsylvania and Chestnut Hill Hospital.

**BRADLEY W. FENTON, M.D.**
**STEVEN A. SILBER, M.D.**
**JOSEPH BOSELLI, M.D.**
Presbyterian Medical Center, 39th and Market sts., Suites 240 and 260, Medical Office Bldg., Philadelphia, PA 19104; (215)662-8347 and (215)662-8806.
Board-certified internists providing health promotion and prevention, primary care, and consultations for complex or perplexing internal medicine problems, with a caring, individualized approach.

**STEPHEN J. GLUCKMAN, M.D.**
Cooper Hospital/University Medical Center, 3 Cooper Plaza, Suite 215, Camden, NJ 08103; (609)342–2439.
Experienced general internists offering comprehensive medical care; specialists in occupational and environmental medicine; travel clinic provides immunizations and complete advice for international travelers.

**ARNOLD L. GOLDSTEIN, M.D.**
**BARBARA H. SHONBERG, M.D.**
**BRUCE A. GOODMAN, M.D.**
170 Middletown Blvd., Suite 101, Langhorne, PA 19047; (215)757–8100.
Diplomates American Board of Internal Medicine. Primary care adult medicine, risk-factor reduction, nutritional counseling, executive physicals. Laboratory facilities. Hours by appointment.

**MARK R. GOLDSTEIN, M.D.**
*Cholesterol Disorders*
Crozer–Chester Medical Center, Upland, PA 19013; (215)447–2655.
Board-certified internist, university affiliated. Director, Cholesterol Center, Crozer–Chester Medical Center, dedicated to the detection, evaluation and treatment of cholesterol disorders.

**GEORGE T. HARE, M.D.**
*Geriatric Medicine*
Cooper Hospital/University Medical Center, 3 Cooper Plaza, Suite 215, Camden, NJ 08103; (609)342–2439.
Comprehensive health assessments and ongoing care provided by geriatricians and geriatric nurse practitioners, addressing the physical, nutritional, emotional and social needs of patients over 60.

**MARIANNE HERMAN, M.D.**
1335 Tabor Rd., Suite 209, Philadelphia, PA 19130; (215)924–1234.
Board-certified in internal medicine. In practice for over 10 years. Strong interest in geriatrics, affiliated with Albert Einstein Medical Center and Germantown Hospital.

# Can you guess which one has the hip replacement?

The Joint Replacement Experts at The Hahnemann Orthopaedic and Arthritis Center can offer expert, affordable treatment ... right here in Philadelphia.

**Quality.** Our world-renowned team of board certified orthopaedic surgeons, rheumatologists and rehabilitation specialists are highly-skilled in state-of-the-art joint replacement techniques.

**Experience.** We've performed thousands of successful hip and knee replacements, as well as provided many other arthrithic treatment alternatives to improve the quality of life for our patients.

**Dedication.** For over 20 years, we've been committed to providing superior treatment, care and rehabilitation support for all our patients.

*Total Hip*

If you or someone you love is suffering from a painful joint damaged by arthritis, illness or injury, we can help. **Call the Joint Replacement Experts at 1-800-762-8500 today.**

### The Orthopaedic and Arthritis Center
#### Hahnemann University
**221 North Broad Street Phila, PA 19107**
## 1-800-762-8500

# Dermatology at PENN

Specialists in **Penn's Department of Dermatology**, the first established in the United States, evaluate and treat the full range of dermatologic problems. Our faculty physicians have developed many of today's innovative methods for treating these problems.

Our board-certified specialists provide:

- **General Dermatology**
  For all types of skin disorders
- **Dermatologic Surgery**
  - Skin cancer and cosmetic surgery
  - Laser skin surgery
  - Moh's cancer surgery
  - Hair transplantation
  - Vein sclerotherapy and laser surgery
- **Aging and Cosmetic Dermatology**
- **Hair Problems**
  Disorders of the scalp, hair
- **Pigmented Lesion Center**
  Moles, pigmented lesions and melanoma
- **Cutaneous Ulcer Center**
  Innovative treatments for hard-to-heal skin ulcers
- **Psoriasis**
  Phototherapy, inpatient and daycare, drug therapy
- **Photopheresis**
  Cutaneous lymphoma and scleroderma
- **Connective Tissue Diseases**
  Lupus, dermatomyositis, scleroderma
- **Dermatopathology**
  Analysis of skin biopsies

For specified disorders, our physicians also see patients at **Penn Medicine at King of Prussia.**

**For information or an appointment, call Dermatology, 215-662-2399, or Penn's referral counselors, 215-662-PENN (7366**

## UNIVERSITY OF PENNSYLVANIA MEDICAL CENTER

University of Pennsylvania School of Medicine
Hospital of the University of Pennsylvania

*Special Advertising Section*

**INTERNAL MEDICINE ASSOCIATES LTD.**
**GILBERT GROSSMAN, M.D.**
**JACOB GOLDSTEIN, M.D.**
**KENNETH J. FORMAN, M.D.**
*Cardiology*
One Abington Plaza, Township Line and York rds., Jenkintown, PA 19046; (215)885–1173.
Practice limited to cardiology and internal medicine.

**ALLAN KOFF, D.O., F.A.C.O.I., LTD.**
**MARVIN SCHATZ, D.O.**
Three convenient locations: Northeast, Juniata, Olney; (215)533–0909.
Focusing not only on symptoms but on the total health of our patients. We involve the patients in a course of education and treatment options.

**RICHARD KONES, M.D., PH.D.**
1525 Locust St., Philadelphia, PA 19102–3732; (215)545–4444.
Scientific, comprehensive yet personal treatment of the entire patient. Allergy, lung, heart, blood/anemia, hormone/metabolic, gastrointestinal, infections, fatigue, food sensitivities, nutrition and prevention emphasized.

**RUSSELL C. MAULITZ, M.D.**
Suite 260, Medical Office Bldg., Presbyterian Hospital, 51 N. 39th St., Philadelphia, PA 19104; (215)662–8870.
Primary-care internal medicine for adults, providing health maintenance and disease prevention. Staff and physician emphasize clear listening and follow–through between visits.

**MEDICAL AND DIAGNOSTIC CENTER**
**RICHARD KONES, M.D., PH.D.**
Medical and Diagnostic Center, 1525 Locust St., Philadelphia PA, 19102-3732; (215)545–4444.
Allergy, lung, heart, metabolic, blood, hormone and nutritional analysis; infections, fatigue, and general medical ailments are treated. A refreshingly sophisticated, thorough, caring, and personalized approach.

**MEDICAL GROUP AT MARPLE COMMONS**
**MARTHA LOGAN, M.D.**
**JANET SPECTER, M.D.**
**MARGARET WALKER, M.D.**
**DANIEL WOLK, M.D.**
**LESTER COHEN, FNP**
2000 Sproul Rd., Broomall, PA 19008; (215)359–1355.
Quality health care for the family from adolescence through senescence. Special interests: prevention, women's health, geriatrics.

**MARC H. NEIBERG, D.O.**
827 Fayette St., Conshohocken, PA 19428; (215)828–2608.
Residency: Sinai/Hopkins, Baltimore; Bryn Mawr Hospital athletic-team physician. Focus on family practice, thorough, compassionate approach to medicine. Convenient location. Hours: weekdays, evenings, Saturdays.

**REGIONAL INTERNAL MEDICINE ASSOC., LTD.**
*Multispecialty*
404 Middletown Blvd., Suite 300, Langhorne, PA 19047; (215)750–6777.
We are a multispecialty group specializing in invasive and non–invasive cardiology, hematology, oncology, and pulmonary diseases. Hours by appointment.

**RUSSELL J. STUMACHER, M.D.**
**ROSALIE PEPE, M.D.**
*Infectious Diseases*
Infectious Diseases Unit, Graduate Hospital, Pepper Pavillion, Suite 502, Philadelphia, PA 19146; (215)893–2415.
Diagnosis, treatment, and prevention of adult infectious diseases: travel-related infections, Lyme disease, HIV, vaccinations, STSs, antibiotic infusion therapy, chronic fatigue syndrome, women's health issues.

**EUGENE E. VOGIN, M.D., PH.D.**
*Geriatrics*
2682 Welsh Rd., Philadelphia, PA 19152; (215)464–7689.
Adult medicine, minor procedures, x–rays, physical therapy, staffed at three hospitals. Hours by appointment. Friendly staff, conveniently located between I–95 and

*Special Advertising Section*

Roosevelt Blvd. All insurance plans accepted.

**LEON J. WEINER, M.D.**
*Geriatrics*
9873 Bustleton Ave., Philadelphia, PA 19115; (215)464–1516.
Specializing in the care and treatment of people over 60 (particularly pain management).

## NEPHROLOGY

**CLINICAL NEPHROLOGY ASSOCIATES, LTD.**
**JOESPH H. BREZIN, M.D.**
**LARRY E. KREVOLIN, D.O.**
**ARTHUR R. OLSHAN, M.D., PH.D.**
**M. BLANCHE LIM, M.D.**
**JOHN E. PRIOR, D.O.**
**MARIA MENDEZ, M.D.**
*Clinical Nephrology*
250 N. 13th St., Philadelphia, PA 19107; (215)762–8043.
All kidney problems: high blood pressure, kidney failure, stones, infections, dialysis, transplantation. Board-certified. Active at Hahnemann University, Episcopal, Saint Agnes, Presbyterian hospitals. Insurance accepted.

**CLINICAL RENAL ASSOCIATES, LTD.**
Suite 303, Professional Office Bldg. I, One Medical Center Blvd., Upland, PA 19013; (215)872–8501, and 710 E. Lancaster Ave., Exton, PA 19341; (215)524–3703.
Drs. Clark, Soricelli, Sorkin, Westby, Arora, Williams, Dorrell, and Zirkman.
Specializing in hypertension and medical kidney diseases.

**MEDICAL COLLEGE OF PENNSYLVANIA RENAL ASSOCIATES**
**SANDRA P. LEVISON, M.D.**
**ZIAUDDIN AHMED, M.D.**
**JEAN LEE, M.D.**
**STEVEN J. PEITZMAN, M.D.**
**BONITA FALKNER, M.D.**
Medical College of Pennsylvania and Medical College Hospitals, Main Clinical Campus, 3300 Henry Ave., Philadelphia, PA 19129; (215)842–6988.
MCP's Renal Associates are leaders in diagnosis and treatment of hypertension and renal diseases, including dialysis. Specialists provide care for all ages—adolescents, adults and elderly.

**MARY C. STOM, M.D.**
*Hypertension*
Cooper Hospital/University Medical Center, 3 Cooper Plaza, Suite 215, Camden, NJ 08103; (609)342–2439.
Expert management of hypertension and diseases of the kidney, including kidney failure requiring dialysis, kidney stones, diabetic kidney disease, body mineral imbalance and incontinence.

## NEUROLOGY

**THE ELLIOTT NEUROLOGIC CENTER OF PENNSYLVANIA HOSPITAL**
3rd floor, Spruce Bldg., 8th and Spruce sts., Philadelphia, PA 19107; (215)829–7550.
Treats all types of neurologic problems. Physicians in the Center were well represented in the "Top Doctors" list in *Philadelphia Magazine*.

**HEIDAR K. JAHROMI, M.D.**
213 Reeceville Rd., Suite 13, Coatesville, PA 19320; (215)383–1355.
Practicing both adult and pediatric neurology in Chester County. Board-certified in neurology, completed fellowship in pediatric neurology, Clinical Assistant Professor of Neurology at Thomas Jefferson University Hospital.

**MEDICAL COLLEGE OF PENNSYLVANIA SLEEP DISORDERS CENTER**
*Neurology/Sleep Disorders*
3200 Henry Ave., EPPI Bldg., Sleep Disorders Center, Philadelphia, PA 19129; (215)842–4250.
Thorough, cost-effective sleep disorders diagnosis and treatment by board-certified specialists. Doctors June M. Fry and Rochelle Goldberg in accredited sleep disorders center.

**THE MEMORY INSTITUTE**
**JOSEPH MENDELS, M.D.**
*Alzheimer's Disease*

# CHILDREN'S SURGICAL ASSOCIATES, LTD.

*Dedicated to providing high-quality, state-of-the-art pediatric surgical services for your child.*

## CARDIAC SURGERY   590-2708
William I. Norwood, M.D.   590-2708
Marshall L. Jacobs, M.D.   590-2708

## GENERAL AND THORACIC SURGERY   590-2730
James A. O'Neill, Jr., M.D.*   590-2727
Louise Schnaufer, M.D.*   590-2733
John M. Templeton, Jr., M.D.   590-2753
Henry T. Lau, M.D.   590-2737
Arthur J. Ross, III, M.D.*   590-2744
Mark A. Hoffman, M.D.*   590-4210
Perry W. Stafford, M.D.*   590-2730

## NEUROSURGERY   590-2780, 2781
Luis Schut, M.D.   590-2780 or 2781
Leslie N. Sutton, M.D.   590-2780 or 2781
Ann-Christine Duhaime, M.D.   590-2780 or 2781

## OPHTHALMOLOGY   590-2791
David B. Schaffer, M.D.*   590-2791
James A. Katowitz, M.D.   590-2791
Graham E. Quinn, M.D.*   590-2791
Richard W. Hertle, M.D.   590-2791

## ORTHOPEDICS   590-1527
Denis S. Drummond, M.D.   590-1527
Richard S. Davidson, M.D.*   590-1523
John R. Gregg, M.D.   590-1539
Malcolm L. Ecker, M.D.   590-1535
Bong S. Lee, M.D.   590-1531
John P. Dormans, M.D.   590-1548

## OTOLARYNGOLOGY   590-3440
William P. Potsic, M.D.*   590-3450
Steven D. Handler, M.D.*   590-3454
Ralph F. Wetmore, M.D.*   590-3458
Lawrence W.C. Tom, M.D.*   590-3461

## PLASTIC AND RECONSTRUCTIVE SURGERY   590-2208
Linton A. Whitaker, M.D.   590-2209
Don LaRossa, M.D.   590-2214
Scott P. Bartlett, M.D.   590-2209
Howard S. Caplan, M.D.   590-2210
David Low, M.D.   590-2210
Marshall Partington, M.D.   590-2210

## UROLOGY   590-2754
John W. Duckett, M.D.   590-2754
Howard McCrum Snyder, III, M.D.*   590-2754
Steve Zderic, M.D.*   590-2754
Douglas Canning, M.D.*   590-2754

*Also has office hours at:
583 Shoemaker Road, Suite 150
King of Prussia, PA 19406
Please call 215-337-3232
to schedule an appointment.

*The numbers listed above are for the main offices located at The Children's Hospital of Philadelphia, 34th St. & Civic Center Blvd., Philadelphia, PA 19104.*

1015 Chestnut St., Suite 1303, Philadelphia, PA 19107; (215)923–8378.
The Memory Institute offers programs using new medications for treatment of Alzheimer's disease and other memory problems. Programs are free of charge and confidential.

**PAUL L. SCHRAEDER, M.D.**
Cooper Hospital/University Medical Center, 3 Cooper Plaza, Suite 320, Camden, NJ 08103; (609)342–2445.
Special expertise in seizure disorders, stroke, neuromuscular diseases, Parkinsonism, other movement disorders, dementia, traumatic brain injury and malignancy affecting the nervous system.

**ROBERT SLATER, M.D.**
304 Medical Center, 2100 Keystone Ave., Drexel Hill, PA 19026; (215)259–9500.
Practice limited to neurology and neuro–tology (vertigo, dizziness and balance disorders). Board-certified in neurology and EEG member American Neurotology Society.

## NEUROSURGERY

**LEONARD A. BRUNO, M.D.**
**GENE SALKIND, M.D.**
1601 Walnut St., Suite 908, Philadelphia, PA 19102; (215)843–8908.
Practice of neurosurgery, cranial, spinal, and peripheral nerve operations, including microsurgical and stereotactic techniques. Hours by appointment, (215)853–8908.

**RICHARD KANOFF, M.D.**
Suite 514, GSB Bala Cynwyd, PA 19004; (215)667–0659.
Board-certified. Professor of Neurosurgery. Practice includes all phases of cranial and spinal adult neurosurgery, with additional focus on surgical management of chronic pain.

**NEUROSURGICAL PRACTICE ASSOCIATES**
**LEONARD F. HIRSH, M.D.**
**VINNIE S. CHITALE, M.D.**
**THOMAS FRANCAVILLA, M.D.**
*Neurological Surgery*
Crozer Chester Medical Center, Suite 428, Chester, PA 19013; (215)874–4044.
University affiliated, Board-certified neurosurgery, all modern techniques for intracranial and spinal surgery. Academic medical care in private community hospitals. Recognized contributors to medical literature.

**GENE SALKIND, M.D.**
**LEONARD A. BRUNO, M.D.**
1601 Walnut St., Suite 908, Philadelphia, PA 19102; (215)843–8908.
Practice of neurosurgery, cranial, spinal, and peripheral nerve operations, including microsurgical and stereotactic techniques. Hours by appointment, (215)843–8908.

## OB/GYN

**ANTENATAL TESTING UNIT**
Pennsylvania Hospital, 800 Spruce St., Philadelphia, PA 19107; (215)829–5108, and 191 Presidential Condominium, Bala Cynwyd, PA; (215)667–1018.
The Antenatal Testing Unit offers high-risk pregnancy consultation, genetic counseling and the most advanced prenatal testing available. Staff Physicians: Robert Atlas, M.D., Joseph Bell, M.D., Ronald Bolognese, M.D., Joseph Bottalico, D.O., Nancy Bridgens, D.O., James Byers, M.D., Geeta Chhibber, M.D., Alan Donnenfeld, M.D., James Huhta, M.D., Ronald Librizzi, D.O., Abraham Ludomirsky, M.D., Garo Megearian, M.D., Munir Nazir, M.D., Stephen Smith, M.D., Jorge Tolosa, M.D., Sharon Weil, M.D., Stuart Weiner, M.D. Call for additional information regarding other locations in Pennsylvania and New Jersey.

**EDWARD L. APETZ, M.D.**
N. Broad and Oak sts., Woodbury, NJ 08096; (609)848–4846.
Full OB/GYN health care, including colposcopy, ultrasound, and the latest technology of in–office surgical procedures. Two female practitioners available. Most insurances accepted.

**BI–COUNTY OB/GYN ASSOCIATION**
**DR. LESTER A. RUPPERSBERGER D.O., F.A.C. O.O.G.**
**DR. NEIL D. BLUEBOND, D.O. F.A.C.O.O.G.**

# Dentistry While You Sleep

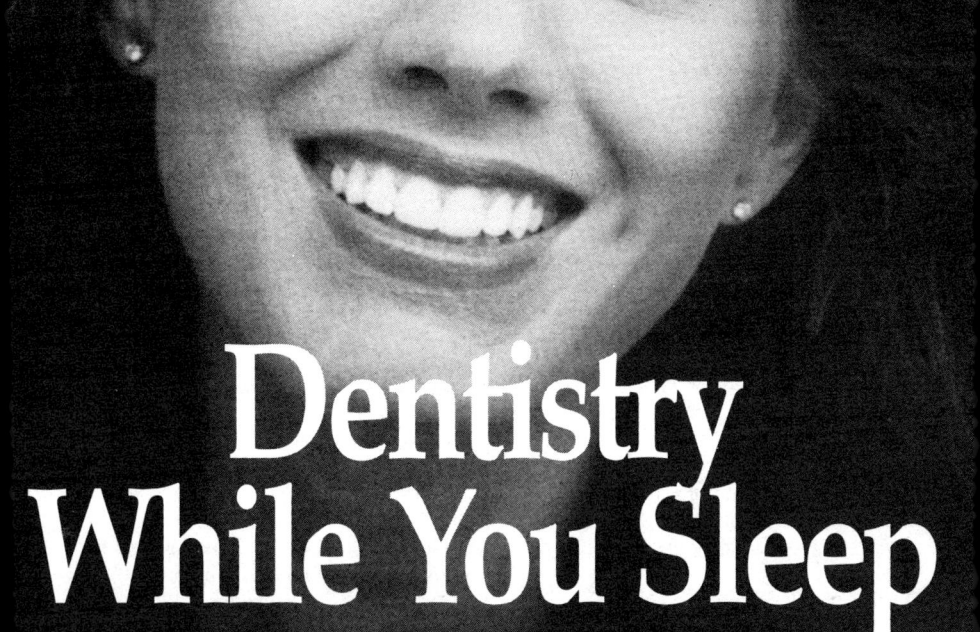

## Dental Anxiety?
## Executive With Time Restraints?
## Medical Limitations?

Single Day Dentistry is for you!
Personalized Dental Care • Several Procedures in One Day:
Capping, Bonding, Gum Treatments, Root Canals, Implants, Other Cosmetic Procedures
Performed While You Sleep • Performed by Dental Specialists • In A Hospital Setting

The result is a healthier mouth and an attractive smile, in a Single Day. If you are part of a select group requiring this type of care, phone (215) 985-1181 for more information on the latest three words of mouth.

## SINGLE-DAY DENTISTRY
### (215) 985-1181

A Member of the Dental Health Network • Dr. Barbara J. Steinberg, Director

*Special Advertising Section*

404 Middletown Blvd., Suite 305, Langhorne, PA 19047; (215)750–6611.
Drs. L. Ruppersberger and N. Bluebond are both board–certifed obstetricians and gynecologists. They engage in a progressive practice in the Lower Bucks County area, which provides total women's health care.

**DRS. BOLTON, VAUGHN AND RONNER, INC.**
700 Spruce St., Suite B–01, Philadelphia, PA 19106; (215)829–7400.
A five-physician practice located at Pennsylvania Hospital. Additional offices: Bala Cynwyd, and Haddonfield, NJ. Complete obstetric and gynecologic services, menopausal care, gynecologic surgery.

**MICHAEL J. CAMPION, M.D.**
*Gynecologic Oncology*
Graduate Hospital, Dept. Of Gynecology, 1840 South St., Philadelphia, PA 19146; (215)893–5477.
A specialist in gynecologic cancers and pre–malignant conditions of the cervix. Dr. Campion is an authority on the use of cervicography for cervical cancer screening.

**REBECCA S. CONRAD, M.D.**
*Gynecology*
822 Pine St., Suite 1–D, Philadelphia, PA 19107; (215)925–4780.
Gynecological surgeon. Pennsylvania Hospital specializes in evaluation of the abnormal PAP smear, care of the menopausal woman, problems of the reproductive years, and gynecological surgery.

**DELLABADIA AND PODOLSKY, PC**
Offices in Blackwood, NJ, Center City and South Philadelphia; (215)271–8000.
Drs. Carl DellaBadia and Michael Podolsky are pleased to announce Dr. Lisa Turri is joining their practice of OB/GYN, laser, and video surgery, including laparoscopic hysterectomy.

**MICHAEL A. FEINSTEIN, M.D.**
**KATHLEEN E. PATRICK, M.D.**
**TIMOTHY F. SHAWL, M.D.**
700 Spruce St., Suite 102, Philadelphia, PA; (215)627–5272, and 2314 S. 3rd St., Philadelphia, PA; (215)467–2205, and 461 Lankenau Medical Bldg., Wynnewood, PA; (215)649–8499.
Board–certified. Specializing in full service women's health care. Affiliated with Pennsylvania and Lankenau hospitals.

**DANIEL C. HARRER, M.D., F.A.C.O.G.**
1600 North High St., Millville, NJ 08332; (609)327–7711.
Board-certified. Obstetrician/gynecologist specializing in obstetric care, including gynecological procedures and surgery. Recently relocated to South Jersey from Lankenau Hospital. Hours by appointment.

**JUST FOR US. PRACTICE FOR OBSTETRICS AND GYNECOLOGY DR. ISA VELEZ.**
301 S. 8th St., Philadelphia, PA 19106; (215)829–7260.
University-affiliated. Board-certified.

**GWEN K. KAPLOW, M.D., P.C.**
*Gynecology*
1015 Chestnut St, Suite 312, Philadelphia, PA 19107; (215)925–8865.
An intimate office–based private practice with special attention to contraception, PMS, menopausal problems, and infertility. Caring, individual attention to our patients is our hallmark.

**MANGAN RIVA GYNECOLOGIC ASSOCIATION**
**RICHARD Z. BELEH, M.D.**
**ROBERT GIUNTOLI, M.D.**
**TIMOTHY McGINNISS, D.O.**
*Gynecologic Oncology*
700 Spruce St., Suite B–00, Philadelphia, PA 19106; (215)829–7111.
Emphasis on pelvic cancer, difficult gynecological surgical procedures, abnormal pap smears needing colposcopy, prevention and research. High-risk patients (family cancer syndrome) encouraged.

**PINE OB/GYN ASSOCIATES, P.C.**
Pennsylvania Hospital, 800 Spruce St., 1 Pine East, Philadelphia, PA 19107; (215)829–5018, Bala Cynwyd (215)667–1018, and Cherry Hill (609)482–1839.
Pine Ob/Gyn physicians provide specialized

*Special Advertising Section*

health care services for women at Pennsylvania Hospital and two suburban offices. High-risk pregnancy: Robert Atlas, M.D., Joseph Bell, M.D., Ronald Bolognese, M.D., James Byers, M.D., Alan Donnenfeld, M.D., James Huhta, M.D., Ronald Librizzi, M.D., Abraham Ludomirsky, M.D., Garo Megearian, M.D., Munir Nazir, M.D., Stephen Smith, M.D., Jorge Tolosa, M.D., Sharon Weil, M.D., Stuart Weiner, M.D. Infertility/gynecology: Andre Denis, M.D., Lenore Huppert, M.D. Urogynecology/gynecology: Richard Isenberg, M.D. Gynecology: Frank Gaudiano, M.D., Mark Woodland, M.D. Obstetrics and gynecology: Kathleen Burke, M.D., Cathy Buch, M.D., Taffy Dorsey, M.D., Deborah Schrager, M.D.

**PROFESSIONAL HEALTH CARE FOR WOMEN, INC.**
**BURTON L. WELLENBACH, M.D.**
**BENJAMIN KENDALL, M.D.**
**DAVID M. GOODNER, M.D.**

**JOSEPH G. GROVER, M.D.**
**OWEN C. MONTGOMERY, M.D.**
**PHILLIP W. HAYES, SR., M.D.**
Thomas Jefferson University Hospital, 111 S. 11th St., Suite G4150, Philadelphia, PA 19107; (215)955–8707, and 1949 Route 70 East, Suite 5, Cherry Hill, NJ 08003; (609)424–5656.
Comprehensive office care in both our Philadelphia and Cherry Hill offices. Complete obstetrical care and a full range of gynecological surgical care, with all hospital services provided at Thomas Jefferson University Hospital.

**THOMAS V. SEDLACEK, M.D.**
*Gynecology, Gynecologic Oncology*
Graduate Hospital, Dept. Of Gynecology, 1840 South St., Philadelphia, PA 19146; (215)893–5477.
A specialist in gynecologic cancers and pre–malignant conditions of the cervix. Dr. Sedlacek is an expert in colposcopy, as well as laser and laparoscopic surgery.

---

# Gentle Caring Services For Oral Surgery Needs...

## Oral & Maxillofacial Surgery

**WISDOM TEETH EXTRACTIONS**
**JAW SURGERY**
**DENTAL IMPLANTS**
**TMJ THERAPY**

Otto Tidwell, D.D.S.
1601 Walnut Street • Suite 215
Medical Arts Building
Philadelphia, PA 19102
215-557-7949

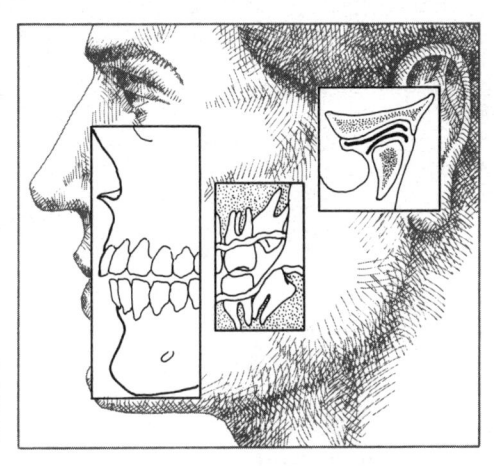

**STEIN–SLOANE MEDICAL ASSOCIATION**
4190 City Line Ave., Suite 315, Philadelphia, PA 19066; (215)871–1970.
Practice limited to general obstetrics/gynecology with subspecialization in vaginal surgery, laser and laparoscopic procedures. Most procedures done in office setting.

**LINDA C. WILSON, M.D.**
**DONALD F. WILSON, M.D.**
**CHRISTINE W. LYONS, M.D.**
**CAROL COLDREN, M.D.**
Brandywine Professional Bldg., 213 Reedeville Rd., Suite 17, Coatsville, PA 19320; (215)383–9400.
Board-certified gynecologists specializing in the management of pregnancy and complete gynecological care, including surgery, infertility, operative laparoscopy and hysteroscopy.

**WOMENCARE OBSTETRICS AND GYNECOLOGY**
**VIVIAN GREENBERG, M.D.**
**SHERRY BLUMENTHAL, M.D.**
**MICHELE PREMINGER, M.D.**
AMH Health Center, 2701 Blair Mill Rd., Suite C, Willow Grove, PA 19090; (215)443–0660.
Women caring for women with empathy. Complete OB/GYN services including gynecological surgery. Menopause support group.

## ONCOLOGY/HEMATOLOGY

**CLINICAL ONCOLOGY AND HEMATOLOGY ASSOCIATES**
**ROBERT L. BOYD, M.D.**
**STEPHEN A. SHORE, M.D.**
Medical and Conference Center, Suite 205, Delaware County Memorial Hospital, 2100 Keystone Ave., Drexel Hill, PA 19026; (215)626–6318.
Board–certified specialists in treatment of cancer and blood disorders. Affliated with Fox Chase Cancer Network and Temple Medical School.

**I. BRODSKY ASSOCIATES**
**I. BRODSKY, M.D.**
**S. BENHAM KAHN, M.D.**
**JAMES F. CONROY, D.O.**
**STEPHEN BULOVA, M.D.**
**PAMELA CRILLEY, D.O.**
**DAVID TOPOLSKY, M.D.**
Broad and Vine sts., Philadelphia, PA 19102; (215)762–7735.
All physicians are certified in hematology/oncology. They are dedicated to state of the art management of hematologic malignancies and solid tumors, including bone marrow transplantation.

**DONNA GLOVER, M.D.**
**STEPHEN GRABELSKY, M.D.**
**RENE ROTHSTEIN RUBIN, M.D.**
Presbyterian Medical Center of Philadelphia, 39th and Market sts. Philadelphia, PA 19104; (215)662-8947.
Oncology/hematology practice for adults. Special expertise in breast, GI and hematologic malignancies. Compassionate board-certified physicians and caring staff in a supportive environment.

**JACK GOLDBERG, M.D.**
Cooper Hospital/University Medical Center 3 Cooper Plaza, Suite 215, Camden, NJ 08103; (609)342–2439.
Comprehensive management for blood diseases and cancer. Therapies include bone marrow transplantation, chemotherapy, immune therapy, systemic radiation, biologic response modifiers, apheresis and experimental therapies.

**LAWRENCE M. SIGMAN, M.D., F.A.C.P.**
7602 Central Ave., Suite 102, Philadelphia, PA 19111; (215)342–3888.
Board-certified. Affiliated with Jeanes Hospital, Fox Chase Cancer Center, and Medical College Hospitals, Bucks County Campus. Special interest in breast cancer and lymphoma.

**JOHN DAVID SPRANDIO, M.D.**
**MONICA E. SMITH, M.D.**
**ROBERT K. ROUSH, JR., M.D.**
2100 Keystone Ave., Suite 502, Drexel Hill, PA 19026; (215)622–3818.
A community-based practice headed by the Director of section. Board-certified physicians with academic orientation. Active participants in Fox Chase Cancer Network.

*Special Advertising Section*

## OPHTHALMOLOGY

**REBECCA J. ADAMS, M.D.**
*Pediatric Ophthalmology*
1930 E. Rte. 70, Suite M–65, Cherry Hill, NJ 08003–4293; (609)424–7749.
Board-certified in ophthalmology. Fellowship-trained in pediatric ophthalmology and strabismus. Member medical staff Wills Eye, Children's Hospital, St. Christopher's, West Jersey hospitals, and Lourdes Medical Center.

**EDWARD H. BEDROSSIAN JR., M.D., F.A.C.S.**
*Ophthalmic Plastic Surgery*
4501 State Rd., Drexel Hill, PA 19026; (215)789–6565.
Cosmetic and reconstructive eyelid surgery, tear duct and orbital surgery. Board-certified; Wills Eye Hospital; American Society Ophthalmic Plastic and Reconstructive Surgery. New York City trained.

**MARC S. COHEN, M.D.**
*Oculoplastic And Cosmetic Surgery, Neuro–ophthalmology*
Wills Eye Hospital, Philadelphia, PA 19107; (215)829–9011, and Pavillions Of Voorhees, 2301 Evesham Rd., Suite 101, Voorhees, NJ 08043; (609)772–2552.
Specializing in eyelid rejuvenation, reconstruction, thyroid-eye disease, tearing problems and skin cancer. Fellowship trained.

**CORNEAL ASSOCIATES**
**ELISABETH J. COHEN, M.D.**
**PETER R. LAIBSON, M.D.**
**CHRISTOPHER J. RAPUANO, M.D.**
*Cornea and External Disease*
Wills Eye Hospital (Cornea Service), 9th and Walnut sts., Philadelphia, PA 19107; (215)928–3180.
Wills Eye Hospital corneal specialists providing expertise in corneal transplantation, refractive and laser surgery and diagnosis and treatment of corneal diseases and contact lens problems.

---

**REPRODUCTIVE and MEDICAL ENDOCRINE ASSOC., P.C.**
**COOPER CENTER FOR REPRODUCTIVE ENDOCRINOLOGY, P.C.**
**COOPER INSTITUTE FOR IN VITRO FERTILIZATION, P.C.**

Dedicated to the Treatment of Female and Male Infertility
Complete On-Site In-Vitro Fertilization Center and Support Facilities
Complete On-Site Semen Evaluation Including New Sophisticated Assays
On-Site Sonography Facility
Sex Selection and Therapeutic Donor Insemination

| | | |
|---|---|---|
| 7447 Old York Road | 1015 Chestnut St. #1020 | 8002 E. Greentree Commons |
| Melrose Park, PA 19126 | Philadelphia, PA 19107 | Marlton, NJ 08053 |
| 215-635-4400 | 215-925-6304 | 609-751-5575 |

Jerome H. Check, M.D.
Jeffrey S. Chase, M.D.
Kosrow Nowroozi, M.D.

Jung K. Choe, M.D.
Althea O' Shaughnessy, M.D.
Ahmad Nazari, M.D.

*Special Advertising Section*

**JAMES L. CRISTOL, M.D.**
*Ophthalmology*
Lawrence Rd. and Sussex Blvd., Broomall, PA 19008; (215)325-9630.
Modern high-tech family eye care accomplished with an old-fashioned conversational, personal approach. Routine examinations and troubling medical and surgical problems thoughtfully managed.

**DR. EUGENE M. DIMARCO**
6557 Roosevelt Blvd., Philadelphia, PA 19149; (215)535-5025.
Surgery and diseases of the eyes and eyelids; Parkview Medical Center and Graduate Hospital. Specializing in single-stitch cataract surgery, glaucoma laser surgery and surgery of the eyelids.

**THOMAS R. HEDGES, JR., M.D.**
*Ophthalmology/Neuro-Ophthalmology*
Pennsylvania Hospital, 700 Spruce St., Suite 507, Philadelphia, PA 19106; (215)829-3421.
Internationally known, university-affiliated, board-certified, does cataract removal and lens-implant surgery. Has reputation for in-depth neuro-ophthalmologic exams and diagnoses.

**DANIEL MERRICK KANE, M.D., F.A.C.S.**
Wills Eye Hospital, 9th and Walnut sts., Philadelphia, PA 19107; (215)352-1166, (215)352-4457, (215)688-2733.
Excimer laser refractive surgery for nearsightedness and astigmatism. Surgical correction of cataract with implant; second opinion, especially for implant difficulties.

**LOUIS A. KARP, M.D., F.A.C.S., P.C.**
Suite 100, Garfield Duncan Bldg., 700 Spruce St., Philadelphia, PA 19106; (215)829-5311.
A general ophthalmology practice affiliated with Pennsylvania Hospital. Special interests: cataract and implant surgery, glaucoma management, including laser and conventional surgery. Also contact-lens care.

**MICHAEL L. KAY, M.D.**
*Cataract/Implant Surgery*
130 S. 9th St., Philadelphia, PA 19107;
(215)925-6402, and 102 Bala Ave., Bala Cynwd, PA; (215)667-6760.
Specializing in outpatient no-stitch cataract implant surgery. Caring office, most insurance accepted. Named by *Philadelphia Magazine* in "Top Doctors" issue.

**FREDERIC B. KREMER, M.D.**
Offices in Philadelphia, Radnor, Pottstown, Hatboro; 1-800-432-EYES.
Specialists in eye surgery. Refractive surgery to eliminate glasses and contact lenses. Cataract surgery; no needles or sutures with lens implantation. Glaucoma surgery. Transportation available.

**JAMES S. LEWIS, M.D.**
*Cornea Specialist; Cataract and Implant Surgeon*
100 Old York Rd., Main Lobby, Jenkintown, PA 19046; (215)886-9090.
Internationally known, university affiliated, board-certified. No-stitch cataract surgery, secondary lens implantation, corneal transplantation. Known for pioneering surgical techniques and management of complicated cases.

**STEPHEN B. LICHTENSTEIN, M.D., F.A.C.S.**
150 Lankenau Medical Bldg. East, Wynnewood, PA 19096; (215)649-2600, outside of PA, 1-800-624-8880.
Old-fashioned approach to high-tech eye care; strong believer that physicians should talk to patients. Expert in high-risk cataract surgery and complication management.

**LARRY E. MAGARGAL, M.D., F.A.C.S., F.I.C.S.**
**HELGA O. MAGARGAL, M.D.**
*Retina-vascular disease*
Wills Eye Hospital, 9th and Walnut sts., Philadelphia, PA 19107; (215)824-3920.
Board-certified specialist in retina vascular disease and laser surgery of the eye. Fellow, American Academy Of Ophthalmology and the American and International College of Surgeons.

**MARLENE R. MOSTER, M.D.**
Lankenau MOB East, Suite 154, Wynnewood, PA 19096; (215)649-9800.
Practice limited to the treatment of glauco-

*Special Advertising Section*

ma and related diseases. Offices located at Lankenau and Wills Eye Hospitals.

**NAIDOFF ALTMAN EYE ASSOCIATES**
1100 Walnut St., Suite 603, Philadelphia, PA 19107; (215)922–2455.
Drs. Michael A. Naidoff and Adam J. Altman. Board-certified ophthalmologists specializing in medical and surgical eye care, with offices in Center City and Northeast Philadelphia.

**LEONARD B. NELSON, M.D.**
*Pediatric Ophthalmology*
900 Walnut St., Wills Eye Hospital, Philadelphia, PA 19107; (215)928–3244, (215)896–7171 (Lankenau).
Co–director of pediatric ophthalmology at Wills Eye Hospital. I treat all childrens' eye problems, such as strabismus, which is a deviation of the eyes, and amblyopia, which is poor vision.

**NEURO–OPHTHALMOLOGIC ASSOCIATES**
*Neuro–Ophthalmology*
Wills Eye Hospital, 900 Walnut St., Philadelphia, PA 19107; (215)928–3130.
At Wills Eye Hospital, treating patients with decreased vision or other visual problems associated with neurologic disease. Named in "Top Doctors" in *Philadelphia Magazine*, *Town and Country*.

**STEPHEN E. ORLIN, M.D.**
Suite 158 Lankenau MOB East, Wynnewood, PA 19096; (215)649–7000.
Cornea, anterior segment and refractive surgery. Treatment of external eye disease. Offices located at Lankenau Hospital, Scheie Eye Institute, Einstein Center One and Marlton, NJ.

**DAVID S.C. PAO, M.D.**
**WILLIAM B. NEUSIDL, M.D.**
*Ophthalmology–Cataract Implant*
1018 Street Rd., Southampton, PA 18966; (215)322–8338.
Fellowship-trained in retina and cornea. Teaching staffs of Wills Eye and Temple

## Reshaping Your Face with Corrective Jaw Surgery

BEFORE

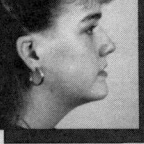

AFTER

With the revolutionary new procedure of RIGID FIXATION her jutting jaw was corrected, without traditional jaw wiring, making eating and speaking easier, as well as reducing the healing time and discomfort.

## Wisdom Teeth: They may do more harm than good:

Are your wisdom teeth threatening the health of your mouth? An evaluation can answer this question.

If your evaluation pinpoints a problem with your wisdom teeth, surgery may be recommended to remove your wisdom teeth and eliminate your symptoms.

If you are apprehensive about dental procedures, the use of general anesthesia can make a more pleasant and simple surgery.

## Oral & Maxillofacial Surgery
**Dr. M. MADANI, Diplomate**
American Board of Oral and Maxillofacial Surgery
Klein Professional Building, Suite 204 • 5401 Old York Rd, Phila., PA 19141
**215-456-7328** EMERGENCY HOURS Available
*Other surgical services available. Dental Implants. TMJ., etc.*

University. General ophthalmology and expertise in cataract implant, retina, cornea, glaucoma. Also Levittown office.

**IRVING M. RABER, M.D.**
Suite 158, Lankenau MOB East, Wynnewood, PA 19096; (215)649–7000. Practice limited to cornea, anterior segment and refractive surgery and external eye disease. Offices located at Lankenau and Wills Eye Hospitals and Marlton, NJ.

**PETER J. SAVINO, M.D.**
The Graduate Hospital, 1800 Lombard St., Philadelphia, PA 19146; (215)893–2457. A full-service ophthalmology department. Dr. Savino has been named in the top 1 percent of physicians in the United States.

**JERRY A. SHIELDS, M.D.**
*Ocular Oncology*
Wills Eye Hospital, 900 Walnut St., Philadelphia, PA. 19107; (215)928–3105. World-reknowned eye specialist in the field of eye cancer and ocular tumors. Written authoritative textbooks on intraocular tumors and orbital tumors.

**SURGICAL EYE CARE LTD.**
**STEVEN B. SIEPSER, M.D.**
*Eye Surgery*
91 Chestnut Rd., Paoli, PA 19301; (215)296–3333.
Surgical ophthalmology practice specializing in stitchless cataract surgery, refractive surgery for nearsightedness, complex ocular surgery. Affiliated with Wills Eye Hospital and Thomas Jefferson University Hospital.

**SOLL EYE ASSOCIATES**
5001 Frankford Ave., Philadelphia, PA 19124; (215)288–5000.
Internationally recognized ophthalmologists treating eye problems, including: cataracts; glaucoma; medical, laser, and surgical retinal problems; pediatric, eye-plastic and low-vision problems.

**GEORGE L. SPAETH, M.D.**
**L. JAY KATZ, M.D.**
900 Walnut St., Philadelphia PA, 19107; (215)928–3197.

Partners specializing in the diagnosis and management of patients with glaucoma and associated conditions, including cataracts.

**RICHARD TIPPERMAN, M.D.**
150 Lankenau Medical Bldg. East, Wynnewood, PA 19096; (215)649–2600, outside of PA. 1–800–624–8880.
Old-fashioned approach to high-tech eye care; believes doctors should talk to their patients. Special interest in high-risk cataract surgery and complication management.

## ORTHOPEDIC SURGERY

**DAVID J. ADAMS, M.D.**
27 S. Bryn Mawr Ave., Bryn Mawr, PA 19010; (215)525-1261.
Temple graduate with 20 years experience in total joint replacement surgery and general orthopedic care. Special expertise in spinal surgery. Team physician for Villanova University.

**JOHN M. CUCKLER, M.D.**
*Hip and Knee Arthritis/Joint Replacement*
Department of Orthopedics, Hospital of the University of Pennsylvania, 3400 Spruce St., Philadelphia, PA 19104;
(215)662–3340.
Practice limited to conservative and surgical care of hip and knee arthritis. "Best Doctors in America," '92 (Hip Surgery), "Top Doctors," *Philadelphia Magazine* '91 (Knees).

**NICHOLAS A. DI NUBILE, M.D.**
*Sports Medicine, Arthroscopic Surgery*
Offices in Havertown, PA and Wayne, PA; (215)789–0150.
Practice focus: knee disorders (injuries, rehabilitation, arthroscopy, surgery). Special advisor, President's Council on Physical Fitness and Sports. Orthopedist, Pennsylvania Ballet. Faculty, Hospital of the University of Pennsylvania.

**WILLIAM D. EMPER, M.D.**
27 S. Bryn Mawr Ave., Bryn Mawr, PA 19010; (215)527–1762.
Practice of general orthopedic surgery specializing in sports medicine, arthroscopic surgery and joint replacement; surgery of

*Special Advertising Section*

the knee and shoulder. Team physician for Villanova University.

**HAHNEMAN ORTHOPAEDIC ASSOCIATES, P.C.**
**ARNOLD T. BERMAN, M.D.**
*Joint Replacements and Adult Reconstruction*
221 N. Broad St., Philadelphia, PA 19102; 800–762–8500.
Internationally known for total hip, knee replacements and other adult reconstructive orthopaedic surgery for arthritis. Professor and Chairman, Department of Orthopedic Surgery and Rehabilitation, Hahnemann University Hospital.

**PALMACCIO–SMITH ASSOCIATES**
*Sports Medicine, Reconstructive Surgery*
12000 Bustleton Ave., Suite 206, Philadelphia, PA 19116; (215)677–2076.
2 Bala Plaza–1L 21, Bala Cynwyd, PA 19004; (215)664–2100.
Arthroscopic surgery, hand surgery, arthritis and fracture care, x–rays on premises, accept most insurances.

**DAVID R. PASHMAN, M.D.**
**ROBERT E. LIEBENBERG, M.D.**
**VICTOR R. FRANKEL, M.D.**
**JONATHAN BROMBERG, M.D.**
5401 Old York Rd., Suite 200, Philadelphia, PA 19141; (215)456–9400.
Specializing in total joint surgery, spine surgery, arthroscopic surgery and sports medicine, occupational injuries and arthritis. 205 Newtown Rd., Suite 103, Warminster, PA 18974; (215)672–3800, and 9880 Bustleton Ave., Suite 201–202, Philadelphia, PA 19115; (215)677–9140.

**WILLIAM G. STEWART JR., M.D.**
27 S. Bryn Mawr Ave., Bryn Mawr, PA 19010; (215)527–1762.
Boston-trained general orthopedic surgeon with specialty interest in area of total joint replacement. Twenty–five years experience using the most modern technique and hospital facilities.

**UNIVERSITY OF PENNSYLVANIA SHOULDER SERVICE**

---

# Have you heard what we're doing at THE NEW MEDICAL AND DIAGNOSTIC CENTER in Philadelphia?

How often have you felt like nothing but a statistic when seeking medical care? Wouldn't you like to find a physician who really listens to you?
...an internist who understands how to diagnose hidden health problems...from uncommon allergies...to hormonal and metabolic malfunctions...and other hard-to-diagnose physical disorders...We believe in thorough testing. We believe in showing you the whole picture.
*Our patients are pleased.*

**THE MEDICAL & DIAGNOSTIC CENTER OF PHILADELPHIA**

1525 Locust Street • Philadelphia, PA 19102 ■ 215-545-4444

**INSURANCE PLANS:** Blue Shield, Major Medical, Private & Commercial Insurance, AFSCME, Teamsters, Mail Handlers Benefit, 1199/MPA, APWU, N.J. State Health Benefits accepted.

*Reconstructive Surgery of the Shoulder*
2 Silverstein Pavilion, 3400 Spruce St., Philadelphia, PA 19104; (215)662–3575.
The service includes four orthopedic surgeons specializing in the diagnosis and treatment of shoulder disorders, including rotator cuff injuries, unstable shoulders, arthroscopy and joint replacement.

### DR. STEVEN J. VALENTINO, M.D.
*Orthopedic Spine Surgery*
Merion Bldg., 700 S. Henderson Rd., Suite 100, King of Prussia, PA 19406; (215)265–5795.
Board-certified orthopedic spine surgeon, specializes in arthroscopic laser microdiscectomy and new reconstructive spine surgery techniques as well as general orthopedics. He is associated with Graduate Hospital, Philadelphia and Suburban General Hospital, Norristown, and has offices in Philadelphia and King of Prussia, PA, as well as Cherry Hill and Blackwood, NJ.

## OTOLARYNGOLOGY

### BENJAMIN S. CHACK, D.O.
*Head and Neck Surgery*
586 Middletown Blvd., Suite C–15, Langhorne, PA 19047; (215)750–6130.
Board-certified. Specializing in ear, nose and throat and facial plastic surgery, including pediatrics and cosmetic surgery.

### EAR, NOSE AND THROAT PROFESSIONAL ASSOCIATES
### MAX L. RONIS, M.D.
### EMIL F. LIEBMAN, M.D.
### MELVIN L. MASLOF, M.D.
2106 Spruce St., Philadelphia, PA 19103; (215)790–1553.
A University-based team with six decades combined experience. Each physician with special skills, including cosmetic surgery, sinus endoscopy, hearing disorders, allergy, pediatric/ENT and dizziness.

### SCOTT R. PARGOT, D.O.
*Head and Neck Surgery/Allergy*
2340 E. Allegheny Ave., Philadelphia, PA 19134; (215)423–6670.
Board-eligible, Osteopathic College of Otolaryngology. Head and neck surgery, facial plastic surgery, allergy. Northeastern Hospital, Pennsylvania Hospital, Thomas Jefferson University Hospital.

### LEE D. ROWE, M.D.
2340 E. Allegheny Ave., Philadelphia, PA 19134; (215)423–6670.
Board-certified and Fellow American College of Surgeons. Surgery of the ear, nose, and throat. Head and neck reconstruction and facial plastic surgery. Northeastern Hospital, Pennsylvania Hospital, Thomas Jefferson University Hospital.

### LYNN F. SUMERSON, D.O.
### DAVID W. GRANOFF, D.O.
### VYTAF B. SILIUNAS, D.O.
*Ear, Nose and Throat*
510 Darby Rd., Suite 202, Havertown, PA 19083; (215)449–2800, and 205 Newtown Rd., Warminster, PA, and 8300 Bustelton Ave., Philadelphia, and HPCOM Parkview, 1331 E. Wyoming Ave., Philadelphia.
Also specialize in pediatrics, adult allergies and cosmetic surgery.

## PEDIATRICS

### ROSEMARY CASEY, M.D., DIRECTOR
Children's Hospital of Philadelphia, Wood Ambulatory Center, 3rd Floor, 34th St. and Civic Center Blvd., Philadelphia, PA 19104; (215)590–2178.
Unique private practice comprised of five academically trained pediatricians from the University of Pennsylvania faculty. Focused on all aspects of children's health. 24-hour availability.

### CHILDREN'S HEALTH CARE ASSOCIATES, INC.
Children's Hospital of Philadelphia, 34th St. and Civic Center Blvd., Philadelphia, PA 19104, 1–800–879–2467.
Listed in "Top Docs for Kids," *Philadelphia Magazine,* as outstanding specialty Pediatricians: allergy, cardiology, dermatology, diabetes, emergency, gastroenterology, genetics, hematology, metabolism, neonatology, nephrology, neurology, oncology, rehabilitation, general pediatrics.

*Special Advertising Section*

**CHILDREN'S SURGICAL ASSOCIATES, LTD.**
*Pediatric Surgical Care*
One Children's Center, The Children's Hospital of Philadelphia, 34th St. and Civic Center Blvd., Philadelphia, PA 19104–4399; (215)590–2700.
Pediatric surgical care in cardiac surgery, general and thoracic surgery, neurosurgery, ophthalmology, orthopedics, otolaryngology, plastic and reconstructive surgery and urology.

**JEFFREY B. ETTINGER, M.D.**
**GERALD ZUBKOFF, M.D.**
**DOROTHY BURDZIAK, D.O.**
7500 Central Ave., Suite 205, Philadelphia, PA 19111; (215)728–7711.
Caring, accessible, board–certified pediatricians serving families in Northeast Philadelphia and neighboring Montgomery County and Bucks County suburban communities. Convenient hours by appointment.

**PEDIATRIC CARDIOVASCULAR RISK REDUCTION PROGRAM**
**BONITA FALKER, M.D.**
**EDWARD FISHER, M.D., PH.D.**
**SUZANNE MICHEL, M.P.H., R.D.**
*Pediatric cholesterol and hypertension management*
Department of Pediatrics, The Medical College of Pennsylvania, 3300 Henry Ave., Philadelphia, PA 19129; (215)842–7142.
Diagnostic evaluation and management of children with elevated cholesterol or blood pressure; promotion of normal growth, primarily by age-appropriate changes in diet and exercise.

**DR. MISCHA F. GROSSMAN**
*Adult Medicine*
9001-C Greentree Commons, Marlton, NJ 08053; (609)983–6999.
Hospital affiliations: University of Medicine and Dentistry of New Jersey; J.F.K. Hospitals; West Jersey Hospitals, Voorhees Div.; Thomas Jefferson University Hospital; Childrens Hospital of Philadelphia.

## Cardiothoracic Surgery at Penn

The internationally recognized surgeons in Penn's **Division of Cardiothoracic Surgery** have developed many of today's innovative techniques for **surgery and transplantation of the heart and lungs.**

Penn's board-certified surgeons treat patients who have:
- Coronary artery disease
- Cardiac valvular disease
- Arrhythmias
- Pacemakers
- Congenital heart disease
- Thoracic aorta diseases
- Pulmonary disease
- Esophageal disease
- Disorders of the mediastinum, pleura, chest wall, diaphragm
- Lung tumors

**Cardiac Surgery**
*Verdi J. DiSesa, MD*
*Joseph Bavaria, MD*
*L. Henry Edmunds, MD*
*Mark B. Ratcliffe, MD*

**Thoracic Surgery**
*Larry Kaiser, MD*
*Joseph Bavaria, MD*
*L. Henry Edmunds, MD*

In addition to traditional surgical methods, our surgeons use advanced, minimally invasive endoscopic and thoracoscopic techniques.

**For more information** about our surgeons or programs, or to schedule an appointment, please call **Penn's referral counselors, 215-662-PENN (7366).**

**UNIVERSITY OF PENNSYLVANIA MEDICAL CENTER**
University of Pennsylvania School of Medicine
Hospital of the University of Pennsylvania

*Special Advertising Section*

## HAHNEMANN PEDIATRIC ASSOCIATION
216 N. Broad St., Feinstein Bldg. 4th floor, Philadelphia, PA 19102; (215)762-PEDS (7337).
We offer a personalized approach to the whole child while providing state of the art medicine in both primary-care pediatrics and all pediatric subspecialties.

## JEFFERSON ASSOCIATES IN NEONATOLOGY
**ALAN SPITZER, M.D., DIRECTOR**
**JAY GREENSPAN, M.D., ASSOCIATE DIRECTOR**
**STEPHEN BAUMGART, M.D. DIRECTOR, ECMO PROGRAM**
**SHOBHANA DESAI, M.D., DIRECTOR, NEONATAL FOLLOW-UP PROGRAM**
**ERIC GIBSON, M.D., DIRECTOR, INFANT APNEA PROGRAM**
*Newborn Medicine (Neonatology)*
Thomas Jefferson University, Department of Pediatrics/College Bldg., 1025 Walnut St., Philadelphia, PA 19107;(215)955–6523.
Jefferson Associates in Neonatology offers complete comprehensive care services for the well and the critically ill newborn, with prenatal consultation for high–risk families.

**CATHY KAISSI, M.D.**
**ELLEN L. SPECK, M.D.**
205 Newtown Rd., Suite 216, Warminster, PA 18974; (215)953–8633.
Academic affiliation: Medical College of Pennsylvania. On staff at Medical College Hospitals, Bucks County Campus; St. Christopher's Hospital for Children. Minor emergencies treated in office.

## NEWBORN PEDIATRICS
**FRANK BOWEN, M.D.**
**SORAYA ABBASI, M.D.**
**VINOD BHUTANI, M.D.**
**JEFFREY GERDES, M.D.**
**LOIS JOHNSON, M.D.**
Pennsylvania Hospital, 800 Spruce St., Philadelphia, PA 19107; (215)829–3301.
Academically oriented practice committed to providing highest level of health care for infants before, during, and following birth, while preserving the balance between technical and psychological needs of the family and infant. Goals are excellence through research and enhancement of understanding infant and parental needs through teaching and community service.

## PEDIATRIC AND ADOLESCENT ASSOCIATES, LTD.
**ELLIS H. SACKS, M.D.**
**JANET MICHAELSON, M.D.**
**BARBARA S. ROLNICK, M.D.**
300 E. Lancaster Ave., Suite 110, Wynnewood, PA 19096; (215)642–6000.
Warm, personal approach to pediatric and adolescent patients and families. Childrens Hospital of Philadelphia–trained, board-certified. Admit to Lankenau, Bryn Mawr hospitals, Childrens Hospital of Philadelphia.

## PEDIATRIC MEDICAL ASSOCIATES
**ALFRED J. CARLSON JR., M.D.**
**JOHN P. RODZVILLA JR., M.D.**
**JEREMY LICHTMAN, M.D.**
**C. ROSS SMITH, M.D.**
**RENEE M. SAMMARITANO, M.D.**
**BRIGITTE K. ROTCHE, M.D.**
*Infants, Children, Adolescents*
420 Township Line Rd., Havertown, PA 19083–5294; (215)449–6200.
Personalized care. Board-certified pediatricians in fully equipped suburban office. Available 24 hours. Daytime, evening, weekend hours by appointment. Bryn Mawr and Fitzgerald Mercy hospitals.

## THOMAS JEFFERSON UNIVERSITY CHILD AND ADOLESCENT NEUROLOGY, PSYCHIATRY, AND GROWTH AND DEVELOPMENT
**CHARLES B. BRILL, M.D., NEUROLOGY**
**GARY CARPENTER, M.D., ENDOCRINOLOGY**
**LEONARD J. GRAZIANI, M.D., NEUROLOGY**
**PETER KOLLROS, M.D., PH.D., NEUROLOGY**
**JEANNETTE C. MASON, M.D., DEVELOPMENTAL**
**RUTH P. ZAGER, M.D., PSYCHIATRY**
Thomas Jefferson University, Department of Pediatrics, 909 Walnut St., Philadelphia, PA 19107; (215)955–6822/2400.

*Special Advertising Section*

Specializing in problems including developmental and language disorders, cerebral palsy, seizures, genetic, endocrine and metabolic diseases, headaches, learning disabilities, and behavioral and emotional disorders.

**NATHAN ZANKMAN, M.D. P.C.
GREGG S. ZANKMAN, D.O.**
Bucks County–area office; (215)943–3600. Board-certified father/son practice. 27 years dedicated to quality care; 24–hour availability. St. Mary, Lower Bucks, Del–Val hospitals affiliation. Most insurances, including HMO, U.S. Healthcare, Keystone.

## PHYSICAL & REHAB MEDICINE

**HAROLD L. BESS, D.O.
THE H.L. BESS NEUROMUSCULAR PAIN CLINIC**
2 Red Rose Drive, Levittown, PA 19056; (215)946–7000.
Auto/work injuries, chronic pain management, exercise rehabilitation, physical therapy, disability evaluation, trauma, neck and pain disorders, sports medicine. Most insurance accepted. Day and evening hours; (215)946–PAIN.

**DENNIS J. BONNER, M.D.
NANCY SHANAHAN, M.D.
GUILLERMO BORNAL, M.D.**
*Physiatry*
St. Mary's Medical Bldg., Suite 304, Langhorne, PA 19047; (215)572–0200. Rehab. Center, 1854 New Rodgers Rd. and Rte. 413, Levittown, PA 19056.
Specializing in PM&R. Treat functional disabilities, strokes, paralysis, amputations, burns, arthritis, osteoporosis, back pain. EMG studies, IMEs, CTS, sports medicine, soft tissue injuries.

**EMMELINE P. GUTIERREZ–ABELLA, M.D.**
1648 Huntingdon Pike, Meadowbrook, PA 19046; (215)938–3630.
Evaluation and management of physical disabilities: strokes, amputations, arthritis, traumatic injuries, and the diagnosis

---

**When it comes to matters of the heart... only the best will do.**

*Dr. Denton A. Cooley · Dr. Arthur A. Hellman*

## The Open Heart Institute
in Philadelphia
**Arthur A. Hellman, M.D.**
Chief Surgeon

When you have to put your heart in someone's hands, you want those hands to be the best:

- skill and expertise with high risk surgery
- uncompromising pursuit of perfect results
- world-class training and experience (with Dr. Denton A. Cooley at The Texas Heart Institute)
- surgery by the surgeon (not by assistants or trainees)
- comprehensive quality care...from consultation through surgery and recovery
- dedication to patient and family
- state-of-the-art cardiac surgery facilities

**THE OPEN HEART INSTITUTE**

301 South Eighth Street
Philadelphia, PA 19106
**215/829-7120**

of nerve and muscle diseases. Electro-myography and nerve nonduction studies.

## PLASTIC SURGERY

**THOMAS J BROBYN, M.D.**
831 Bethlehem Pike, Erdenheim, PA 19118; (215)233–4005.
Board-certified in plastic surgery. Reconstructive, cosmetic, and hand surgery. Medicare, Blue Shield and most HMOs accepted.

**MARC S. COHEN, M.D.**
*Oculoplastic and Cosmetic Surgery, Neuro–Ophthalmology*
Wills Eye Hospital, Philadelphia, PA 19107; (215)829–9011, and Pavillions Of Voorhees, 2301 Evesham Rd., Suite 101, Vorhees, NJ 08043; (609)772–2552.
Specializing in eyelid rejuvenation and reconstruction. One of the few cosmetic surgeons trained to treat eyes. Fellowship-trained.

**COOPER PLASTIC SURGERY ASSOCIATES**
**ARTHUR S. BROWN, M.D.**
**LENORA R. BAROT, M.D.**
**MARTHA S. MATTHEWS, M.D.**
*Reconstructive Surgery*
702 E. Main St., Moorestown N.J. 08057; (609)234–7073.
Full range of cosmetic and reconstructive surgery—breast surgery, liposuction, facial, hand, birth defects, microsurgery, maxillofacial, difficult wounds, post–traumatic reconstruction. Affiliated with Cooper Hospital.

**COSMETIC SURGERY CENTER**
**MARVIN T. HUNTER, M.D., F.A.C.S.**
**DAVID A. SILBERMAN, M.D., F.A.C.S.**
205 Newtown Rd., Suite 108, Warminster, PA 18974; 1-800 223–1190.
Certified by American Board of Plastic Surgery. Facial, nasal, eyes, breast, liposuction and chemical peels. Payment plan available. Second location: 301 S. Main St., Doylestown, PA.

**DR. CARMEN DIMARIO**
*Cosmetic Surgery*
Offices in Bala Cynwyd, Chadds Ford, Philadelphia and Yardley; (215)667–2005. People seek cosmetic surgery for various reasons. The results should be natural looking and give the feeling of confidence. My concern is for the patient.

**RICHARD L. DOLSKY, M.D.**
Cosmetic Surgery of Philadelphia,
191 Presidential Blvd., Suite 105, Bala Cynwyd, PA 19004; (215)667–3341.
Specializing in facial surgery, liposuction and breast contouring. Dr. Dolsky is the only Philadelphia plastic surgeon certified by the American Boards of Plastic Surgery, Otolaryngology and Cosmetic Surgery.

**JAMES W. FOX, IV, M.D.**
135 S. 18th St., Philadelphia, PA, 19103; (215)–563–8557.
Board-certified plastic and reconstructive surgeon, Chief of Plastic Surgery Thomas Jefferson University Hospital, Professor of Plastic Surgery Jefferson Medical College. Specializes in cosmetic surgery, breast surgery, liposuction, and skin cancer surgery.

**BRUCE E. GENTER, M.D.**
Foxcroft Apts.,1250 Greenwood Ave., Suite 10, Jenkintown, PA 19046;(215)572–7744.
Board-certified, medical-school-affiliated. Expert in post-mastectomy breast reconstruction, facelift, eyelids and nasal surgery, dermabrasion, chemical peel, tummy tucks, liposuction, body contoring, breast enhancement.

**STEPHEN HARLIN, M.D.**
*Reconstructive Surgery*
210 West Rittenhouse Square, Philadelphia, PA 19103; (215)731–9490, and Delaware County Medical Center, Broomall, PA 19008; (215)356–4499.
Thoughtful counsel, sound surgical judgment, precise technique. Aesthetic, breast, reconstructive, hand, dermatologic, and pediatric plastic surgery.

**PAUL S. KIM, M.D.**
*Reconstructive Surgery*
Oaklands Corporate Center, 460 Creamery Way, Suite 110, Exton, PA 19341; (215)524–8244.

*Special Advertising Section*

Gary Wingate, M.D., Mario Loomis, M.D. Full spectrum of plastic surgery, emphasis on cosmetic surgery of face, eyes, nose, breast, and liposuction. Reconstructive hand surgery.

**PHILIP LIPKIN, M.D., P.A.**
Pepper Pavilion, Suite 1006, 19th and Lombard sts., Philadelphia, PA 19146; (215)732-3445, and 750 Rte. 73 S., Suite 108, Marlton, NJ 08053; (609)985-5888.
My practice includes all plastic surgical procedures, with a special emphasis on cosmetic surgery, breast reconstruction after mastectomy, and breast reduction. An in-office surgical suite contributes to the caring environment which is my practice philosophy. Faculty appointment, University of Pennsylvania, and certified by the American Board of Plastic Surgery.

**DOUGLAS G. MANN, M.D., F.A.C.S.**
*Facial Plastic Surgery*
Suite 201, Riddle Health Care Center 1, Media, PA 19063; (215)566-4100.
Our cosmetic imaging computer can give you a full color image of what you could look like after surgery. Board-certified. Committed to your satisfaction.

**MANSTEIN PLASTIC SURGICAL ASSOCIATION**
**MARK ERIC MANSTEIN, M.D.**
*Plastic and Hand Surgery*
7500 Central Ave., Suite 210, Philadelphia, PA 19111; (215)742-6700.
Friendly, intimate but multifaceted practice involving all aspects of plastic surgery. Areas of special enterprise are breast surgery, cosmetic surgery and hand surgery.

**JOHN H. MOORE JR, M.D.**
*Reconstructive Surgery*
135 S. 18th St., Philadelphia, PA 19103; (215)563-8557.
Plastic and reconstructive surgery, Thomas Jefferson University; aesthetic and reconstructive breast surgery, cosmetic surgery, liposuction, skin-cancer surgery. Certified, American Board of Plastic Surgery.

---

**GRADUATE HOSPITAL GASTROENTEROLOGY ASSOCIATES, P.C.**

Julius J. Deren, M.D.
George Ahtaridis, M.D.
Steven M. Greenfield, M.D.
S. Philip Bralow, M.D.
Jeffrey N. Retig, M.D.
Anthony Infantolino, M.D.
Donald O. Castell, M.D.
David A. Katzka, M.D.

Pepper Pavilion, Suite 100
19th & Lombard Streets
Philadelphia, PA 19146
(215) 893-2532

Crohn's & Colitis Comprehensive Care Center

Functional Gastro-Intestinal Syndromes

Acid Reflux Disorders    Swallowing Disorders

G.I. Cancer Risk Assessment

Gastro-Intestinal Cancer

Gallstone Center

Hepatitis Evaluation & Management Service

Anal Incontinence Center

Pancreatic Disorders

(addt'l locations in Upper Darby & So. Phila.)

*Special Advertising Section*

**J. BRIEN MURPHY, M.D.**
*Reconstructive Surgery*
888 Glenbrook Ave., Bryn Mawr, PA 19010; (215)527–4833.
Attending Plastic Surgeon Bryn Mawr, Children's, and Lankenau hospitals; specializing in all aspects of aesthetic and reconstructive surgery with emphasis on breast, pediatric and laser surgery.

**R. BARRETT NOONE, M.D.**
*Reconstructive Surgery*
888 Glenbrook Ave., Bryn Mawr, PA 19010; (215)527–4833.
Chief of Plastic Surgery and Surgery Department Chairman at Bryn Mawr Hospital. Dr. Noone specializes in all aspects of cosmetic surgery and in breast reconstruction.

**CHARLES E. PAPPAS, M.D., F.A.C.S.**
The Institute for Aesthetic Plastic Surgery, 467 Pennsylvania Ave., Suite 202, Fort Washington, PA 19034; (215)628-4300.
A board-certified plastic surgeon specializing in facial-aesthetic and body-contouring surgery; Director of the Institute for Aesthetic Plastic Surgery, a regional center for plastic surgery.

**JOESPH H. REICHMAN, M.D.**
*Reconstructive Surgery*
Executive Mews, Suite E–30, 1930 Rte. 70 East, Cherry Hill, NJ 08003; (609)988–8400.
The latest cosmetic surgery and breast reconstruction techniques are combined with personalized consultation. Requests for information are encouraged. Certified by the American Board of Plastic Surgery.

**MURRAY W. SEITCHIK, M.D., F.A.C.S., LTD.**
Suite 202, Yorktown Courtyard, Elkins Park, PA 19117; (215)572–6888.
American Board of Plastic Surgery, specializing in reconstructive and cosmetic surgery. Chairman, Division of Plastic Surgery Albert Einstein Medical Center, Medical College Hospitals, Elkins Park campus.

**HENRY J. ZACKIN, M.D.**
*Reconstructive Surgery*
One Brick Rd., Suite 206, Marlton, NJ 08053; (609)985–7370.
Trained at New York Hospital, Cornell, certified by American Board of Surgery. Extensive experience in cosmetic surgery; concerned, caring, personally available for all surgery and care.

## PODIATRY

**BUX–MONT FOOT AND ANKLE CARE CENTER**
**JACK B. GORMAN, D.P.M. AND ASSOCIATES**
*Podiatric Medicine and Surgery/Pain Management*
399 N. York Rd., Warminster, PA 18974; (215)672–3222.
Board-certified. Ambulatory surgical center; micro–surgery, laser and arthroscopic surgery, computerized sports medicine. Pain management, diagnostic studies. Friendly staff, day, evening and emergency hours.

**RONALD F. CARROLL, D.P.M.**
*Podiatric Medicine and Surgery*
2780 W. Country Club Rd., Philadelphia, PA 19131; (215)879–0277.
Specializing in diabetic foot care, sport-related injuries, heel pain, ingrown toenails, warts, fractures, geriatric foot care, arthritis, sprains, bunions, hammertoes, orthotics. Day, evening and Saturday appointments.

**DR. EDWARD CHAIRMAN**
The Foot Center, Suite 604, Pepper Pavilion, One Graduate Plaza, Philadelphia, PA 19146; (215)732–0200.
Dr. Edward Chairman is Director of The Foot Center and a pioneer in combining cosmetic surgery with podiatric surgery to make feet feel and look better. Diplomate, American Board of Podiatric Surgery; Fellow, American College of Foot Surgeons.

**RICHARD A. CICCATELLI, D.P.M.**
*Podiatric Medicine and Surgery*
8314 Germantown Ave., Philadelphia, PA 19118; (215)248–0710 and 158 Main St., Pennsburg, PA 18073.
Board-certified, American Board of Podiatric Surgery. Chestnut Hill Hospital, Grandview Hospital, Montgomery Hospital. Total foot care, birth to maturity.

# Surgery at PENN

Our surgeons are at the forefront of today's dramatic advances in surgical techniques and research discoveries. Their contributions are recognized throughout the world in transplantation, heart and lung, cancer, gastrointestinal, plastic, vascular and trauma surgery. These advances have made possible the extraordinary level of care available to our patients.

## Specialty Centers for Surgery:
- Center for Lung Cancer and Related Disorders
- Center for Minimally Invasive Surgery
- Mitral Valve Center
- Multi-Organ Transplant Center

## Department of Surgery Divisions and Faculty Surgeons:

### Cardiothoracic Surgery
Verdi J. DiSesa, MD
Joseph E. Bavaria, MD
L. Henry Edmunds, MD
Larry R. Kaiser, MD
Mark B. Ratcliffe, MD

### Gastrointestinal Surgery
Ernest F. Rosato, MD
Gordon P. Buzby, MD
Julius A. Mackie, MD
Leonard D. Miller, MD
Jon B. Morris, MD
James L. Mullen, MD
John L. Rombeau, MD

### General Surgery
All of our surgeons participate in the Division of General Surgery.

### Plastic Surgery
Linton A. Whitaker, MD
Scott P. Bartlett, MD
Ralph W. Hamilton, MD
Don LaRossa, MD
David W. Low, MD
Marshall Partington, MD
Peter Randall, MD

### Surgical Oncology
John M. Daly, MD
Lori A. Jardines, MD
Michael H. Torosian, MD

### Transplantation Surgery
Clyde F. Barker, MD
Kenneth L. Brayman, MD
Amy Friedman, MD
Ali Naji, MD

### Trauma and Surgical Critical Care
C. William Shwab, MD
Peter B. Angood, MD
Donald R. Kauder, MD
Michael D. McGonigal, MD
Michael F. Rotondo, MD

### Vascular Surgery
Clyde F. Barker, MD
Jeffrey P. Carpenter, MD
Michael A. Golden, MD
Ali Naji, MD
Leonard J. Perloff, MD

For more information about our surgeons or special programs, please call **Penn's referral counselors, 215-662-PENN (7366).**

**UNIVERSITY OF PENNSYLVANIA MEDICAL CENTER**

University of Pennsylvania School of Medicine
Hospital of the University of Pennsylvania

*Special Advertising Section*

**DR. ELLIOT DIAMOND**
*Medicine and Rehabilitation*
2429 Brown St., Philadelphia, PA 19130; (215)236–4088.
Non–surgical techniques emphasized. Advanced Rehabilitation, acupuncture for lower extremity conditions, pain control, circulation problems, trauma, arthritis, etc. Routine care offered. Board-certified pain management.

**MALLORY L. EISENMAN, M.D.**
1900 Rittenhouse Square, Suite 3, Philadelphia, PA 19103; (215)735–3668.
General podiatry, office and hospital surgery, orthotics, sports medicine, surgeon board-certified by American Institute of Foot Medicine. Day and evening hours, most insurance accepted. Also Northeast office.

**EDMOND L. FREED, M.D.**
*Diabetic and Vascular Complications*
Graduate Hospital Medical Bldg., 2nd Floor, 520 S. 19th St., Philadelphia, PA 19146; (215)546–3668.
30 years experience, foot and leg problems. Board-certified. Podiatric orthopedics. Offices also at Franklin Square Hospital, 8th and Vine sts.; (215)238–2122.

**THE GRADUATE HOSPITAL WOUND CARE CENTER**
**MICHAEL S. WEINGARTEN, M.D.**
**CHARLES WOLFERTH, M.D.**
**RICHARD M. JAY, D.P.M.**
**HAROLD SCHOENHAUS, D.P.M.**
**DENNIS MONTEIRO, M.D.**
**EDWARD CHAIRMAN, D.P.M.**
*Multidisciplinary specialists in wound care*
1740 South St., Suite 306, Philadelphia, PA; (215)893–7655.
Unique team approach, comprehensive care. Medical and nursing specialists use latest techniques to treat non–healing wounds resulting from diabetes, poor circulation, pressure, and other causes.

**STUART JACOB, D.P.M.**
*Podiatric Medicine and Surgery*
Bridge Plaza Professional Center, 319 W. Broad St., Burlington, NJ 08016; (609)386–0217.
Graduate of the Pennsylvania College of Podiatric Medicine, and member American and New Jersey Podiatric Medical associations. Committed to quality foot care. Medicare and PA/NJ BC/BS participating.

**LEG ULCER AND VEIN CENTERS OF AMERICA**
*Wound Care/Ulcer Treatment*
Jamestown Medical Bldg., 525 Jamestown Ave., Suite 206, Philadelphia, PA 19128; (215)483–3666.
Board-certified physicians specializing in all aspects of wound care and healing, varicose veins, and sclerotherapy (nonsurgical destruction of unsightly leg veins).

**THEODORE G. MUSHLIN, D.P.M.**
3319 West Chester Pike, Newtown Square, PA 19073; (215)356–5911, and Westtown Business Center, 1593 McDaniel Dr. Rtes. 3 and 352, West Chester, PA 19380; (215)431–0200.
Board-certified, American Board of Podiatric Surgery; Fellow, American College of Foot Surgeons, Chief of Podiatry, Mercy Haverford Hospital. General and surgical care, foot and ankle.

**PODIATRY CARE CENTER**
**DR. STEPHEN WEISSMAN**
725 Walnut St., Philadelphia, PA 19106; (215)592–4504.
We specialize in correction of fungal nails, ingrown toenails, hammertoes, bunions, heel spurs. In-office correction, free parking. Board-certified in foot surgary.

## PREVENTIVE MEDICINE

**BENJAMIN FRANKLIN CLINIC**
*Preventive Medicine*
Public Ledger Bldg., 6th and Chestnut sts., Suite 104, Philadelphia, PA 19106; (215)925–4300.
Dedicated to prevention and early detection of disease for corporations and individuals. Programs include: Annual exams, cancer and cardiovascular screening, nutrition, exercise facility, and occupational medicine.

**INDUSTRIAL HEALTH-CARE CENTER**
**NATALIE P. HARTENBAUM, M.D., MEDICAL DIRECTOR**

*Occupational Medicine*
1854 New Rodgers Rd., Rte. 413, Levittown, PA 19056; (215)750–6426. Specializing in occupational/industrial medicine; treatment of work–related injuries. D.O.T. physicals, executive health screens, substance-abuse testing, physical therapy, x–ray, work hardening, TMEs, lab.

## PSYCHIATRY

**JON BJORNSON, M.D.**
Suite 808, 1601 Walnut St., Philadelphia, PA 19102; (215)963–0668, (215)836-7700. Adult psychiatry. Individual, marital, and family therapy, 25 years experience treating a wide variety of psychiatric disorders. Affliated with Jefferson and Eugenia hospitals. Specializes in P.T.S.D.
**MARTIN GOLDBERG, M.D.**
**INSTITUTE OF PENNSYLVANIA HOSPITAL**
111 N. 49th St., Philadelphia, PA 19139; (215)471–2081.
Specialist in relationship problems, psychotherapist for couples; board–certified. Life fellow: American Association Marital Family Therapy; past President, Philadelphia Psychiatric Society.

**THE GRADUATE HOSPITAL EATING DISORDERS PROGRAM AND DEPARTMENT OF PSYCHIATRY, MICHAEL J. PERTSCHUK, M.D.**
*Eating Disorders*
1740 South St., Suite 305, Philadelphia, PA 19146, and 200 West Lancaster Ave., Wayne, PA 19087; (215) 985-2242. Specialized services for eating disorders; off-site residential and day treatment programs at Graduate Hospital and outpatient treatment in Philadelphia and Wayne. Experienced, degreed staff treat anorexia, bulimia, compulsive eating, weight problems. Individualized treatment, transition and family counseling. Covered fully or partially by many insurers including HMOs. Listed under "Top Doctors," *Philadelphia Magazine*.

---

# Thoughtful counsel.
# Sound surgical judgment.
# Precise technique.

stephen harlin, m.d.
plastic and reconstructive surgery
surgery of the hand

210 west rittenhouse square
philadelphia, pa 19103
215•731•9490

*Special Advertising Section*

**IN PERSPECTIVE**
**GARY KRAMER, M.D**
**JAY SEGAL, M.ED.**
*Gay, Lesbian, HIV Counseling*
100 Old York Rd., Suite 218, Jenkintown, PA 19046; (215)572–7282.
Couples, individuals, gay parents and their children; families of gay individuals; HIV-affected individuals and their families. Also Bensalem and Center City Philadelphia offices.

**STEPHEN E. LEVICK, M.D.**
*Psychotherapy/Psychopharmacology*
111 N. 49th St., Philadelphia, PA 19139; (215)471–2869.
Board-certified, Yale-trained; staff, Institute of Pennsylvania Hospital; faculty, University of Pennsylvania. Evaluating and treating individuals 18–60 with depression, mood swings, stress, anxiety, addictions, schizophrenia.

**DAVID E. NESS, M.D.**
225 Newtown Rd., Warminster, PA 18974; (215)441–6908.
Board-certified. Comprehensive psychiatric services, including emergency assessment, psychotherapy and psychotropic medication management. Emphasis on family involvement and community mental health education.

**EDWARD OPASS, M.D.**
18 N. State St., Newtown, PA 18940; (215)579–9850.
I am board-certified in psychiatry and specialize in intensive individual psychotherapy using medication where appropriate. I also see older individuals, older adolescents and couples.

**PHILADELPHIA MEDICAL INSTITUTE (PMI)**
**JOSEPH MENDELS, M.D.**
*Depression/Anxiety*
1015 Chestnut St., Suite 1303, Philadelphia, PA 19107; (215)923–2583.
PMI provides quality health care using newly developed treatment programs for depression, anxiety, panic and sexual dysfunction.

**SUSAN PORITSKY, M.D.**
800 Spruce St., Pennsylvania Hospital, Philadelphia, PA 19107; (215)471–2413.
Adult and adolescent psychiatry, specializing in treatment of anxiety, depression, relationships and career difficulties. Evening hours available. Additional office: 111 N. 49th St., Philadelphia, PA 19139.

**PSYCHIATRIC CARE ASSOCIATES**
**GARY H. KRAMER, M.D.**
1260 Virginia Dr., Suite 225, Ft. Washington, PA 19034; (215)643–8680.
Psychiatric Care Associates is a mental health practice of licensed multidisciplinary professionals treating children, adolescents, adults and older adults, also providing 24-hour emergency care.

**MARK SHULKIN, M.D.**
**SUNNY SHULKIN, A.S.C.W.**
300 E. Lancaster Ave., Wynnewood, PA 19096; (215)667–7645.
Sunny and Mark are specialists in helping couples stuck in chronic upset increase their willingness to express tenderness and understanding. Offices on Main Line, Media.

## PSYCHOLOGY

**AGORAPHOBIA AND ANXIETY TREATMENT CENTER**
*Anxiety Disorders*
112 Bala Ave., Bala Cynwyd, PA 19004; (215)667–6490.
Internationally recognized program for research and treatment of anxiety disorders, including: agoraphobia, social anxiety, obsessive-compulsive and panic disorders, and P.T.S.D. for adults and children.

**BIOCARE ASSOCIATES, DIRECTORS:**
**DR. CHRIS ELEFTHERIOS, PSYCHOLOGIST**
**LESTER JONES, LICENSED CLINICAL SOCIAL WORKER**
*Stress Management*
Offices King of Prussia, Bala Cynwyd and Center City; (215)783–6592.
Experienced in stress and pain management, biofeedback, individual, family and marital counseling. Psychological testing and employee assistance programs for trou-

*Special Advertising Section*

bled employees and their families.

**ABBY GOLOMB COLE, PH.D.**
*Clinical Psychology*
70 W. Oakland Ave., Suite 201, Doylestown, PA 18901; (215)348–2850.
Psychotherapy for anorexia nervosa, bulimia, and compulsive overeating; depression, anxiety, marital and identity problems. Specialty on women's issues, individual and group therapy available. Insurance accepted.

**EAGLESMERE PSYCHOLOGY ASSOCIATES**
**MARY KREMPA GILLESPIE, PH.D. DIRECTOR**
*Behavioral Medicine and Clinical Psychology*
2350 Pheasant Hill Lane, Malvern, PA 19355; (215)647–2888.
Brief strategic therapy, stress management, pain control, anxiety, panic attacks, depression, marriage and family conflicts, sexuality, children/teens behavior and school problems, hypnosis, biofeedback, psychological testing, custody evaluations.

**THE PSYCHOLOGY CENTER OF PHILADELPHIA**
**LEONARD LEVITZ, PH.D., DIRECTOR**
*Eating Disorders*
1616 Walnut St., Philadelphia, PA 19103; (215)731–9510.
Group and individual treatment programs for compulsive eating, bulimia, anorexia, and obesity provided by a coalition of specialists in eating disorders.

**SCHUYLKILL VALLEY COUNSELING**
**LYN STEWART, MSW, LSW**
**ERICA BRENDEL, M.D.**
**ANNE MARIE BUCK, M.A.**
**ROCHELLE GREENFIELD, M.ED.**
**HANNAH JACOBSON, MS, MSW, LSW,**
**EUGENE O'NEILL, ACSW, LSW**
*Sexual Abuse/Relationship Issues*
538 Walnut Lane, Philadelphia, PA 19128; (215)487–7210 (24 hours).
Provides services to children, adolescents,

# Urology at Penn

Specialists in **Penn's Division of Urology** have developed many of today's most advanced treatment methods and surgical procedures in the following areas:

- Prostate disease
- Prostate cancer
- Urologic cancer
- Incontinence
- Reconstructive surgery, including bladder reconstruction
- Interstitial cystitis
- Male infertility
- Male sexual dysfunction
- Stone disease
- Voiding dysfunction

**Penn's board-certified urologists:**
*Alan J. Wein, MD, Chief*
*Keith Van Arsdalen, MD*
*S. Bruce Malkowicz, MD*
*Gregory A. Broderick, MD*

For more information about our physicians or services, please call **Penn's referral counselors, 215-662-PENN (7366)**, or **Urology, 215-662-2891.**

**UNIVERSITY OF PENNSYLVANIA MEDICAL CENTER**
University of Pennsylvania School of Medicine
Hospital of the University of Pennsylvania

*Special Advertising Section*

and adults in individual, couples, family and group therapy. Addictions counseling, psychological testing/psychiatric evaluations. Insurance accepted, sliding scale fees.

**JULIAN W. SLOWINSKI, PSY.D., A.B.P.P.**
*Clinical Psychology/Sex and Marital Therapy*
Pennsylvania Hospital, 700 Spruce St., Suite 501, Philadelphia, PA 19106; (215)829-5534.
Board-certified: Affiliations: Pennsylvania Hospital, University of Pennsylvania Medical School: professionally active nationally, specialties: sex and martial therapy, gender problems; general practice: individuals, couples, families.

**"THE TREATMENT CENTER FOR RELATIONSHIPS." MARRIAGE COUNCIL; DIVISION OF FAMILY STUDY; UNIVERSITY OF PENNSYLVANIA SCHOOL OF MEDICINE**
*Marriage and Family Therapy.*
4025 Chestnut St., Philadelphia, PA 19104; (215)382-6680.
Relationship and sex therapy for individuals, couples and families; offices in Montgomery, Bucks, and Chester counties and South Jersey. Sliding fee scale.

## PULMONARY DISEASE

**FRANK J. MONDSCHEIN, M.D.**
**THOMPSON H. BOYD, III, M.D.**
*Internal Medicine*
2126 Fairmount Ave., Philadelphia, PA 19130-2603; (215)236-4600.
General medical practice in the Art Museum area, caring for patients with multiple medical problems. Board-certified, University-affiliated.

**NORRISTOWN PULMONARY ASSOCIATES**
**ALAN S. JOSSELSON, M.D., F.C.C.P.**
**GARY DRIZIN, M.D., F.C.C.P.**
**RONALD BARNETT, M.D., F.C.C.P.**
1330 Powell St., Suite 508, Norristown, PA 19401; (215)275-2446.
Board-certified physicians specializing in diseases of the chest, including asthma, bronchitis, emphysema, pneumonia, asbestos poisoning. Most insurance accepted.

**MELVIN R. PRATTER, M.D.**
Cooper Hospital/University Medical Center, 3 Cooper Plaza, Suite 215, Camden, NJ 08103; (609)342-2406.
Specialists in respiratory disorders with emphasis on cough, shortness of breath, asthma, chronic bronchitis, emphysema and sleep disorders, including apnea, daytime drowsiness and insomnia.

**PULMONARY DISEASE ASSOCIATES, LTD.**
**JAMES H. DOVNARSKY, M.D.**
**JULIA B. BRODY, M.D.**
**BRUCE S. MARGOLIS, D.O.**
*Internal Medicine*
2300 S. Broad St., Suite 204, Philadelphia, PA 19145; (215)463-5008.
Three board-certified pulmonologists specializing in the diagnosis and treatment of diseases of the lung. Offices in South Philadelphia and Northeast Philadelphia.

**SHINNICK-FREEDMAN-KARLIN PULMONARY ASSOCIATES, P.C.**
Presbyterian Medical Center, 39th and Market sts., Philadelphia, PA 19104; (215)662-8060.
Drs. Shinnick, Freedman, and Karlin specialize in lung problems with particular interest in chronic cough, breathing difficulty, asthma, emphysema, occupational disease, lung cancer, neuromuscular disorders, tuberculosis.

## RADIATION ONCOLOGY

**GIULIO J. D'ANGIO, M.D.**
Department of Radiation Oncology, University of Pennsylvania Medical Center, 3400 Spruce St., Philadelphia, PA 19104; (215)662-3074.
Board-certified, specializing in pediatrics.

**BARBARA L. FOWBLE, M.D.**
Department of Radiation Oncology, Hospital of University of Pennsylvania, 3400 Spruce St., Philadelphia, PA 19104; (215)662-3075.
Board-certified, specializing in the treatment of breast cancer.

*Special Advertising Section*

**JOEL W. GOLDWEIN, M.D.**
Department of Radiation Oncology, University of Pennsylvania Medical Center, 3400 Spruce St., Philadelphia, PA 19104; (215)667–7147.
Board-certified, specializing in pediatric radiation oncology, associate staff member Department of Pediatrics and Department of Radiology; Children's Hospital of Philadelphia.

**MORTON M. KLIGERMAN, M.D.**
Department of Radiation Oncology, University of Pennsylvania Medical Center, 3400 Spruce St., Philadelphia, PA 19104; (215)662–3198.
Board-certified, specializing in head and neck cancer.

**ROBERT E. KRISCH, M.D., PH.D.**
Department of Radiation Oncology, University of Pennsylvania Medical Center, 3400 Spruce St., Philadelphia, PA 19104; (215) 662-3109.
Board-certified, specializing in lung and prostate cancer.

**DEBORAH MARKIEWICZ, M.D.**
Department of Radiation Oncology, University of Pennsylvania Medical Center, 3400 Spruce St., Philadelphia, PA 19104; (215)662–7449.
Board-certified, specializing in head and neck cancer.

**W. GILLIES MCKENNA, M.D., PH.D.**
Department of Radiation Oncology, University of Pennsylvania Medical Center, 3400 Spruce St., Philadelphia, PA 19104; (215)662–3147.
Chairman, Department of Radiation Oncology, board-certified, specializing in sarcoma, melanoma and lung cancer.

**MERCY ASSOCIATES IN RADIATION ONCOLOGY**
**LESLIE TUPCHONG, M.D.**
**MERRILL SOLAN, M.D.**
**C. JULES ROMINGER, M.D.**
Mercy Catholic Medical Center, Lansdowne

---

# SPRUCE Chiropractic Centre
## In Center City
*Specializing in Conservative Gentle Treatment*

### Call for immediate appointment.

headaches • stress management • arthritis • child & family care
sciatica • nutrition • lower back, leg, neck, hand & arm pain
numbness • auto accidents/personal injury • work injuries
disc problems • sports injuries • exercise programs

Morning, lunchtime & evening hours for working people
Most insurances - Blue Cross, Blue Shield,
Personal Choice, Worker's Compensation

*Call for a free information booklet.*

Free Parking **735-2997**
1421 Spruce (at Broad) • Phila.

**Dr. Andrew Indriso**
Member of Int'l Chiropractic Assoc.
American Chiropractic Assoc.
Member Chiropractic Fellowship Of PA
And also PA Chiropractic Society

Ave. and Bailey Rd., Darby, PA 19023; (215)237–4370.
Radiation oncology practice staffed by three board-certified radiation oncologists. Hospital–based. We offer the most advanced technology available for cancer treatment. Consultations and emergencies seen 24 hours a day, 7 days a week.

**WILLIAM D. POWLIS, M.D.**
Department of Radiation Oncology, University of Pennsylvania Medical Center, 3400 Spruce St., Philadelphia, PA 19104; (215)662–6934.
Board-certified. Specializing in Hodgkin's disease and non–Hodgkin's lymphomas, hematologic malignancies, brain tumors, and radiosurgery for brain tumors.

**LAWRENCE J. SOLIN, M.D.**
Department of Radiation Oncology, University of Pennsylvania Medical Center, 3400 Spruce St., Philadelphia, PA 19104; (215)662–7267.
Board-certified, specializing in breast cancer.

**RICHARD WHITTINGTON, M.D.**
Department of Radiation Oncology, University of Pennsylvania Medical Center, 3400 Spruce St., Philadelphia, PA 19104; (215)662–6515.
Board-certified, specializing in gastrointestinal and genito–urinary cancers, prostate cancer, organ preservation, and implants.

## RADIOLOGY

**THE BREAST HEALTH CENTER**
**JANE S. HUGHES, M.D.**
*Mammograghy*
600 Jessup Rd., Suite 104, West Deptford, NJ 08066; (609)845–4200.
Mammograms are done in a relaxed and feminine setting. Our specially trained staff performs the exams in an efficient and sensitive manner. Accredited by the ACR.

**DOOLEY-LYNCH ASSOCIATES**
**ROBERT E. LYNCH, M.D.**
**ALLAN M. COHEN, M.D.**
**MICHAEL H. BLESHMAN, M.D.**
**JOHANNA KALEMBA, M.D.**

**DAVID W. LEVY, M.D.**
*Diagnostic Imaging Specialists*
491 Allendale Rd., Suite 104, Professional Bldg., King of Prussia, PA 19406; (215)265-6790.
Dooley-Lynch Associates provides quality diagnostic imaging, including: mammography, OB ultrasound, fluroscopy, routine x-rays, routine ultrasound, CT, nuclear medicine, and MRI studies. Convenient offices in: King of Prussia, Royersford, Lionville, Trappe, and Phoenixville.

**HUGH J. MULLIN, M.D., DIPLOMATE, A.B.R., CERT. N.I.O.S.H. B–R.D.R.**
**RICHARD M. PURSE, D.O., DIPLOMATE, A.O.B.R., DIPLOMATE, A.O.B.N.M.**
Oxford Valley Imaging Center, Inc., 330 Middletown Blvd., Suite 402, Langhorne, PA 19047; (215)752–8080.
Serving Lower Bucks community for 20 years. O.V.I.C. provides full diagnostic imaging services, including general radiology, mammography, ultrasound, nuclear medicine, including cardiac, CT and MRI.

## REPRODUCTIVE ENDOCRINOLOGY

**LORRAINE C. KING M.D., P.C.**
834 Chestnut St., Philadelphia, PA 19107; (215)922–2442.
Board-certified specializing in infertility, endometriosis, laser surgery and hormonal replacement; sensitive care coupled with state of the art technology. Staff, Thomas Jefferson University.

**MAIN LINE REPRODUCTIVE SCIENCE CENTER**
**ABRAHAM K. MUNABI, M.D.**
**MILLICENT G. ZACHER, D.O.**
**KATHRYN C. WORRILOW, PH.D.**
950 West Valley Rd., Suite 2401, Wayne, PA 19087; (215)964–9663.
Specializing in treatment of male and female infertility disorders. Full-service, out–patient facility. IVF\GIFT\ZIFT, andrology, donor insemination, sperm freezing, micromanipulation. Board-certified staff, hospital-affiliated.

# Plastic Surgery

The American Medical Association (AMA) and
its American Board of Medical Specialties (ABMS)
certifies *just one* board in this field,
**The American Board of Plastic Surgeons**.
The following Greater Philadelphia Physicians
are the certified members of the
American Board of Plastic Surgeons,
the American Society of Plastic and
Reconstructive Surgeons and
the Philadelphia Society of Plastic Surgeons.

Thomas J. Brobyn, M.D.
Arthur S. Brown, M.D.
Lawrence Chase, M.D.
Howard S. Caplan, M.D.
Hector Carlos, M.D.
Francine A. Cedrone, M.D.
James Columbo, M.D.
Francis X. Delone, M.D.

James W. Fox, IV, M.D.
Marcia Fitzpatrick, M.D.
John E. Gatti, M.D.
Bruce E. Genter, M.D.
Marvin T. Hunter, M.D.
Paul Jackson, M.D.
Theodore Katz, M.D.
Paul S. Kim, M.D.

John L. Krause, Jr., M.D.
Joseph Kusiak, M.D.
Phillip Lipkin, M.D.
Barbara Lundy, M.D.
R. Michael McClellan, M.D.
Amit Mitra, M.D.
John H. Moore, Jr., M.D.
J. Brien Murphy, M.D.
Guy Nardella, Jr., M.D.

J. Barret Noone, M.D.
Charles Pappas, M.D.
Joseph Rabson, M.D.
David E. Saunders, M.D.
James E. Slavin, M.D.
Roslyn C. Souser, M.D.
Mark Solomon, M.D.
Chris D. Tzarnas, M.D.
Linton Whitaker, M.D.

Members

AMERICAN SOCIETY OF PLASTIC AND RECONSTRUCTIVE SURGEONS
PHILADELPHIA SOCIETY OF PLASTIC SURGEONS
1-800-635-0635

**STEPHEN L. CARSON, M.D.**
**FRANCES R. BATZER, M.D.**
**BENJAMIN GOCIAL, M.D.**
**MAUREEN KELLY, M.D.**
**JAQUELINE N. GUTMAN, M.D.**
815 Locust St., Philadelphia, PA 19107; (215)922–2206.
Philadelphia Fertility Institute. Care from puberty through menopause, focused on infertility, endocrinology, menopause, IVF, and reproductive surgery. Suburban: 5217 Militia Hill Rd., Plymouth Meeting, PA; (215)834–1230.

## SURGERY

**RICHARD J. CITTA, D.O., P.A., F.A.C.O.S.**
**MICHAEL J. SASSO, D.O.**
25 Laurel Rd., Stratford, NJ 08084; (609)784–4740.
Practice is limited to general surgery in the South Jersey area with expertise in laparoscopic gall bladder removal and laparoscopic herniorrhaphies, with major hospital affiliations.

**HERBERT E. COHN, M.D.**
*Thoracic and General Surgery*
Thomas Jefferson University Hospital, Suite G8290, 111 S. 11th St., Philadelphia, PA 19107; (215)955–6602.
Extensive experience in the diagnosis and treatment of malignant and benign disorders of the lung, esophagus, breast, thyroid, and parathyroid gland, experienced in thorascopic and laparoscopic surgery.

**JOSEPH H. ENTINE, M.D., F.A.C.S.**
9892 Bustleton Ave., Suite 206, Philadelphia, PA 19115; (215) 673-0343.
General surgical practice with special emphasis on breast-sparing procedures for cancer, hernia surgery and laparoscopic abdominal surgery. Board-certified.

**GLENN D. HOROWITZ, M.D.**
9892 Bustleton Ave., Suite 206, Philadelphia, PA 19115; (215) 673-0343.
Complete surgical care for Northeast Philadelphia. Specialties include laparoscopic, abdominal and chest surgery, cancer detection and management, and intravenous nutrition.

**LISA K. JABLON, M.D.**
*General Surgery*
Albert Einstein Medical Center, 5501 Old York Rd., Klein Building, Suite 501, Philadelphia, PA 19141; (215)457–4444.
Specializing in breast disease; Director, High-Risk Breast Program, a comprehensive evaluation of women at increased risk for breast cancer; participant in Breast Cancer Prevention Trial.

**MARK J. KAPLAN, M.D.**
*General Surgery*
Albert Einstein Medical Center, 5501 Old York Rd., Klein Building, Suite 501, Philadelphia, PA 19141; (215)457–4444.
Board-certifed in general and critical-care surgery. Specializing in laparoscopic, laser, and oncologic surgery, breast cancer and critical-care management.

**MATT L. KIRKLAND, M.D.**
301 South 8th St., 2-L, Philadelphia, PA 19106; (215)829–3697.
Board-certified surgeon practicing the full spectrum of general surgery, including extensive experience with laparoscopic cholecystectomy and other laparoscopic procedures.

**LAWRENCE J. MAYER, M.D.**
2100 Keystone Ave., Medical Office Bldg., Suite 406, Drexel Hill, PA 19026;. (215) 259-5007.
Chief of Surgery Delaware County Hospital; Board-certified; Fellow American College of Surgeons. Training: Hospital University of Pennsylvania. Specializing in breast, laparoscopic, abdominal and office surgery.

**ROBERT G. SOMERS, M.D.**
*Practice Limited to Breast Disease*
Albert Einstein Medical Center, 5501 Old York Rd., Klein Bldg., Suite 501, Philadelphia, PA 19141; (215)457–4444.
Chairman, Department of Surgery, surgical oncology fellowship at Memorial Sloan–Kettering Center. Board-certified in general surgery. Practice limited to diseases of the breast.

## UROLOGY

**CENTER FOR SEXUAL HEALTH**
**RICHARD MILSTEN, M.D.**
**DANIEL GOLDBERG, PH.D.**
**FRED O. DOREY, M.D.**
**KARL H. EBERT, M.D.**
Medical Arts Building, Suite 16, W. Red Bank Ave., Woodbury, NJ 08096; (609)853-5050.
Founded in 1985, a team of doctors helps patients experiencing such difficulties as erectile dysfunction (impotence), orgasm difficulties, premature ejaculation and loss of sexual interest.

**BRUCE B. GARBER, M.D., F.A.C.S.**
*Urologic Surgery*
Graduate Hospital, 606 Pepper Pavilion, Philadelphia, PA 19146; (215)893-2643.
Dr. Garber directs the Philadelphia Impotence Foundation, and specializes in the treatment of male impotence, urinary tract tumors, prostate problems and urinary stones.

**DR. PHILLIP C. GINSBERG**
*Urology and Urologic Surgery*
Albert Einstein Medical Center, Klein Professional Bldg., Suite 204A, 5401 Old York Rd., Philadelphia, PA 19141; (215)456-1177.
Board-certified, emphasis on non-surgical treatment for prostate enlargement. Laser surgery including kidney stones; urologic problems of the elderly and comprehensive urologic cancer management.

**KRISTENE E. WHITMORE, M.D.**
**PHILADELPHIA UROSURGICAL ASSOCIATION**
1 Graduate Plaza, 606 Pepper Pavilion, Philadelphia, PA 19146; (215)546-2280.
Female urology: bladder disorders, cystitis, interstitial cystitis, incontinence, prostate problems, bladder cancer.

## VASCULAR SURGERY

**JEFFREY P. CARPENTER, M.D.**
University of Pennsylvania Medical Center,

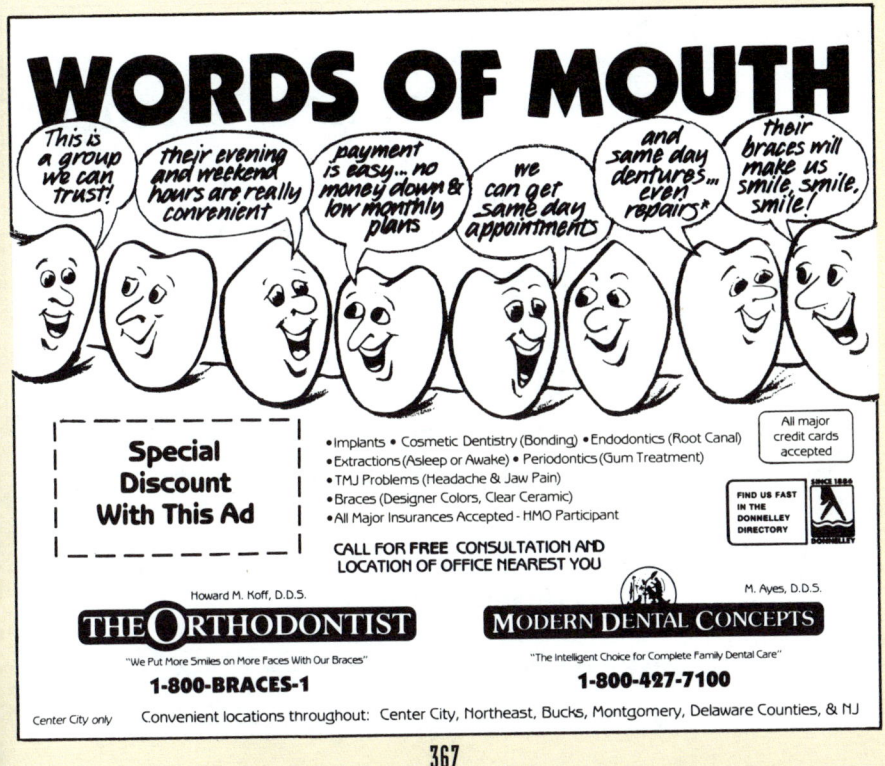

---

# WORDS OF MOUTH

*This is a group we can trust!*
*Their evening and weekend hours are really convenient*
*Payment is easy... no money down & low monthly plans*
*We can get same day appointments*
*And same day dentures... even repairs*
*Their braces will make us smile, smile, smile!*

- Implants • Cosmetic Dentistry (Bonding) • Endodontics (Root Canal)
- Extractions (Asleep or Awake) • Periodontics (Gum Treatment)
- TMJ Problems (Headache & Jaw Pain)
- Braces (Designer Colors, Clear Ceramic)
- All Major Insurances Accepted - HMO Participant

All major credit cards accepted

FIND US FAST IN THE DONNELLEY DIRECTORY

**Special Discount With This Ad**

CALL FOR **FREE** CONSULTATION AND LOCATION OF OFFICE NEAREST YOU

Howard M. Koff, D.D.S.
**THE ORTHODONTIST**
"We Put More Smiles on More Faces With Our Braces"
**1-800-BRACES-1**
Center City only

M. Ayes, D.D.S.
**MODERN DENTAL CONCEPTS**
"The Intelligent Choice for Complete Family Dental Care"
**1-800-427-7100**
Convenient locations throughout: Center City, Northeast, Bucks, Montgomery, Delaware Counties, & NJ

Silverstein Pavilion, 4th floor, 3400 Spruce St., Philadelphia, PA 19104;(215)662-2029. Dedicated to patient care, specializing in aneurysms, circulation problems and carotid disease. Yale-and Penn-trained, his award-winning research has attained international recognition.

**LEG ULCER AND VEIN CENTERS OF AMERICA**
*Wound Care/Ulcer Treatment*
The Jamestown Medical Bldg., 525 Jamestown Ave., Suite 206, Philadelphia, PA 19128; (215)483-3666.
Board-certified physicians specializing in all aspects of wound care and healing, varicose veins, and sclerotherapy (nonsurgical destruction of unsightly leg veins).

**MICHAEL GOLDEN, M.D.**
University of Pennsylvania Medical Center, Silverstein Pavilion, 4th floor, 3400 Spruce St., Philadelphia, PA 19104;(215)662-7831. Harvard-trained, board-certified vascular surgeon; 1992-1993 American College of Surgeons award-recipient specializing in vascular diagnosis and treatment, including aneurysms, carotid disease and leg circulation.

**LEONARD J. PERLOFF, M.D.**
University of Pennsylvania Medical Center, Silverstein Pavilion, 4th floor, 3400 Spruce St., Philadelphia, PA 19104; (215)662-2090.
Comprehensive clinical vascular surgical practice as well as a modern vascular laboratory. Particular interests include carotid disease, abdominal aortic aneurysms, hypertension, and peripheral arterial and venous disease.

**CAROL A. RAVIOLA, M.D.**
Suite 2A, 301 S. 8th St., Philadelphia, PA 19106; (215)829-6520.
Affiliation: Pennsylvania Hospital. Board-certified in Vascular Surgery. Treatment of arterial disorders: carotid and aortic reconstructions, lower extremity arterial revascularization. Diabetic foot ulcers; non–invasive diagnostic testing.

---

# Can you smile without shame?

*Are you one of those unlucky people with the misfortune to have terrible teeth?*
*Have things reached the stage where you must do something?*
*Do you know where to turn?*

Perhaps we can help. We have marvellous modern facilities. We can provide everything from implants right through to the final æsthetic reconstruction. Dr. Hunt has impeccable credentials. There's no need to put it off any longer. Call today.

**DR. PETER HUNT & ASSOCIATES IN DENTISTRY, P.C.**
116 South 18th Street
Philadelphia, PA 19103
215 . 564 . 0408   —   fax: 215 . 564 . 6731

*Notes*

*Notes*

*Notes*

*Notes*